THE LONELY FURROW

Farming in the United States,
Japan, and India

The Lonely Furrow

Farming in the United States Japan and India

by Kusum Nair

Ann Arbor
The University of Michigan Press

Preface

1

If a reason must be assigned for every book that is written, this one originated in a question. The question arose out of my earlier study, *Blossoms in the Dust* (New York: Fredrick A. Praeger; London: Gerald Duckworth & Co. Ltd., 1961), in which I reported mainly economic attitudes and opinions of a number of farmers in India.

The person who posed the question is a good economist and a better friend, who firmly believes that for anyone to be noneconomic is to be perverse. Since the behavior and views of several Indian farmers interviewed by me appeared to deviate from the path of orthodox economic rationality, my friend asked: "Well Kusum, I don't disbelieve your findings. But how do you know that these peasants would not have acted and answered your questions differently if they had the economic opportunity; easy access to various inputs like improved seed, water, fertilizer, credit; and a technology that was really profitable to adopt, along with appropriate price incentives, and so on?"

I did not know the answer to the question. Admittedly, Indian farmers did not have most of the listed items. Moreover, they were not likely to have them *all* for some time to come. In 1961 that day was clearly far off. The importance of knowing the answer, on the other hand, was immediate. It could make a critical difference to the course of agriculture in India. Or so I thought.

And so, somewhat in the spirit of Miyazaki Antei, whom the reader will meet later, I decided to go to countries where farmers have everything, to find out how *they* think and act in their more fortunate situation. A combination of circumstances, intuition, and deliberate choice led me to the United States and Japan. They have both achieved notable success in developing agriculture. No two countries are exactly alike. But few are as dissimilar. If I could discover a common clue to their success, I thought I might be able to answer not only my friend's question, but also be of help to India's planners and policy makers in their efforts to induce an exceedingly rapid rate of growth in agriculture in a very short time.

2

I set out on this venture in September 1962. I spent one year in the United States in the course of which I interviewed farmers in thirteen states: North Carolina, Mississippi, Tennessee, Louisiana, New Mexico, California, Pennsylvania, Wisconsin, Minnesota, Illinois, Utah, Washington, and Alaska. Prior to field interviews, I met with faculty members of the state universities in the departments of agricultural economics, rural sociology, anthropology, history, extension education—every discipline connected with farmers, agriculture, rural development, and its history. I visited also the universities of Chicago, Cornell, Michigan State, and Pennsylvania. At Harvard, where I was based, I did considerable library research and later spent another year writing.

To learn about American crops and technology of farming I went to experiment stations in the states in which I did field work. The Department of Agriculture in Washington, D.C., briefed me on policy and problems. And I stayed with several farm families to get a more intimate view of their life and work. In this manner I covered every major region, type of farming, income group among farmers, and school and shade of thinking in the academic and official world. Interviews with farmers were arranged through county agents and representatives of the Farmers' Home Administration.

I followed a similar procedure in Japan, where I spent three months—in the fall of 1963, and again in 1965. I visited the Ministry of Agriculture in Tokyo, the four Imperial universities of Tokyo, Kyoto, Kyushu, and Hokkaido, and several experiment stations. Here also, my field study covered all the important regions, types of farming, and categories of farmers. Inevitably, however, concentration was heaviest on rice, Japan's main crop.

Interviews with farmers in Japan were arranged by the university or experiment station of the region in collaboration with the extension service and were conducted through an interpreter. For historical and secondary data also, I had to draw on the work of Western scholars and Japanese sources available in English. Fortunately, these are plentiful and excellent.

As in *Blossoms in the Dust*, interviews with farmers were unstructured but within a uniform framework and approach—to assess their attitudes concerning work and production. Notes were taken verbatim during the interview or immediately after. Again, as in *Blossoms*, I have reported the situation in the raw, as I found it, and as it appeared to the man (or woman) at the other end. I have not attempted to sound deeper depths, because for our purpose what is believed is what counts. If I have used concepts such as modern and secular, without defining them very precisely, the connotation is in the commonest and most widely understood sense.

The study is not computerized. Neither statistics nor people have been put through the machine. Though their names have been changed, the farmers in the text are all real characters. I have portrayed them as accurately and objectively as I could. For those who have a taste for it, there is a great deal of background statistical information. Some of it is in the text, but most of it will be found in the notes.

3

The major part of the book is devoted to a comparative description in detail of agricultural development, current and historical, in the United States and Japan. A résumé of the situation in India is given in the end along with the conclusions.

In the course of my travels, I had the opportunity to look at farming in Australia, the Philippines, and Thailand as well, which I found extremely useful. I have not included the experience of these countries in this study, however, because I did not want to make it too complex. Even of the countries covered, the story is not complete. Economists, historians, and sociologists will not be happy on account of what has been left out. But that was unavoidable, unless I wrote several volumes.

Also, at places a situation might appear to be overdrawn because all the factors have not been dealt with adequately. If they do not make a material difference to the point at issue, I have left them out deliberately. The role of the landlord in Meiji Japan, for example, is a much discussed topic among scholars. But I have not allotted much space to it. Similarly, there are angry controversies among historians regarding the *exact* rate of growth in agriculture during the Meiji period. I have simply mentioned the different views, because they do not alter the essence of the argument. The nonagricultural sectors of both economies have been omitted almost entirely, although their impact on farming is considerable.

The study does *not* in fact even attempt to deal with all the variables in agricultural production and growth. Land, capital, prices and profits, technology, social and economic institutions, and government policy have been considered, but only as a stage and backdrop to the horizon, beliefs, and behavior of the cultivator. The focus throughout is on the response and role of farmers in deployment of whatever the opportunities and resources: *Why do they work and produce as they do?*

4

Requirements for the functioning and growth of agriculture are akin somewhat to the three legs of a tripod. One leg consists of off-farm resources, including technology and the research that sustains its progress. Another leg consists of services and the institutional arrangements and organization at various levels for different purposes and needs of the farmer. The third leg represents the producer. The tripod must have all three legs to stand.

The analogy applies to all but the most primitive forms of human enterprise. But whereas in a large industrial corporation, operating at an advanced level of technology, the individual is clearly subordinate to organization and technology; in family-type farming, even if it is mechanized, the most critical single input is still the initiative and effort of the individual operator. (See John Kenneth Galbraith, *The New Industrial State*, Boston: Houghton Mifflin Company, 1967.)

Unlike the managers of a business corporation, moreover, farm operators do not act in concert. They do not determine the prices of goods and technology that they purchase, or of their own produce that they sell. They have no collective or corporate identification with each other and the larger national goals and policies. The majority are unaware of the several theories that are supposed to govern their conduct, and do not always act as they are expected to. And as the reader will discover, their goals and motives are complex; and of the components thereof, there could be as many mixes as the number of farmers. The result is, that although it must always pay to be efficient, the agricultural vista offers an astonishing range of variations in production behavior and efficiency in even a highly developed situation, as of the United States.

Of all the variables in agriculture, therefore, the farmer is the most crucial and the least predictable. He plows a lonely furrow. It can be deep or shallow. Accordingly, and as demonstrated in the world's two most brilliant success stories, the richest soil can yield poorly, and vice versa, depending on the will and skill of the cultivator. This study is limited to and gives primacy to him—the third leg of the tripod. This is not to imply that the other two legs can be dispensed with.

Historical focus, too, is primarily on events and actions of men concerned with and engaged in agricultural production, rather than on abstract concepts and theories. The latter have a strong tendency to break away from reality, to become independent satellites. Over time, they cease often to represent reality, or do so only partly.

5

My inferences, hypotheses, and suggestions on how to develop agriculture in an undeveloped situation, as that of India, will be found at the very end, in the last chapter. The conclusion is stated in brief bare outline. Details of how it could be applied in specific situations must be the subject of further research and investigation. This study is limited to and culminates only in the formulation of a principle for policy guidance.

I should perhaps caution the reader, and more so the economist to whom pecuniary compensation is about the only explanation and key to all effort, that he may be shocked somewhat by the conclusion. It does not conform to growth liturgy. It questions several traditional virtues associated with the nature of men. And it refutes explicitly and by implication many hallowed images, beliefs, and maxims of the day. As T. W. Schultz, having seen an early copy of the manuscript, stated somewhat impatiently and not without exaggeration: "The elegant prose of a Kusum Nair, enriched by travel over India, the United States and Japan, has farmers saying, 'Economics is dead.'" (T. W. Schultz, *Production Opportunities in Asian Agriculture: An Economist's Agenda* (Michigan State University, Asian Studies Center, June 1968), mimeo, pp. 4–5.)

For this, what might appear to many as irreverence and heresy, however, I am not to blame. It was not intended.

What farmers say is in any case beyond my control. But as mentioned earlier, I set out on this venture with a question in my brief case and not a hypothesis. The conclusion derives from and emerges from the empirical data in the text. Unless it is established that the evidence is false, I see no alternative to the final argument and inference. However, even if my thesis should fail immediately to convert all readers, I hope it will provoke them seriously to question and debate in light of the proffered evidence, many of the assumptions that underlie current development theories and policies, as for example, the dogma that mass movement of population *out* of farming is a necessary precondition (and inevitable outcome) of modernization of agriculture.

It will not come easily to the learned, but the truth is that we do not have as yet a practical policy for inducing agricultural growth that will work *by design*. We do not even know what *will* persuade a given number of farmers to produce more, more efficiently, in a given manner and time, especially when the shop windows are largely empty. And the exact sequence and nature of circumstances under which agriculture developed wherever it did, differed in each case, and could not possibly be duplicated. Generally, they resulted from a wholly fortuitous combination of human will and blunders and divine accidents.

It has become essential, therefore, instead of urging the developing nations to do more of what has been tried before, that key premises of the social sciences concerned with agricultural development be reexamined. What may have been believed to be valid once in one part of the world, especially the Western world, need not be valid forever, everywhere, under all conditions. That many such beliefs have acquired an aura of universality and revealed truth is because the lowly peasant is not alone among men to cling to ancestral wisdom long after it has become obsolete.

August 1968

Acknowledgments

My obligations are so extensive as to eliminate virtually any possibility of acknowledging them fully. My first thoughts, however, go out to the hundreds of farmers and their families who gave so generously of their time and hospitality to help me understand their views, attitudes, and problems, even though my questions so often delved into the privacy of their personal lives and budgets. That I could do it on such a scale was due primarily to the cooperation of extension officers who arranged for the farm visits. For much of the local folklore and insights also, they were my initial source of information. For the more scholarly background materials and views, my thanks are due the faculty and staff of the universities and agricultural experiment stations that I visited. I am obliged to them for their time and patience. Since the farmers, extension agents, and institutions of learning and experimentation are spread over six countries, it is impossible to list them individually.

There is, however, a smaller set of institutes that provided the fuel that made this undertaking of what was a dream project a reality. The first was the Radcliffe Institute of Independent Study, Cambridge (Mass.). It gave me a year's grant for 1962-63, supplemented by a Fulbright travel grant. My expenses in Japan on two occasions, in 1963 and 1965, and in the Philippines and Thailand, were met by the Agricultural Development Council, New York. The Australian National University carried the burden of my visit to that continent, while the Center for Economic Development and Cultural Change, University of Chicago, provided invaluable support for two years' work in India, from 1964-66. In 1967 the Center for International Affairs, Harvard University, offered me a home and facilities for writing. I put the final touches on the manuscript and saw it through the press while at Michigan State University. Among individuals who made this generous support possible, my grateful thanks go to Ken and Kitty Galbraith. They were in India in 1962 and were responsible for getting me started. From ADC, I received much more than financial support, and for that I have to thank Arthur T. Mosher, A. M. Weisblat, A. B. Lewis, and most of the Foundation staff at headquarters. I am deeply grateful to Sir John Crawford for my Australian venture and for general encouragement. I could never repay these debts, except in the arrogant hope that the final outcome may have justified the investment in some measure.

Another critical kind of help in the venture has been from the many friends and scholars who have spared the time to read the manuscript at various stages and to offer valuable criticism and suggestions. These include Edward C. Banfield, Willard W. Cochrane, Dale E. Hathaway, Albert O. Hirchman, Bert F. Hoselitz, Nathan M. Koffsky, William W. Lockwood, Edward S. Mason, Gunnar Myrdal, Richard L. Park, Henry Rosovsky, William T. Ross, Thomas C. Smith. If the book is still imperfect, the blame must rest wholly with me. J. Singh and Alice K. Mellian, I have to thank for secretarial assistance and for typing the manuscript.

My final salutations go to my family. It always suffers, as it must, if I am so preoccupied with travel and writing for such inordinate lengths of time. To that, however, there appears no easy solution, unless it be not to write.

Contents

Contents

CHAPTER I

Four Faces

1

Graying, genial, slow; a tear in the right leg of his unpressed pants; he owns 160 acres of land.

Cannot be persuaded to use lime that the soil needs. Does not rotate the crops either. Crops his pasture too close. Hay in the barn is of poor quality.

He sold the horses nine years ago. Milked with his hands till three years ago. Rebuilt the barn a year ago. It had been condemned by the milk plant, and he could not have sold the milk any more.

He is milking seventeen cows. They average a yield of 4630 pounds of milk per cow in a year. It is less than what used to be the average for the county more than twenty years ago, in 1940. The yield could be doubled. A neighbor milking twenty-two cows is getting 10,225 pounds. Another gets 10,383 pounds per cow. But Robert will not make the effort. Stored in cans, all the milk goes for processing because it is not good enough for fluid consumption.

He will retire probably in eight to ten years. Their three children are grown up and settled. His total assets, however, are worth less than $20,000.

They live in a small frame house; bare floors and blank walls, except for a cross hanging in the kitchen. It has no running water. The wife must fetch it from outside. There is a hand pump in the yard. They were offered a loan by the Farmers Home Administration to install piped water. Robert refused it. Said: "It'll cost too much."

2

"My grandfather was given a grant for this land a hundred years ago. It was signed by the President himself. By President James Buchanan," he repeats proudly.

He owns 180 acres and rents 120. It is pretty, rolling. The soil is good; not light and sandy. The county ranks fourth amongst all counties in the nation for its income from the sale of milk and dairy products. He is milking twenty-eight cows. Also has chickens, hogs, heifers, and beef animals.

The barn is equipped with an automatic cleaner and a stainless steel bulk tank to hold the milk. He has three tractors; all the necessary tillage, planting, and harvesting machinery; also a shining blue car and a truck. The property would be worth nearly half a million dollars.

To help around the farm he hires a hand. Children also help—two boys and two girls. "But they are still young, because we married late." She sounds sorry.

"That is why we have such a small family, and we are past the age for adopting. There are rules. . . ." He has just turned fifty.

They are concerned about the children they have. They do not have a television set in the house lest it make them lazy. He is not planning much education for them either. He thinks that young people do not stay on the farm any more because they go to school.

"Give a kid a car and send him to school. That's the end of him. You've spoilt him."

He studied up to the eighth grade. Big of build, in a check shirt and suspenders, he is hearty, talkative. She too is lively; with buck teeth, thin and scrawny.

Both of them *love* farming. They would not leave it for anything; not even if they could earn *much* more than the $9000 and odd that they now gross in a year.

United States of America

WASHINGTON

MINNESOTA

WISCONSIN

ILLINOIS

PENNSYLVANIA

NORTH CAROLINA

TENNESSEE

MISSISSIPPI

LOUISIANA

UTAH

NEW MEXICO

CALIFORNIA

HAWAII

ALASKA

"Money is not everything," she says with an air of occidental detachment. "You can't eat it."

"Yeah," he confirms. "You could drink it; but you can't eat it." He likes to drink. He is fond of whisky.

He thinks it over. He repeats. He has chosen to stay in farming, "because I like it." He likes it because it is hard work. Many farmers quit because they do not like hard work. "I enjoy it."

For information about new techniques and developments in agriculture, however, "You get it by experience." He does not get it from anywhere else. The county has had an agricultural extension agent since 1919. "But," he insists, "experience, and experience *alone*, can teach you. . . ."

It is three in the afternoon. John has yet to shave. He is cutting his first crop of hay. He is nearly a month behind several of his neighbors. It is almost straw.

After a century of cultivation, stones, small and loose, are scattered around his fields. They could be removed by hand. Vegetables in the yard are infested with thistle.

The house is old. Without paint, it is black as the barn; untidy. The kitchen has been remodeled recently. But the sink is dirty; very dirty.

3

One could live in the barn, it is so clean; painted white. Even the grass around it has been mowed, as carefully as the front lawn. The house, too, is lovely; with carpets, curtains, white lace on the dining-room table.

Yet, he is milking only twenty cows. And the country is hilly, rocky, wooded. The fields are small and scattered. In narrow circular strips they skirt the contour of the land. Often the slope is steep.

The little town nearby, where he went to school, is struggling to survive. The old grade school has moved out. There is no industry. A lumber mill—it used to be operated by water power—stands idle. There are few churches; not even a bookstore.

"My grandfather decided to settle here probably because it was like home." In his time, a man could have had practically the pick of what he wanted. Plenty of land was available virtually for the taking. Ray has not tried to move to gentler, more fertile pastures. But he purchased a bulk cooling tank for his milk, way back in 1946. "They ridiculed me."

The silo, however, is small. He does not have an automatic unloader; pitches by hand. Most of the heavy machinery he shares and owns jointly with his brother-in-law. They also swap labor. "Oh, yes. It can be done," without hurting timeliness of operations.

He does not have much equipment in fact, because he thinks that "beyond a certain point, further mechanization becomes pointless; a vicious circle and a burden." It is not necessary. Nor does he agree with the belief and trend of the times, that farmers must have larger and larger units in order to make a decent living. "We think we are making a good living."

Across the road, a farmer from Iowa has recently bulldozed a thousand acres—woods, contours, and all. "His only concern is bigness—as in Iowa."

Ray finds his hundred cultivated acres sufficient. In the ultimate analysis, he feels, "It is not the size of the operation but the quality and efficiency of work that counts."

His first crop of hay was in three weeks ago. Corn in the fields is good. The cows are beauties. Sells Grade A milk of the highest quality. He works from five in the morning till nine at night; sometimes ten. The wife helps. A handsome family, they have three children, two girls and a boy.

4

There was not a tractor on the place in 1941, when Carl took over the 160-acre farm from his father for $15,000.

"Father did not like tractors." So, he had only horse-drawn equipment.

Now, there is not a horse left on the farm. It is totally mechanized; a superb, modern dairy unit, well above the average. The double four herringbone milking parlor is the latest in vogue; spotless. One man can milk forty-five to fifty cows in an hour; four at a time.

The cows are never pastured. They stay in a "loafing" barn, out in the open, all through the year. There is only a shed for them to lounge in, to eat and drink. He built it a year ago. Some neighbors say he does not know what he is doing. The cows' teats will freeze in the cold. Only one teat froze, and it was an unusually severe winter.

Almost every year, Carl introduces some such innovation, some new device; adds some more machinery, a few more cows, and many more acres. Forty-nine years old, he is milking seventy-six cows. He owns as much young stock for replacement and has 460 acres. His two silos are probably the tallest in the county.

He is, however, modest, gentle, soft spoken; a handsome man of few words. He completed high school, the only one in a family of nine to do so. But he worked on his father's farm from the age of ten. His own youngest son, a cheerful eleven-year-old, wakes up at five. The boy feeds the calves and does other chores around the barn every day, before and after school. The whole family helps—four sons and a daughter. No help is hired.

The wife and daughter also freeze meat and can the vegetables. They bake their own bread and tend the kitchen garden. It has flowers as well. The old two-story frame house they live in is large. It has been remodeled and is elegantly furnished. The lawn, the hedges, and the bushes are all very neat and trim.

Only the office in the milkhouse is frugal—an unpolished desk with a figurine of Mary and Jesus. On the wall hangs a wooden cross, and above it a board with the number and daily up-to-the-minute record of each cow. The cows have numbers. They are too many to have names. Besides, names for cows are obsolete.

5

Four random faces: they are all white, professional dairy farmers from the heart of "America's Dairyland," the midwestern state of Wisconsin. In terms of volume and value of milk products, Wisconsin has been the foremost state in the country for more than half a century.

Although their pioneer forefathers came of different ethnic stocks, from different countries in Europe, possibly for different reasons and from different backgrounds, Robert, John, Ray, and Carl are all at least third-generation American.[1]

They have had the same routine rural schooling of their times. None has had very much more of it, or less, than the rest. None has had any specialized off-the-farm instruction in agriculture, animal husbandry, or farm management. On the other hand, they have had equal access, as their parents did before them, to similar opportunities, extension and other services, technology, credit, and markets, under identical constraints and incentives of public policy and private institutions.

The soil on their farms is not identical. But in no case is it particularly superior or infertile. In any event it is not a critical factor, because American cows do not live by the soil alone, so to say; not any more. Three of the farms are situated in adjacent counties in the predominantly agricultural area of central Wisconsin. The fourth is farther east, in the region of Fox River Valley. In all four counties, milk is the most important source of farm income.

Full-time, commercial "dirt" farmers, earning mainly from milking cows, the four men started working independently on their own farms, all of about the same size, very early in the 1940's. The decade witnessed a dramatic rise in the price of agricultural commodities, and in value and quantity of dairy products sold per farm, the upward trend continued subsequently. Also, development in dairying, as in the entire range of agricultural technology in the United States, has been more rapid in the twenty years after 1940 than in the preceding century. The milk on the market is wholly standardized. No farm commodity in Wisconsin is so closely regulated and governed by as much special legislation as the production and marketing of fluid milk.

Yet, one farmer out of the four has spent a lifetime shuffling his feet, heaving and carrying cans of indifferent milk, milked indifferently, from indifferent cows. He let the opportunities at his doorstep slip by.

Another, despite his vehement affection for agriculture and hard work, has yet to notice the rocks in his fields nor has he troubled to harvest the hay on time.

The third farmer is most impressive and efficient. He operates on a static scale, however, that would be more appropriate in the country of his grandparents' birth, where arable land is scarce and largely infertile. What is more, he is content with it.

Only the fourth, alone among the four operators, is striving continually to improve, innovate, add; to use the latest techniques, plant, and machinery. He produces more milk than the rest of the three together.[2] He is earning roughly four times the gross income of John and ten times that of Robert. There is little or no comparison between their levels of life and work. Carl's cows live better probably than the families of the first two.

And *he* is not even a progeny of the Puritan revolution. His great-grandfather did not flee home and Europe as a dissenter persecuted for his faith. Carl is neither Protestant, nor secular. A devout Catholic, he will ordinarily not cut a crop on Sunday. If the weather should compel him, then he will do it, but with prior permission of the parish priest.

"Some folks do it, even if it is not absolutely necessary," says his wife. "We don't."

Only the milking they do on the Sabbath. It is permitted by the church.

CHAPTER II

The Invisible Ladder

1

A favorite American fable tells of a ladder, one end of which rests on the ground. It stands erect, like the rope in the Indian rope trick. Any farmer, at least any white farmer, could start at the lowest rung of this ladder without a nickel in his pocket and climb to the very top. The ladder is not visible any more. Nevertheless, it describes a situation more or less accurately, as it obtained once upon a time.

Ideally, a farm boy began as an unpaid worker on the home farm. At the age of seventeen or so he started to work on a neighbor's farm for cash wages. He lived with the family and saved the cash, with which he purchased a team of horses and some equipment. Then he rented a piece of land that he cultivated independently. If he was frugal, he saved enough to make a down payment to purchase a farm, the balance being secured by mortgage. Normally, by the time he was sixty-five years old, he was an owner-operator.

To climb this ladder became a national dream, a part of the American creed and ethic. Not only did a farm boy generally want to climb it, but he was expected to climb it, just as he was expected to attend church or send his children to school. Yet, over the recent decades, more farmers appear to have slipped down the agricultural ladder than risen up on it. After World War II, tens of thousands were finding it difficult to keep a foothold on whichever rung they happened to be.

In 1935, for example, there were 6.8 million farms, the most ever in American history. By 1965, there were the fewest since 1870. In three decades they had dwindled to less than one half. Only 3.3 million farms remained, on a total land area of about 2.3 billion acres, of which 80 percent is classified as agricultural, including forests. Some 3 to 4 percent of the farmers were still quitting farming each year.[1]

Moreover, of those who remained, as many as 1.8 million, that is 55 percent, were like Robert, first of the four dairy farmers of Wisconsin. They had cash sales of less than $5000 in a year, of whatever they produced. They earned 8.2 percent of the total receipts from farm marketings. Those like John sold $5000 to $10,000 worth of commodities. They made up 14.8 percent of all farms, and earned 9.5 percent of the market proceeds. Only 499,000 farms were akin to Carl's enterprise, each selling farm products worth $20,000 and over. Among them, about 140,000 had sales of $40,000 or more.[2] Altogether, they also comprised 14.8 percent of the total number of farms, but received as much as 63.8 percent of the market sales.

Of the first group, however, nearly a million and a half farmers did not have enough produce to earn even $2500. And so, 42.9 percent of all farm operators in the United States in 1965 shared 4.3 percent of the total cash from market receipts.[3]

2

In a message to Congress on February 4, 1965, President Lyndon B. Johnson stated: ". . . Lack of a decent life is almost twice as prevalent in rural America as it is in urban America. Only 30 percent of our families live in rural areas, but they include 46 percent of those American families with incomes under $3,000." It placed them in the "poverty" classification as defined by the administration at that time.

In the same farm message of February 4, however, the President also affirmed that "Rural America is the scene of one of the greatest productive triumphs in the history of man."[4] This is true. Agricultural technology in the United States is one of the most highly developed in the world. In the decade of 1950 it developed more rapidly than technology did in industry. Output per man hour of farm workers increased at more than twice the rate for workers in manufacturing. Agriculture had come a long way since the days of Charles Newbold's cast iron plow of 1797. Thus:

> The plows of the eighteenth century were heavy and awkward contrivances. The moldboard was constructed of wood according to some rule-of-thumb that might or might not result in a plow that would turn the soil. . . . It took two men, or a man and a boy, using two or three horses or four to six oxen, an entire day to plow one or two acres. . . .
> The first patent issued for a plow went to Charles Newbold of New Jersey in 1797. The plow, except for the handles and beam, was to be of solid cast iron. Although Newbold's plow worked well, it was not accepted by the farmers, as they claimed the iron poisoned the land and made the weeds grow.
> The next great improvement in the plow was Jethro Wood's cast iron plow, first patented in 1814. . . . (But, at) the first plowing match at Brighton, Massachusetts, held in 1817, no cast iron implements were used.[5]

By 1960, however, in a single year farmers were purchasing plowing and other equipment containing more than five million tons of steel. It was difficult to find anything wooden operating on a field, unless it was the farmer himself.

The statistics are staggering. Whereas in 1820 a farm worker produced enough food and fiber for only three people, he now supplies more than thirty consumers, besides himself. One hour of farm labor in the early 1960's produced more than five times as much food and other crops as it did in 1919–21. An Iowa farm that needed seventeen men to operate in the 1930's could be worked by three men —the same acreage and enterprises.

Four million fewer workers therefore produced 50 percent more farm products in 1960 than in 1940. Corn yields were 92 percent higher per acre, with 86 percent less work per bushel; and wheat 47 percent more, with 73 percent less work per bushel. Cotton was giving 79 percent more per acre, with 73 percent less work per bale. There was a 57 percent increase in the yield of milk per cow, with an equivalent decrease in work per gallon; while broilers took 88 percent less labor per pound.

The only farm creature to resist modernization, mechanization, or increased efficiency in the process of production—up to 1965—was the pig. He appeared to be immune to progress. Although a number of developments were under way, it still took as many pounds of feed to produce a hundred pounds of hogs as was the case a decade earlier. Feed fed per 100 pounds of broilers and turkeys had, in the same period, dropped by 25 and 15 percent, respectively. Feed fed to layers per 100 eggs produced, also dropped 15 percent; while 20 percent more live weight of grain-fattened cattle was produced for every 100 pounds of feed than in the early 1950's.

3

The impressive gains in production efficiency came about not only by improvement in yields owing to better varieties of seed, stock, and cultural techniques but through a massive investment in plant and machinery as well. Increase in drawbar power of tractors, for instance, has been phenomenal on U.S. farms. In nine years from 1955 it went up by 40 percent. It was five times as much as in the 1920's, on fewer harvested acres.

In 1910 virtually all power on the farms was supplied by horses and mules. Even in 1940 more animal than mechanical power was being used. In another twenty years, however, only three million horses survived on farms. Since 1920, one-fourth or more of the total cropland that had been used for feeding horses has been released for other purposes. The engines now used for agricultural production have a total of 205 million horsepower. This is more than the combined power of mechanical engines and turbines of all of the nation's factories, private and commercial aircraft, railroads, merchant ships, and mines.

In 1965 farmers invested over $4.2 billion in motor vehicles, tractors, and other farm machinery and equipment. New tractors alone cost them $991 million.[6] The tractor is basic. It is, however, one piece of equipment among many, such as milkers and milk coolers, feed mixers, harvester-threshers, and mechanical pickers of various kinds for diverse crops. Some of them are highly complex and ingenious. Thus, giant self-propelled combines cut the wheat and simultaneously thresh it. The grain flows from a chute into a wagon running alongside. These machines can harvest up to 150 acres a day. Some combines also bale the straw and deliver it ready for storage to a second wagon. There is another adaptation for picking corn and yet another that plucks the cotton bolls, two rows at a time. Mechanical dryers are fitted with a temperature control device for quick drying of the harvested grain. Similarly, a potato machine digs, gathers, grades, sacks, weighs, and delivers the potatoes to the waiting truck; while the sugar-beet harvester not only digs and sacks the beets but also ties a string around the sacks and drops them off at the end of the row. Some devices combine several operations, as, for instance the mulchmonster, used for preparing the soil. It has spring teeth to raise clods, pulverizer wheels to smash them and level the soil, peg teeth to smooth, aerate, and loosen it, and a dragboard to finish. Corn and peanut planters open the bed, plant the seed, place the fertilizer—all in a single operation. There is also a machine that cultivates and at the same time shoots flames that kill the weeds. Several thousand aircraft are employed for spraying chemicals for weeds and pests and for aerial seeding.

Practically all operations, of plowing, planting, irrigating, spraying, harvesting, threshing, storing, and transporting, are performed by machines. Whatever remains, and it is largely stoop work on specialized farms producing vegetables, fruit, sugarcane, or cotton, is done by hired hands.

The value of machinery and other assets in agricultural production in America (inclusive of farm real estate but less the value of dwellings) was estimated at $201.7 billion in 1966. Average investment per farm came to $65,960; and per farm worker to $35,958.[7]

Aside from capital expenditure, the average annual operating expense per farm was $9110. To mention a few of their current expense items, farmers consumed more petroleum in a year than any single industry; also as much electric power as required to supply Baltimore, Chicago, Boston, Detroit, Houston, and Washington, D.C. They purchased $5.9 billion worth of feed for livestock and $599 million worth of seed.[8] Similarly, primary plant nutrients, lime and chemical fertilizers cost the farmers $1.7 billion. A critical factor among various inputs, the usage of fertilizers in U.S. agriculture by the way, has an interesting history.

CHAPTER III

"Like Pigs in Clover"

1

Chemical fertilizers were introduced in the United States around the middle of the nineteenth century. But very much earlier, in the spring of 1621, shortly after the Pilgrims had landed in New England, an Indian named Squanto or Tisquantum, taught the Pilgrims how to plant corn and fertilize each hill with fish. Squanto showed "them both the maner how to set it, and after how to dress & tend it. Also he tould them, excepte they gott fish & set with it (in these old grounds) it would come to nothing. . . ."[1]

Despite Squanto's warning, however, the pioneers appear to have preferred literally to "butcher" the virgin soil they cleared to exhaustion, "till it will bear nothing more."[2] They would plow up fresh land rather than fertilize the old.

But then, as the settlements spread, often there was no good land left nearby to clear, and soil exhaustion became a problem. In eastern New England for instance, the situation early became serious, and wheat had to give way to the cultivation of corn or rye and livestock raising. Similarly, in Maryland and Virginia, yields of tobacco and wheat declined as the soil became impoverished, and cotton suffered the same fate in the South Atlantic states. According to Lewis C. Gray, "In the upland areas from Virginia to

Georgia the expansion of cotton and tobacco left behind an ever-widening circle of lands suffering from soil exhaustion. Year after year the old lands were depleted until it was no longer profitable to farm them. By 1850 a large proportion of Virginia and Maryland east of the Blue Ridge was a waste of old fields and abandoned lands covered with underbrush and young cedars."[3]

Through the century, the American farmer generally continued to impoverish the soil. On new Western lands also, reports showed rich harvests for a few years. As Oliver Ellsworth wrote to his brother from Bloomington, Illinois: "The soil is as black as your hat and as mellow as a(n) ash heep. . . . If you, John, will come on, we can live like pigs in the clover. . . ."[4] Said Morris Birbeck in 1818, "Manure has been often known to accumulate until the farmers have removed their yards and buildings out of the way of the nuisance. They have no notion of making a return to the land, and as yet there seems no bounds to its fertility."[5] But then, as the soil became exhausted, here too, there would be a sharp decline in yields to the point of unprofitability. However, the typical attitude was: "To talk of manuring all our farms while they are so large is simply ridiculous. With the present scarcity and high price of labor, how is the farmer to find time and money or labor to manure his farm of from one hundred and sixty to fifteen thousand acres?"[6]

The average farmer therefore "would dream at the plow handles, and then throw the stable manure into the ditches, or on the mud roads."[7] Declining fertility of the soil was perhaps an important reason why the average output per worker in agriculture in 1850, when about two-thirds of the population was engaged in its production, was very nearly the same as half a century earlier in 1800.[8]

By 1860 chemical fertilizers were being manufactured commercially by seven factories in the United States. Two decades later, an English observer expressed the hope that "when no virgin land is left to exhaust" farmers would turn to the practices of more experienced countries and save American agriculture before it was too late. Several agencies within the country, such as agricultural colleges, experiment stations, farm journals, and the Grange, also began to urge better conservation and tillage practices. Even so, by 1900 expenditure on commercial fertilizers was 11 cents to the average acre in Ohio and 1 cent in most of the prairie country of the North Central states.[9] In 1909 the Commission on Country Life, appointed by Theodore Roosevelt, viewed with concern the "lessening of soil fertility . . . in every part of the United States."

2

Till after the outbreak of World War II, in fact, there was little systematic manuring of American soils. The evidence is mostly of serious depletion of fertility, countered by constant shifts to better lands and expansion of acres. In 1937–38, the North American continent (including Canada) used 1.7 million metric tons of plant nutrients, as against 4.7 million tons consumed in West Europe alone. Twenty-one years later, North America was still lagging behind Western Europe in this respect. Nearly 60 percent of the harvested crop in the United States was not fertilized, although there had been a 300 percent increase in the consumption of commercial fertilizers since 1940, and most of the increase in yields in this period had accrued from it. Only 11 percent of the American farmers in 1959 used the recommended and most profitable rate of fertilization.

In the summer of 1963, my first engagement in a county in Minnesota, agriculturally rich and progressive, was to attend a meeting late in the evening at which the county agent addressed a group of farmers in their church basement. The entire talk revolved on the theme of fertilizers—why and how they should be used. It was illustrated by a film. The county agent stated that not more than 15 percent of the local farmers had their soils tested. Although most were perhaps using some plant nutrients, he estimated the majority did not apply them on all crops. Nor did they always apply the right type of fertilizer, correctly or in sufficient quantity. In its content and presentation the lecture was elementary. It could have served an audience of illiterate peasants in India.

Also, as one drove through the corn country, variation in quality and color of foliage was often striking, at times astonishing, in standing crops in adjacent fields, mainly because of a differential in the rate of fertilizer application. Interstate variations in average yields in 1962 ranged from twenty-seven bushels an acre in Mississippi to eighty-three bushels in Illinois, though most of the corn came from states with an average output of fifty bushels an acre or more.

Corn, a major crop in the U.S., is the most important of the feed grains.[10] It is also the pride of American agriculture. Grown under more nearly ideal conditions of soil and climate than any place else in the world, it has been developed to near perfection in the three and a half centuries since the Jamestown settlers first planted thirty to forty acres of it, their efforts to grow European crops having ended in disaster.

Yet, even in the eight Corn Belt and Lake states that together account for 73 percent of the grain, studies showed that in 1963 farmers could have profitably obtained twenty to twenty-four bushels more per acre. They could have increased over-all production of corn in the same acreage by one-third, simply by using more fertilizer. Yield response under farm conditions in these states indicated that with corn at a dollar a bushel and fertilizer at prevailing prices, if farmers had doubled the (1963) average rate of application, they would have got back $1.20 on the last dollar spent on fertilizer, with other practices at existing levels.[11] It should have provided a very attractive incentive. Moreover, fertilizer salesmen were established in most of these communities with equipment and credit, and farmers could have had the fertilizer applied as and when required and paid for it after the crop had been harvested.[12]

3

However, with or without fertilizers, the United States is the world's leading producer and exporter of farm produce, and its farmers are the most productive on the planet.[13]

The country has never known a famine. Tall silver elevators filled with golden grain glimmer everywhere in the sunshine. Tables at home are loaded with calories, and countless ships carry as much grain abroad as the needy countries can and will take, with or without payment.[14] From around 1952, production became seemingly unlimitable and almost out of hand. Farm output increased at 2 percent a year. But every year, it has been more than the increase in demand. It has kept agriculture in a state of chronic oversupply.

In an effort to deal with the problem, compulsory acreage allotments were imposed in 1953. A Soil Bank program was authorized in 1956 to pay farmers for a period of years to reduce acreage of the major supported crops in which unwanted stocks were accumulating. Also, a Conservation Reserve program was introduced, under which entire farms could be retired and the owner of the land receive payments for keeping it out of crop production. Under this scheme 6.4 million acres were retired in 1957, 9.9 millon acres in 1958, 22.4 million acres in 1959, and 28.6 million acres in 1960. By 1965 about 60 million acres of cropland were being withheld from production under the Conservation Reserve and grain programs.

In 1961 a special feed-grains program was introduced. Farmers were paid for idling land on which these grains had been grown for the previous two years. As a result, in a year the acreage under corn declined 18 percent, and that under grain sorghum dropped by 29 percent. Output of corn, however, was reduced only 7 percent, and of sorghum 22 percent. Their yields per acre had risen 13 percent over that in 1960.

At peak in 1961, carryover stocks of corn amounted

to two billion bushels, or about half a year's output. Of wheat, there were 1.4 billion bushels in storage—more than twice the annual domestic consumption. Stocks held by the Commodity Credit Corporation had risen every year for almost a decade, in spite of acreage allotments, soil banks, lower price supports, and special surplus-disposal programs. Interest and storage charges alone on the surplus were costing the federal government around a billion dollars annually; losses on disposals about two billion dollars; and other programs another billion. In eight years from 1953 the administration spent more than forty billion dollars on agriculture. By the middle 1960's the cost of maintaining farm prices and incomes and disposing of surplus products was running close to six billion dollars a year.

In 1964–65, Commodity Credit Corporation expenditures were estimated to equal 25 percent of the value of feed grains produced, 19 percent of the value of wheat, and 26 and 27 percent, respectively, of the value of cotton and rice production.

4

Not only did agricultural produce persist in rising regardless of a variety of controls and disincentives designed and administered by the government to restrain it, it did so despite rising costs and declining prices and returns on resources engaged in farm production. "The continued expansion of farm output in the United States, in the face of falling product prices and falling incomes to factors of production," has been described by Dale Hathaway as "one of the great economic phenomena of the postwar period."[15]

Except for a brief interlude of the Korean War, the 1950's saw a chronic downward pressure on prices and equally chronic surpluses. Realized gross income from farming (including government payments) was $34 billion in 1957, as against $34.1 billion in 1947. Cash receipts from farm marketings were $29.7 billion in 1957, as against

$29.6 billion in 1947. Yet total agricultural output in the decade had increased by 20 percent.

Despite the massive government programs, the absolute level of farm prices in the late 1950's was well below the high point reached in 1951. And since the general price level had risen in the meantime, the relative price of farm products in 1960–61 was the lowest in twenty years. Production expenses were rising, both because the farmer was purchasing a greater volume of inputs and because there was a persistent increase in the price of inputs. These rose from $6.7 billion in 1940 to $16.9 billion in 1947, to $26.1 billion in 1960, and $30.5 billion in 1965. Land values more than doubled between 1947 and 1964.

The aggregate realized net farm income (including government payments) was about the same for the fourth consecutive year in 1964, at around $12.5 billion, although the value of farm marketings had increased from $36.4 billion in 1961, to $39.1 billion in 1964.[16] Net income rose to $14.2 billion in 1965, but it was still less than in 1947, by nearly $3 billion. Moreover, by 1965 it was a mere 31.6 percent of the gross farm earnings, as against 50.1 percent in 1947.

Farmers also received substantially lower returns for their capital and labor than comparable investment in other industries.[17] The great majority of them received less than parity returns on their productive assets, effort, and enterprise.[18] Even with the record gross farm income of $44.9 billion realized in 1965, the per capita disposable income of the farm population from *all* sources was about 63 percent of that received by nonfarm people in the same year.[19] It was 54.2 percent a year earlier.

Furthermore, the absolute level of national income originating in agriculture fell from $20.9 billion in 1948 to $15.7 billion in 1960. In 1965 it was $19.5 billion and constituted 3.5 percent of the total national income as against 9.4 percent seventeen years earlier.

To quote Dale Hathaway again: "The absolute decline in national income originating in agriculture meant that the people and resources contributing to the steadily increasing farm output were receiving a declining payment for doing so. Here again we see the amazing contrast: rapid increases of output not as a response to rising product prices and an increasing income stream but, instead, in the face of falling prices and a declining income stream."[20]

The phenomenon was both confounding and frustrating. It had Americans in general thoroughly confused. Nor were the economists quite able to comprehend it. Each offered his own explanation, but they could not agree with one another or on a course of action that would persuade farmers to behave as they wanted them to.

Nor were the politicians able to devise effective and yet satisfactory means of restraining production, either by legislative or divine intervention. For the eight years that Ezra Taft Benson was secretary of Agriculture, his staff meetings opened with a prayer, as did the meetings of the National Agricultural Advisory Commission.

Democrats discontinued the ritual of invocation when they took office in 1961, but they tightened the controls on production of the problem commodities in an effort to stem the mounting surplus. However, Republicans or Democrats, prayers or no prayers, and whatever the controls, prices, and profits, production in agriculture in this period, of roughly a decade and a half, continued to increase relentlessly, to the point virtually of absurdity.[21]

The American consumer already spent a smaller proportion of his income on food than did any national anywhere else in the world.[22] On the other hand, reduction of labor required in the production of farm commodities continued so steeply that a growing number of farmers became surplus. They were unable to find employment in other sectors of the economy, and they could not stay in agriculture.

Still another group sat on the river bank watching the weeds grow in their fields, because the government paid them to do so. As one of them in Texas wrote to his Congressman:

"Like Pigs in Clover"

My friend over in Terebone Parish received a $1,000 check from the government this year for not raising hogs. . . .

What I want to know is, in your opinion, what is the best kind of farm not to raise hogs on and the best kind of hogs not to raise.[23]

CHAPTER IV

The Treadmill

1

In this, what looked like a runaway phenomenon in agriculture, the individual farmer was the primary producer. His effort still constituted perhaps the most important input. As an abstraction of statistical averages, he appeared to be an embodiment of secular progress, efficiency, enterprise, and innovation, thought not always of conventional economic wisdom.

But there is no abstract average farmer. There are individuals in farming, whose multitude of detached decisions, actions, and achievements collectively make up the national and regional aggregates. How did this individual view the trends and problems in his country's agriculture? What did he think of government policies, of controls and subsidy? Why did he work so hard to produce more, when quite obviously the market could not take it, at the price that he could produce and accept?

In March 1967 dairy farmers in twenty-five states took to dumping several million pounds of milk in order to press their demand for about two cents a quart more for their produce. One of them described his tribulations in a letter to the *New York Times*, as follows:

> *To the Editor:*
>   My mother used to tell of the farm in Minnesota, where they had to tie the dog up on Sunday

nights so that he would be around on Monday morning to operate the treadmill that ran the churn. That dog, it seems, had more sense than the average dairy farmer.

The farmer works ten hours a day, seven days a week, to maintain and enlarge a property to which he is never out of debt, the taxes, constantly increasing, costing him the value of the property every ten years or so.

The oxen and team of horses that used to supply the power are now replaced by gasoline-driven machinery and the farmer is a slave to big industry. In order to get increased production, he must cover his acres with a yearly spread of manufactured fertilizer and poisonous pesticides. These cost as much as his land is worth.

Originally, he milked by hand in a tin pail, swept up with a broom and fed the herd hay with a pitchfork. The creamery supplied the can for the milk, which he kept cool in the spring. The tin pail has been replaced with thousands of dollars' worth of pipelines, bulk tanks, wash tanks, refrigerators, water heaters, vacuum milkers and large ranch-type masonry buildings. More thousands of dollars are poured in to replace the broom, gutter cleaners, slurry tanks, tank spray trucks, tractor loaders, concrete paved barnyards and anything else that the tyrannical state milk inspector can think of. The Augean stables? Hercules had a cinch.

Nearly 90 per cent of the farmer's production must now go to pay the interest on his investment, and so more thousands of dollars must pay for several silos, and the loading and unloading equipment, granaries, haylofts, combines, balers, choppers, seeders, grinders and conveyors. The pitchfork hangs up beside the broom and the tin pail.

Besides the state milk inspector, the dairyman is also under the lash of the creamery's bulk truck driver, who shows up whenever he feels like it, usually twice a week, weighs, tests for butterfat and temperature and, if he feels so inclined, takes the milk.

The weather determines whether he breaks even. Three out of four years he owes the bank. His barns burn or the tractor tips over on him or disease wipes out his herd, but he never just sells out and retires. He doesn't know, as the treadmill dog did, what freedom is.

He sides with his masters when some of his fellow farmers rebel, and when their half-hearted attempts fail he is glad that he stayed home on the treadmill.

P. F. MacDonald
Shohola, Pa., March 21, 1967

Generally, farmers do not create the new technology that helps to increase production. Often they are indifferent or even hostile to it. Why then, like MacDonald, did they hang up the pitchfork, the tin pail, and the broom and buy more and more equipment in the face of falling farm prices and declining incomes?[1] If they are rational and profit maximizing, why do they mechanize so heavily even though, apart from the problem of surplus and lower prices for their products that it creates, the equipment costs so much more every year to purchase and to operate, and the cost more often than not exceeds the additional revenue?[2]

But for government price supports, in fact, the bigger, commercial, modern, and highly mechanized farms would have been in serious financial difficulty in this period —more so than the smaller ones.[3] Why then did so many farmers continue to farm when for most the economic returns on their labor were submarginal and the returns on investment very much less than in the prosperous and expanding nonagricultural sector of the American economy?[4] Like MacDonald, were they also on a treadmill they could not get off?[5] How did some of these farmers in various income groups in the year of 1963 figure it out, or didn't they?

2

"My problems are debt and machinery." He used to be in the Navy. He purchased his farm seventeen years ago, soon after the war. The leading agricultural enterprise in his county and state is dairying.[6]

Peter Kerl now owns 159 acres, 30 cows, 16 heifers, and has a debt of $18,696.[7] He also has an automobile, a truck, three tractors, and a full line of equipment. The machines, however, "are breaking down all the time." He tries to repair them, as much as he can. "But sometimes I seriously think I would be better off without the machinery —with horses."

The television set also is not working. It shows no pictures. The house is in a run-down condition and shabby. The wife is thin, haggard. Nevertheless, he would like to continue farming.

"Why?"

"I don't know why. I always wanted to farm." After a pause; "It's good for the children—wouldn't know what to do with them in a city."

He has ten children. Seven of them are in school.[8] The youngest is one year old.

3

Wallace, also a dairy farmer in the same state and county, on the other hand, feels trapped in a situation that he cannot get out of. He started out by renting his farm and then purchased it with borrowed money. He now has 143 acres, 21 cows, 15 heifers, and all the necessary equipment.

Wallace took to farming because after the war he swore he would never serve under anyone, "*never* again." He wanted to be independent. "Now, I don't think I am that independent."

Machinery costs more than the returns justify. "The cost of equipment is too high. A small farmer cannot afford it." Then the health department's requirements "make it impossible for me to earn enough on the scale of my operation. I have had to spend fifteen hundred dollars just to repair that bridge down there and the approach road to the milk house," so the truck could drive up to take delivery of the milk.[9]

He feels very strongly against government controls as well and thinks they favor the large producer. He is convinced that there is nothing to beat the law of demand and supply for adjusting production and prices. He realizes that it would be rough for a while if the price of wheat, for instance, fell to a dollar a bushel. Wallace has fifteen acres in wheat. But then, "It will hurt the big farmer more than the small one," and that is what he wants. That is why he voted against the administration's proposal for stricter production and marketing controls for the 1964 crop in return for a higher support price.[10] He believes that if agricultural prices fall, the big operators will be eliminated. "They will have to quit." His notion of the "big" farmer is the urban professional man, doctor or lawyer, who has the necessary capital to invest in a farm. Under present policy, however, he does not think the small farmer has any future. "The family-size farms must die. We cannot compete."

He does not think the government's new recreation program (aimed at improving small farmers' income) can rescue them either. "It is not as if we have simply to put up a sign on the road and tourists will start flocking in."[11]

Wallace would be willing to quit farming if he had an alternative. He does not, however, see any. He and his wife, both high-school graduates, have four sons to raise.

"No," they do not think people work and earn first to purchase something they want badly. "People always buy first and try to pay for it later." This, they think, is especially true of families that try to keep up with their neighbors. They deny they are similarly motivated. "We are not concerned. We don't care what the neighbors have."

Nevertheless, whenever they make a large purchase, they also incur a debt. Their latest buy is a new automobile, a blue Ford, on which they still owe $2500. The house is extremely untidy and poorly furnished. Their clothing is shabby. However, "I purchased this car new this time, because I did not want to buy other people's troubles. But this too is giving me trouble. The radio doesn't work. . . ."

4

Thirty-one years old, Philip Brooks was born on this farm in the corn country, in southeastern Illinois.[12] So was his father, now living with him.

He owns ninety acres and rents 264.[13] The lease is oral, and he pays one-third of the produce to the landowner, who also provides lime and potash and shares the cost of fertilizer. The house is their own. But it is falling apart, quite literally. In winter the whole family huddles into a single room to keep warm. There is a bed in the living room beside the TV. The yard is littered with debris. Philip has lost all his teeth. Hers look diseased.

One reason for the low income apparently is that he carries too little stock—only eight cows and seventeen sows.[14] He does so because both father and son firmly believe in the legend that "Corn is King." While it used to be true once upon a time, it is not so any more. Corn in the fields also could clearly do with more fertilizer.[15] But most of the income from the farm, he claims, goes into machinery, which he finds very expensive.

When asked what he wants most, however, Philip's reply is instantaneous: "Two hundred acres of my own with some stock. I would be perfectly happy and content with that much."

"No, *no*," he would not "dream of giving up agriculture and going to the town," however much more attractive the financial prospect of an urban job may be. He would not give it a thought even, "not for *anything*."

"Why?"

"The farmer is independent." The son and the father repeat it several times with great feeling and vehemence. Moreover, as an afterthought, "Children cannot be reared in a city. They become delinquents."

They have two girls and two boys, between the ages of eight and three.

5

Ralph Fick also is farming in Illinois, in Vermilion County. In this, the state's east-central region of rich and highly productive soils, 72 percent of the farmland is tenant operated.[16] Full owner-operators cultivate only 15 percent. Ralph too is a tenant. He does not own any land. His father was a tenant as well, all his life.

Thirty-six years old, Ralph has been having a rough time, however, ever since he started to farm a decade ago. In eight years, he has had to move three times, with family, machinery, livestock, and all.[17] Twice he had to leave because the farms he had rented were sold, and he was asked to quit. The third time, he was given notice because he had dairy cows. The landlord did not approve of them.[18] In the end he lost both the farm and the cows, because he had to vacate on March 1, and till February, he had not found another place to move to. He has no home of his own.[19] So he sold his cows. It broke his heart.

The farm that he is renting now belongs to a woman who lives in Florida.[20] It is managed on her behalf by a local bank. Ralph was able to get it only because "I knew some one in the bank."[21]

The tenant's house on the farm, in which they live, is in poor repair, but this landlord is prepared to let him have livestock. The lease is on a 50–50 share basis, in grain and animals.[22] This time, Ralph has a hog operation going. His twelve sows just farrowed 112 pigs. He hopes to farrow two groups of twelve sows twice a year. "May be, I could increase it to three groups, in another year or so."

The hogs have better living facilities than the family, wife and two kids. But Ralph is proud of them: the hogs.

"Would you like to own your own place?"

His face lights up. "Yes," is the unhesitating reply. He would, however, like to own only as much as he rents now—that is, 240 acres.[23] "No, not more."

Ralph worked in a factory once for a year and was earning $2.50 an hour.[24] But he quit. "I did not like it. It was the same every day."

He has had a surfeit of variety in farming, especially of landlords. And he has no illusions of ever being able to own a place, however small.[25] It was not easy getting into farming in the first place. The only land he could find initially to rent was eighty acres, and even the Farmers Home Administration refused to give him a loan for an operation that small.[26] A local bank put him into business eventually on the signature of his father.

Since then, Ralph has had ample experience of the hazards and insecurities of tenant farming. He has no legal protection or security of tenure.[27] Nor is he happy with the prices he is getting for his produce. However, he is not prepared to give up and leave. He has invested more than $14,000 in equipment and livestock.[28] He is determined to stay in agriculture and simply "hope for the best."

CHAPTER V

Why Work?

1

Like Ralph, he also did not own any land when he started. He married and began to farm on his own in the still largely rural region of the Red River Valley in Minnesota. That, however, was way back around 1940. It was a different era.

The first farm Anderson rented was of 420 acres. He then possessed one tractor and a couple of cows that his father had given him. Forty-four years old, he now owns 680 acres and rents 500. He purchased a quarter in 1946 and the rest of this farm in 1951, but only because he had to. The landowner decided to sell it, and Anderson bought it, although he had to borrow money to do so.

Now, again, the 500 acres that he is renting is up for sale. Anderson is being given the option to overbid the highest offer. "I will either have to let it go or buy it." If he decides to buy it, he will have to take another loan.[1]

According to Anderson, this is happening all the time. As soon as a tenant has improved the land, the owner sells it. Often, he does not even inform the tenant, who is left out in the cold, stranded. "It has happened to several farmers." Also, tenants outbid each other, for land to lease is not easy to come by any more.[2] "Even your nearest neighbor will do it to you."

He is worried about the growing size of farms, although his is not a small unit.[3] He thinks the trend will continue, because the margin of profit is so low. "You have to have an awful lot to get enough." He has 177 acres of wheat allotment and 127 acres in sugar beets. The rest is in oats, barley, and sunflowers.

For himself, he would not care to have a larger operation. But he is bothered by the fanatical drive and concern for efficiency. "Everybody keeps emphasizing efficiency," he complains with hands outstretched. Anderson, with several farmers in the community, believes that they work extra hard as it is—"Much harder than say to the east here and in many other regions."

He cannot explain why they work harder. His wife thinks it is because each one is trying to keep up with the neighbors.

"There is also the factor of how you are brought up." Anderson has been taught to believe that since land is God's most precious gift, he must take good care of it and leave it better than when he took custody of it. One of the bishops they had recently also drove them hard. "He did not believe in play."

Even so, "How efficient *can* you get?" he asks, with a note of exasperation in his voice. "You work and work and work. But is it worth all that in the end?"

He is not so sure any more. He has driven a tractor for thirty-six hours at a stretch. After more than two decades of hard work, he has a beautiful new home, into which they moved a couple of years ago. He has two cars, a good living, and a delightful family—of eleven children. Twelfth is on the way.[4]

He also has a debt, however, of more than $70,000.[5] He is not unduly perturbed about it. But it is unlikely that he can repay all of it in his lifetime, no matter how hard he works and how efficiently.

2

"It is precisely that debt" which drives the farmer to work endlessly to produce more and more efficiently, according to young Charles Kingston in northern Utah. "They are all so heavily mortgaged that they have no choice. They've got to produce the most they can to repay those debts."[6]

His own farm of 180 acres and thirty-five dairy cows is mortgaged for $45,000. "I don't think I'll ever be debt free. I feel as if I've rented the place for life."

He had borrowed $8000 for his first batch of cows and tractors in 1954. He still owes $5000 on it. "I have to re-borrow every time I purchase more equipment," although he buys mostly used machinery and does not trade it till it is about to fall apart.[7] He thinks most farmers are over-capitalized and live beyond their means because of social pressures and of advertising. "They feel they've got to."

Charles came into farming for the simple reason that he felt he could make good money at it. "I had no illusions whatsoever about agriculture being a superior way of life, or more independent, and so on; none of that nonsense. I grew up on a farm."

For a while, he had gone to town and worked at different jobs—mainly as a carpenter. He had two years at a college as well. Then he purchased the farm from his father-in-law: "Because I thought I could earn more money here. It was the edge of the Korean boom then and prices of farm products were good." Now, as he looks back, "I don't think I made a very wise decision."

They have a small house that he built himself, and five children. Last year he grossed $22,000, of which net income was $4700. He would like to increase his dairy cows to sixty, but not the acreage.

3

Harvey, in the same county as Charles, has no regrets. But then he was born to it. "Been farming all my life. Started sixty years ago. I am sixty-seven now." He never had an occasion to make a choice.

When first settled, this area was dry and sandy, suited only for pasture. Water from wells was brackish. The first small stream of irrigation from the mountains came in 1873.

"Father came here around 1878. He bought this land and built this house. I was born here"—fifteenth child in a family of twenty-five. His father had two wives.[8] "We have six children." Harvey now owns 764 acres and rents more to make it a round thousand. About two-thirds of it is irrigated.[9]

"We also feed livestock—lambs and cattle. Have 10,000 lambs and 200 head of cattle—feeder cattle. We just fatten them. I like it because it gives us work in winter."

"But why do you want more work? Why work so hard at your age? You already have plenty, don't you? You must be the biggest farmer in the community."

"I don't know" is the first reply. "I was always told work is good for you. Before my boy was big enough to go to school he could drive the tractor. My father milked a hundred cows by hand."

He thinks it over and then adds: "We've got to work hard because we can't help it. We are heavily mechanized."

Mechanization was gradual—first automobile in 1917. "Since he had two wives, father did not want to buy just one car. So he said, all right give me two. It was the same with the piano. He purchased two. I got my first tractor in 1928, or was it 1930. It had steel wheels. We are still purchasing new machinery. The hay swather came three or four years ago. There are only three of them so far in the community. I may buy one next year. I do not have one." However, he says, "We did not used to use any fertilizer here, till ten years ago. Only when they put the restrictions on, we started using it. When returns are small, we've got to produce more to make ends meet."

Harvey has an allotment of 220 acres in wheat. But like Wallace he also voted against the administration's offer of a higher price support in the May 1963 referendum. "I would rather have less and be free, than have more income and be told what to do and what not to do. I was afraid that similar controls would be extended to dairy and other products as well. In fact, Secretary Freeman said so."[10]

Another farmer, who is present during the discussion,

thinks differently—as to why they work so hard to produce more.

"You know," he intervenes, "I think a person who is in permanently like us, we produce either way, irrespective of whether the return is high or low. For one thing, we have fixed overheads like taxes, etc. If prices go down, we have to have more to make the same income. If profits are high, we may still want to increase the volume.

"I don't think returns make much difference to us folks who are permanent," he repeats. "We produce as much as we can irrespective of returns. We think in terms of capacity—of what we can produce rather than in terms of returns." .

More specifically and for himself, however, Albert's goal is to work enough only to help his children get a start in life, "and if they want to go in for education." He would also like to take a vacation every year in California or Florida. "I would work like a nigger the rest of the time to be able to do that," he says earnestly, with a far-off look in his gray-blue eyes.

"I wouldn't want money endlessly," he hastens to add, "money for the sake of money. Just so I could afford that vacation!"

4

Mrs. Daniere also believes that, "we set goals and try to attain a certain standard of living. We work for that." She has a very nice home, with a lovely garden.

Both her husband and son, however, who are farming in partnership in the state of Washington, deny categorically that they are motivated by the income aspect in agriculture. Her son Verl is very clear and forthright. "I would rather do farming than anything else," he says, "but *not* for economic reasons. I *know* I can make more money elsewhere. But I like farming."[11] He thinks that is a good enough justification.

On essentially similar grounds, neither of them would like to farm farther to the west, in the Columbia Basin, where there is an extensive scheme for irrigation.[12]

In fact, the father was farming there till 1937, when he moved over to this site, not far outside Pullman. The ground here is rolling and at places quite steep. They have an elaborate tiled underground drainage. About $75,000 is invested in machinery alone, and this the old man resents. He thinks the cost of mechanization is making it impossible for people who want to stay in farming to do so. He considers it most undesirable that a man should not be able to farm simply because he cannot afford the machinery and the requisite acreage. "This is a free country," he says, but sadly, shaking his head, as if it were no longer true.[13]

Together, they are cultivating 920 acres. Half of it is owned, and half is rented. For wheat, they have an allotment of 280 acres. The rest is under dry peas, barley, oats, alfalfa. With irrigation their output of wheat could be more than doubled, even tripled.[14] According to the director at the Experiment Station in Pullman, "Yields from newly irrigated lands are phenomenal."

On the other hand, dry wheat cultivation can be a "risky, costly business," says Cliff Tollett, farmer and Wheat Commission member. "Sometimes you get forty-five bushels to the acre, all right, only twenty-two bushels of that is Canada thistle."[15] Winter kill, hail, erosion, weeds, and/or disease can cut the yield so that a farmer makes less than wages. He has to work hard ten months a year and be lucky to beat the average 2 percent return on investment. However, yields or no yields, the Danieres refuse to consider the proposition of irrigated farming.

"But tell me: why?"

"We can't do it" is the frank and somewhat vehement reply. "It is much harder work. An American can look big—six feet tall. But he *cannot* work hard. Now the orientals and Mormons can do that kind of work. They don't mind it. But not Americans. It's too hard. It's different. We don't understand it."[16]

It is not as if they did not work hard at present. They have to. It is the *type* of work that poses the problem. Verl would consider cattle. "But not irrigated farming. It's different. It requires too much manual labor." He would not even like to try it.

Furthermore, he is skeptical of the allegedly high returns and believes that the problem of weeds and pests is aggravated under irrigated conditions. In the Columbia Basin, according to him, it is rarely the first farmer who succeeds with wet cultivation. "It is usually the third or fourth."[17]

"Why do you think the orientals can do it?"

"Why? Because they are a different people!" says the senior Mr. Daniere. "The Japanese are small. They can stoop, and they have been used to it for generations." Besides, "they pitch in their women and children you know, to work on the farm. They don't mind."[18] And the Mormons "learnt to do it only because they *had* to. It was a desert in Utah, and there was no place else they could have gone to."[19]

5

Eric Stoll does operate an irrigated farm in the Quincy Irrigation District of the Columbia Basin. And he is "American," and not a Mormon either.

Of his thousand acres, 889 are irrigated. In the project records, twelve separate units are shown under multiple ownership. Actually, it is a single farm.[20] He purchased 800 acres from a man who had been on it since 1900 and left because, like the Danieres, he was not interested in irrigated farming. The rest was owned by two absentee owners who had never seen the property.[21]

Stoll grew up on a small farm in the western part of the state and then went into real estate business. He bought this farm because "The moment I saw the country, I felt I would like to live here." He also fancied the notion "that I could make rain as and when I wanted."[22]

However, unlike the Danieres, who work themselves, he has a foreman under him, and even through the winter he employs three men full time to take care of maintenance and repair of machinery. "We could do with one man perhaps. But we have three." At peak, he hires thirty to forty hands.

Stoll is wearing dark brown woolen pants, a white shirt and tie, polished shoes, and a soft brown felt hat. He is watering the lawn with a sprinkler. He is clean and spruce— not even tanned. His yield on wheat, he says, is 125 bushels an acre. But he does *no* work on the farm, stooping or standing. "I manage."

CHAPTER VI

Men, Mules, and Tractors

There would be several "gentlemen" farmers like Stoll in the irrigated Columbia Basin. But they are not typical in the North-Central and Eastern states of the country, in grain or dairy enterprises.

Almost nowhere does the "American" stoop to stoop labor, and in many communities wives do not work in the fields.[1] Migrant labor is usually hired for crops and operations that are not yet mechanized, that require stoop or strenuous manual work.[2]

Nevertheless, in the north generally, whatever his income status, the farmer-operator hires help only for extra or special work that he cannot handle.[3] For the rest, he works himself and looks it. His hands are grimy, rough, and horny. The face is weather worn, and his complexion is a deep tan. His boots are never polished except on a Sunday maybe, when he dresses to go to church. He has always worked himself, from the days of the ox and the mule.

By contrast, the South is the region for genteel farmers with soft, clean hands.[4] For here they have always had plenty of Negro, practically serf labor, to do the hard and dirty work, and also a dominant agrarian tradition for gracious living and leisure.

40

Here too, agricultural labor is being replaced by machinery, and as elsewhere, farms in the South are becoming fewer and larger. But whereas machinery is ousting the traditional sharecropper and his mule, it continues to be operated mostly by a hired hand—not by the farmer.[5]

Along the road everywhere in the South stand rows of pathetic wooden shacks, shabby, small, silent—empty of erstwhile tenants. The man on the tractor, however, is generally a Negro, and he does not own the land he is plowing or the machine. Rarely, if ever, does the typical "Southern" white landowner in the group of the larger commercial farmers, work on the land himself or even alongside his hired men. He simply stands and supervises, while Negroes dig, lift, carry, or whatever it be. The ground is being plowed in Mississippi for the sowing of cotton. Over and across more than a hundred miles, I do not see a single white man working in the fields.

It is different only in the mountain areas, where there are few or no Negroes and few commercial farms, and in Louisiana, in counties with a heavy concentration of small farmers of French descent. The poor white peasant elsewhere in the southern plains also works on the land himself. He outnumbers the large planters, but he cultivates much less acreage and markets an insignificant proportion of the region's total farm produce.

2

Harold Whitman is typical of the large commercial operator. He has forty tractors and twenty tractor drivers. "Half of them are illiterate, but they can count." He also has thirty-five families on a wage basis. Two overseers, a machineman, and a supervisor stay out in the field with the tractors.[6] There are three families of sharecroppers besides.

"No, I don't work myself. How *can* I? I can't. My work is coordination—over-all management."

He keeps in touch with operations in the field from

the cool comfort of his large living room, through his own radio system. If need be, he rides out in a pickup truck.

Grandfather built the house in 1858. "He had plenty of slaves. These are homemade doors. In father's time, the entire estate was given out on crop-sharing basis."[7] He used to have sixty to seventy families of croppers on the plantation.

"I have more torn down houses than labor. We had to throw them out. What is left is from those times." He still has forty-seven tenant cabins on the grounds. "I have two carpenters who spend half their time just keeping those houses in repair."[8]

Harold is operating 5300 acres, in the Delta region of Yazoo County, in the state of Mississippi. Eight hundred and fifty acres are in cotton.[9]

"My investment is $160 per acre in cotton. That doesn't include the initial investment of $200,000 that I have in machinery. In fact, it is more than that. I've spent another $30,000 on irrigation equipment. Irrigating is expensive." Part of the land is irrigated. For his operating expenses alone, he claims, he often has to borrow $100,000 in a year. "If the crop were to fail, I could never pay it back. In 1960 I faced complete disaster. . . ."

If he produces a bale an acre, "I break even. Anything over a bale is profit." His yields average a bale and three quarters an acre. "But then, bad years also come in." He is somewhat vague about his actual costs and returns. But he does know that: "The bigger you are, the more money you make."

He explains at length. "The cost of machinery has been going up, and the price of cotton going down. It has dropped every year almost, over the past ten years." With this price structure and the price of machinery, "We can keep in business only with volume."[10]

He does not think he is making more money "than we would working with hands. But you can't get hand labor. Young men do not like to do manual work; not any more." However, he appears to distrust both men and machines.

That is why he employs so many wage men in addition to the machines—as a standby. He can have them whenever they may be wanted. "Transient laborers—I wouldn't hire them."[11]

He expects to keep on mechanizing. The reason is "kind of both. Mechanization is a desire to get ahead—try and outdo your neighbor." But also, "That is the only way to do it. You can't buy mules now.[12] And you can't get share-croppers. There is plenty of cash renting. But you can't find sharecroppers. They don't want it—can't make a living."

According to him, small farmers have no choice any more. "They might exist. But sixteen acres of cotton can't sustain them at a decent standard of living—refrigerator, washing machine, change of clothes."[13]

The man with a single tractor cannot hope to survive. "The day his tractor breaks down, he can't afford to buy another. So he goes out of business. You've got to have three tractors at the least." Then, even a second-hand one-row cotton picker would cost $6000. "He couldn't afford a big combine. And he couldn't pick the cotton by hand, with his family labor."

Therefore, "If a man wants a decent standard of life, he would need at least a hundred acres of row crops, in cotton and soybeans." To work it, he would require machinery worth about $20,000. "I don't know of one small farmer who has a decent income who doesn't have an industrial job."

3

Statistics would appear to endorse Whitman, but Joe Brown does not agree. He has a cotton allotment of thirteen acres and twenty-five in soybeans.[14] He has no off-farm income; no industrial job. He rents another twelve acres for cotton and fifteen acres for beans. But he owns only sixty acres of land.

"I got two tractors. I hire the cotton picker. A bale is cheaper picked by 'em than by hand. I have two tractors, a cultivator and planter." His entire equipment, inclusive of an automobile, is worth less than $5000. "I work myself and hire help when I need to—for harvesting and chopping." Nor does he borrow much. "Only from the Farmers Home Administration. And they don't let us have very much."[15]

He thinks, however, that he is making a satisfactory living, although of course, "We do our own work and don't live on luxuries—ordinary common living. Year before last, I made forty-two bales. Pretty cotton—just like a snow bank. I got $4000 out of that crop—just the cotton."[16]

Fifty-eight years old, Brown is wearing a gray shirt and faded blue overalls. He has been here forty-five years. It is his nineteenth year on this farm. It used to be a big plantation. The government purchased the estate and divided it into small plots that were sold to tenants like Brown at eighty-five dollars an acre on an easy payment basis.

"Been a lot of improvement in living," according to him. "But they don't work as hard any more. I have a tractor, and it is not the same as working with mules. With mules I walked. With the tractor I ride. When we moved here we had wood heat. Now we have gas, refrigerator, electricity, washing machine, deep-freeze, TV, radio."

The house went with the land. It had four rooms. "We have three bedrooms now, bath and kitchen. And the pantry got four closets," the wife says proudly. It is a neat house, modestly but well furnished. The garden has sweet corn, strawberries, and flowers.

"When I bought this land, we had mules. Land back here was all in woods. Now it is all cultivated. There was no house between here and Greenville."[17]

Both their children are grown up and settled. One son works in a store in Leland. The wife does some farm work—attends to the yard and takes care of the chickens. "Used to have a lot." But now she has only eleven layers and a rooster. They are fenced in.

"There used to be a market," according to her, for eggs, butter, and milk. "But not any more. People are gettin' funny about their food. I would much rather have home-raised stuff. We still raise our own meat, but we can't sell it. We have a nice cow, but you've got to drink all the milk yourself. People want government-inspected stuff. Eighteen years ago, I had fifty hens. For several years I sold eggs in the town. I got thirty-five to fifty cents a dozen, the year round. I used to raise all my fryers. Now they are cheaper to buy. These broiler houses—they put us out of business."

She has a surplus of eggs, "but nowhere to sell 'em. Neighbors, even country people, say they won't eat 'em because they're too rich."[18] She cannot understand them. Moreover, now her hens "won't sit on their eggs." She thinks it may be because of the new feed. "Everythin' is gettin' so specialized."

Nevertheless, Brown is positive. "Yes, I do think a small farmer can survive. They claim it requires too much work, and they don't want to work. That's why they're quittin'."

There is another limitation, he warns. "You can't work on a small farm and keep up with the practices recommended by them county agents and folks at the experiment station." They have no recommendations that a small farmer can use.

"I can't buy the equipment to use all that modern stuff with." He uses very few chemicals. "Otherwise you have to buy so much machinery to put those chemicals out with. It's not the chemicals, but the machinery required to put 'em out with. I can't afford it." He has to rely on manual labor, and this is becoming difficult. "Big farmers can afford all the equipment and use chemicals, and grass won't come up. I keep my grass down with the plow and hoe. Don't do no flame cultivation. It requires machinery."

Chemicals are tied in with machinery, he repeats. "You need an awful lot of money to afford the machinery." Volume as well. "Those implement places will rip you down the back, if you go to buy one. One thing leads to another."

Recommendations of the county agent and the experiment station therefore "aren't much good to the little farmer." In any case, Brown has never met the county agent. "They don't operate at our level."

In his opinion government programs also favor the big farmer. Cotton allotment, for example, that is surrendered is turned in to a pool. There is a committee to distribute this acreage. "We will apply. But we will be given only a percentage of what we have." That would be much less than what the big farmer gets. "I got one acre last year."[19] Again, although price support is the same for all, the bigger farmer has larger volume and lower cost of production.[20]

There is no problem about the market. But unlike Whitman, Brown does not sell through the Cotton Association, because he has no faith in it. "I don't think it is fair. Lot of times they give us bad grades over there—three or four grades on one trailer. Cotton picked the same time, and it'll get four grades off the same trailer. You can't argue about the grading."

He sells to the local merchant. "Merchants ain't fair either. They don't bargain. But with the Association, we got to wait so long.[21] Sometimes, it takes two weeks even to know the grade. Besides, we always done it this way."

Both husband and wife are amply "content with what we have." He loves hunting. "Through winter I stay mostly in the woods." Rest of the time, "I work myself. Others don't. Reason why even big farmers don't make anything is, they don't want to get their hands dirty like I do. See 'em." He holds them out. They are rough. "They spend so much on labor. They're mechanizin' to cut down on labor."

Brown admits, however, that people like him get fewer and fewer. "Labor at Stoneville—I know 'em all. They used to be sharecroppers," as Brown was until he bought his farm. "They quit and took jobs in Stoneville. They used to work with me—rent farms. They got tired of it and took jobs. They wanted the weekend off to come out to the country," he adds, with a shrug and a wrinkled smile.

CHAPTER VII

Harvest Labor

1

"They don't *want* to work." The cry reached a cre-
scendo farther west, on the Pacific Coast, where many crops
did not lend themselves yet to complete mechanization. As
the South is different, so farmers and farming in California
are a world apart, unique in many respects.

The state produces more fruit and vegetables than
any other state in the country. In the postwar years it was
mechanizing faster probably than any other region.[1] Yet in
1961 hired labor was still the largest single item of expense
for farmers in California. At the peak of harvest season in
that year, there were 370,000 hired workers on the farms, as
against 328,000 in 1950, when mechanization began in earnest, and 120,000 fifty years earlier. California farmers' dependence on hired labor was much greater than elsewhere in
the nation.[2] Moreover, most of these wage workers were
seasonal—at the peak 77 percent of the total.[3] They were required for only sixty to ninety days in the year. A great
number of them were hired on a day-to-day basis, either by
farmers directly or by farm labor contractors. They would be
transported daily to their job location and back by bus or
truck. This came to be known as the "day-haul" system.

The usual picture is of a large group of men
slowly forming in front of the Farm Placement office

as early as 4:00 A.M.; men milling around on sidewalk
and street as trucks and buses pull in; drivers calling
out job and pay rates; men filing in and out of two or
three cafes; a few vehicles fill quickly and are gone,
while some sit occupied by only a handful of men;
occasionally a request for workers blatting out over
the Farm Placement public address system; the crowd
surging across the street and back again as more vehicles arrive; a small knot of men standing just inside
the office, looking in the direction of the "help
wanted" board on the far wall, escaping the early
morning chill; one or two private cars stop, pick up
friends, and squeal off down the street; traffic decreasing as dawn becomes day until by 7:00 A.M. the
unfilled carriers reluctantly move away from the curb
and the remaining men drift slowly back into cafe,
bar, hotel.

Similar scenes are enacted that same morning in Los Angeles, Modesto, Oakland, Bakersfield,
Salinas, Stockton—in tens of other large and small
cities up and down California.[4]

These workers would be paid off every evening. They
were expected usually to supply their own lunch and find
their own housing. They may or may not have been tran-
sients; and they lived mostly in the skid rows which existed
in many cities. Some farmers used the day-haul skid-row
men to meet their entire seasonal need for farm labor.[5]

Essentially, the agricultural labor market in California
at this point was, as it always has been, "without any structure of job rights or preferences." According to Lloyd Fisher,
"Not only are unions virtually nonexistent, but there is literally no relationship between employer and employee upon
which any claims to recurrent employment might be built.
To the employer the harvest hand is anonymous; he has not
even a social security number for identification."[6]

In 1935 the U.S. Congress had excluded farm labor
from the legislation that enabled industrial workers to orga-

nize and engage in collective bargaining. More than thirty years later, the exclusion still held. Farm workers and their employers were virtually exempt from federal and state labor laws that governed the conduct of both sides in labor disputes. All bills attempting to extend these common conventional rights to agricultural labor had been defeated.

And so, when in April 1966, after a strike lasting several months, a few grape pickers in the Delano area won recognition for their right to unionize, it was hailed as a historic event. *Time* magazine described it as follows:

> Wearing rosaries and carrying a sequined banner that pictured the Virgin of Guadalupe, along with crudely lettered union slogans, 100 Mexican-American grape pickers last week finished a month-long, 300-mile march of penance and protest through California's Central Valley from Delano to Sacramento. Marching with them were Roman Catholic priests and nuns and Protestant ministers, and the mood of the demonstrators was triumphant. For shortly before the protesters reached the state capital, they had won recognition of their embryonic union, the National Farm Workers Association, from Schenley Industries Inc., which owns about 2400 acres of vineyards in the Delano area.
>
> More than anything else, this first breakthrough in the bitter fight between growers and workers, who have been on strike for recognition since last September, had been achieved by the massive support given to the strikers by California's churches. "It is the single most important thing that has helped us," says César Chávez, organizer of the Union.[7]

2

Historically, the usage principally of hired hands, as opposed to the national norm and ideal of self-employment in agriculture, has long been a notable and integral feature of farming in California. Unlike the South the state never had a supply of slaves. However, from earliest times, it has had a free farm labor force on the stream, "on terms which competed favorably with slavery."[8]

Even when it was a pure cattle and grain country and there was no intensive cultivation of specialized crops, a local newspaper in 1869 reported: "We hear of the Mongolian binding grain by contract in many parts of the state . . ."[9]

Concentration and specialization in production also developed early. "By the eighteen seventies large-scale wheat-growing was the monoculture of great sections."[10] By the close of the nineteenth century, although extensive cultivation was predominant in most crops, one-sixth of the farms in the state were producing more than two-thirds of the crop by value (Census of 1900). It was feasible, however, only because of a plentiful supply of cheap Chinese labor. According to another newspaper account:

> The grower looked over his goodly acres, calculated his crop, and went to his Chinese labor boss. "John," he would say, "you find me fifty men. Come Thursday."
>
> The square brown man would consider the question, and say "all lite, I get 'em" . . . and there you were. Thursday next fifty replicas of John would appear with mess kit and such bedding as they needed. They lived in the fields, worked as the locusts, cleared the crop and melted away.[11]

Thus, crop specialization, large-scale ownership of land, and foreign labor made up the complex of conditions framing the farm structure in California even ninety years ago. The only factor in this structure to change subsequently was the type of crops raised.

By 1930, for example, agriculture in the state had become specialized; dependent primarily on nuts, fruits, and grapes, all of them labor intensive. Nevertheless, a high degree of concentration remained an outstanding characteristic of production and employment. Some 2 percent of the farms produced 28.5 percent of the state's crops by value and disbursed 35 percent of the cash paid to agricultural wage workers (Census of 1930).

A generation later again, there was a change in the pattern of cropping. Without any decrease in the absolute value of production of intensive crops such as fruit and vegetables, there was a significant shift back to livestock products and field crops. By 1960, while the relative economic importance of fruit and vegetables had dropped "very, very, very sharply in 20 years," the output of field crops, such as cotton and rice, had more than doubled the annual average production in the decade of 1930.[12] The basic structure of ownership, production, and labor employment, however, remained intact. Of all the farms in the state, 3.2 percent accounted for 65 percent of the total farm land. To break it down further, 494 farms, or less than 0.5 percent of the total, owned as much as 35.2 percent of the farm acreage.[13] Similarly, about 4.93 percent, or 4848 of the 99,232 farms, engaged 61.1 percent of the hired labor in the state and paid $304,859,554 in wages out of a total expenditure on hired farm workers of $498,742,765.[14]

3

Sources of supply for labor, upon which California's agriculture—whatever the crops—became so dependent nearly a century ago, have been several. The duration and reliability of each source varied, but it became available "mainly through immigration, depression, and racial discrimination. . . ."[15]

Chinese were the first. In the 1870's, their numbers in the state increased from 49,000 to 75,000. By 1880 they represented one-third of the agricultural labor force and provided the major source of seasonal and casual workers.

As a ban was imposed on their immigration in 1882 under pressure of organized labor, the farmers turned to Japan. More than 41,000 Japanese were in California—and also approximately 10,000 Indians—by 1906, when the Japanese supply also was cut off.[16] Then Mexicans and Filipinos followed. The latter swelled to 30,500 in 1930, and there were 368,000 Mexicans in the same year.

By 1930 unrestricted immigration of orientals had been halted. But then poured in the domestic white migrants from the dust bowls, from the Great Plains and Southwestern cotton states, driven by the Depression. In the 1930's, some 1,250,000 Americans entered California. Of these, 11.5 percent became agricultural laborers. For once, it looked as if the state might have all the hands it could use. But the war broke out, and urgent demands were voiced for the importation of more Mexican workers.

The U.S. government accordingly concluded a treaty with the government of Mexico, under which more workers were imported into California and indentured to agriculture. In addition, uncounted thousands of wetbacks regularly crossed the border illegally to work on farms. Since World War II, with minor exceptions and aside from the permanent immigrants who have been permitted to settle in the country, all foreign contract workers in agriculture have been Mexican nationals, known as *braceros*, meaning literally, "arm laborers."[17]

In 1963 a total of 65,100 foreign contract laborers, mainly Mexican, were engaged by farmers in California—by far, the most in the country. California farms also employed 47,700 domestic migrant workers; again, a great many more such workers than in any other state. Whereas in the thirty years following 1925–29, total agricultural labor input in the United States decreased fifty-five index points, in California it dropped only one index point.[18]

Moreover, through the decades, from back in the last century, as each source of immigrants began to dry up, most farmers' reactions have been identical: "We all know we need labor. . . . There is only one thing that will furnish the labor for the State of California. . . . What we need is 40,000 to 50,000 good young Chinamen. . . ."[19]

The nationality of the "solution" varied. The "solution" itself remained constant. Always, it was to obtain fresh supplies of workers to fit the needs of whatever was the existing structure of agricultural organization. No attempt was made ever to modify the structure to fit the available supply of labor. The structure itself was never questioned. The need and justification for it in the farmer's mind was clear; and that also survived the several generations. A spokesman for the Agricultural Legislative Committee of California put forward the farmer's point of view somewhat bluntly as follows: "We must have somebody in this country to do our work. Somebody, somewhere, has to do hard physical labor, because it is here to be done. If the American people refuse to do it, then what are we to do? Why, we must bring somebody else in from the outside who will do it. Under our present system of education, we must either bring somebody in here to do our hard work or we must go elsewhere for our foodstuffs and clothing."[20]

That was in 1928. Thirty-five years later, the situation in California agriculture was still very much the same.[21] According to a senior Farm Placement official: "Seven hundred Americans were unemployed in Stockton last week, as of April 24th.[22] They are in the streets now without work, while 1500 Mexicans are cutting asparagus in the same area.

"Fifteen hundred jobs are available today," he repeats, tapping the table for emphasis, "if the Americans want them. They have a right to the job—the first option. Mexicans can be given only what they refuse. But they are choosing to stay in the streets. The buses came and went back empty.

"Since 1942 we have constantly advertised jobs open for American workers. But they don't come. They just will not accept farm labor. Filipinos used to make $2000 in a season, when they worked in asparagus."

"But why? Why don't they come?"

"It is stoop work. They are too tall maybe. It is hard work. Man has the right to choose. There is no way to force anyone to work. But there is something missing. It is not right that foreigners have to come in, and our own men be without work."[23]

CHAPTER VIII

Too Tall to Stoop

1

Tom Chavez is farming in California in 1963. According to him, "We *have* to import all help from Mexico. Local labor don't want to do this stoop labor and *can't* do it. We have to accept some local help, like Negroes. But they too won't work. If we pay by the hour, they won't work enough. Bracero will work, but not the Negro."[1]

Local labor "would rather pick fruit than cucumber. You have to bend down to pick cucumber." He had his own son take care of the cucumber lot "this past season. He couldn't pick 'em. He is six feet two inches tall. He could only boss over 'em."[2]

Tom's permanent hands also are Mexican, because "labor from Mexico has the desire. A local man works in canning and then goes on relief—white or Negro. The whole state is becoming a welfare relief state, I tell you."

On the other hand, he repeats, to drive the point home, the Mexicans who come in every year "are really good workers. Earlier, we used to have the Filipinos. But they are all sixty and over now. New ones can't come in. The few left around here are drunks. They are more intelligent than Mexicans. But they are no more."

Tom himself is only a tenant, the son of a tenant; in Alameda County in the Central Coast region. He rents 480 acres on a sharecropping basis. "Never been able to purchase a farm of my own. Never have acquired anything except a livin'. Acquired nothin'."

However, he has $50,000 invested in equipment. "The only money a farmer makes is on depreciation. So we've got to buy new machinery. It's the main source of income. It is for me." He also hires four or five tractor drivers on an annual basis and some sixty temporary hands for three to four months in the year. "Crews often run seventy men at a time." They are his problem.

"My wage bill often runs into $10,000 a week, at harvest time." His preharvest loan is usually around $40,000 at 6.5 percent interest. Tom is cultivating cucumbers, peppers, tomatoes, sugar beets, barley, and walnuts. Only barley is wholly mechanized. Beets still require hand hoeing. And cucumbers, peppers, and tomatoes must be picked by hand. It is the kind of squat or stoop work that, according to Tom, the locals will not do.[3]

He is not overfond of students either, although he himself went to college for a brief period. "Indian students (from India) didn't last very long. Picked cucumbers—were too slow—couldn't do it. They wanted to come at half-past eight, instead of at six in the morning. Wanted an afternoon nap and overslept. For American students we have a special name—'counsel jockeys.' No, students are no good for stoop work either." Besides, "Young people now do not like to put in the hours. Don't let us kid about it. We didn't know no better. We were raised to it."

His preferences and prejudices for the hands he hires run to pattern, on racial and ethnic basis—it is correlated with skill, efficiency, and general desirability.[4] Tom cannot, however, have his choice any more of men or crops. Till very recently, he used to have a plot of string beans. "Now they've gone out of cultivation because the men will not work on a hot day, and that is the day for harvesting beans. I had to drop $80 a ton, because they wouldn't come on that day." He is indignant. "They *won't* work on a hot day," he repeats.

2

Mario DeBeneditto, another California farmer, raises two hundred acres of fall lettuce. It is shipped everywhere in the country, including New York on the east coast. All his work in lettuce, however, is done by hired labor—by braceros under contract.

According to Richard Pike, there is a tremendous resentment against foreign labor. "Yet nobody is able to provide a substitute." Pike manages a corporation farm of 10,000 acres, mostly under fruit and vegetables.

He too believes that "Mexicans are excellent workers. When it comes to harvesting fruit, no national has a better eye for color. Many Americans are partly color blind."

Besides, "Domestic workers will not do stoop labor. No domestic worker will do it—thin sugar beets and lettuce, or harvest vegetables. Most of them perhaps are not built for it. It is the same with budding fruit trees close to the ground. Now the Japanese are built for it. . . ."

What does a Japanese farmer think?

Sam Nakamura is the son of an immigrant who came to California just before World War I. Now, Sam is one of the largest carnation (and rose) growers in the whole of the United States.

It is a very specialized and technical line. Nakamura has over 120 employees, apart from the family members, all of whom work. Of the hired men, twenty are Japanese. "But it is difficult to get them any more." He has brought a few trainees all the way from Japan. Then there are forty Filipinos. They are all specialists, but getting old. And there are sixty Mexicans. "All the younger people for hard work are Mexicans."

"No Americans?"

"No." He does not have a single native white working in carnations or roses. "Only a couple of mechanics and welders."

"Why?"
"Caucasians are poor workers" is the brief reply.

3

The situation was similar, though on a lesser scale, in
the irrigated tracts of Mesilla Valley, in the neighboring state
of New Mexico. In some respects it was more interesting.
A great deal of cotton is cultivated here, and most of it is of
a special long staple American-Egyptian variety. It is white
and fine, "almost like silk."[5] However, its fiber is liable to
damage if picked by a machine. In 1963 farmers in the region
were confronted with a difficult choice—of damaging the
cotton and not being able to sell it, or not having it picked.
The mechanical picker was not quite satisfactory yet and
labor was not available.[6]

"Up till last year I could get hand pickers. Last year I
couldn't get any." Farmer Roy DeCoste has thirty-five acres
in cotton.[7] So, he rented a mechanical cotton picker, being
too small a farmer to purchase one. "I lost twenty-five
dollars a bale," on grade and through waste "of what drops
on the ground."

He switched to mechanical picking a year ago, because
"till then we were gettin' Mexican labor. We were payin'
them piece wage, accordin' to how much cotton they picked."

His main problem now is labor. "Lot of farm products
in this valley can't be handled by machines. Mechanization
can't help. I got a couple of tractors with all the equipment—
to farm better than a hundred acres. So that makes it more
overhead. Don't think we don't miss the mule. There's lots
of things you can't do with a tractor. But you can't hardly
find a mule, no more."

Here also, and despite the machines, preference for
the bracero is emphatic. However, as a result of various re-
strictive measures imposed by the government, he is not
easily available.[8] Roy had a steady man. "We retired him
because he's old and sick now. We are trying to get a Mexican with a permanent passport."

Unlike California, however, "In New Mexico, until the war we used to have local workers; and they were good.[9] All family used to work—including the children. They used to close the schools for cotton pickin'. We also got men from Arkansas and the south and east, mostly Anglos. We had no trouble here, gettin' cotton picked.[10] Laborers used to compete among themselves. But now we can't get local labor. I ask for five men, and they send me two women and three children." A neighbor asked for six men, and the employment office sent him two.[11]

Moreover, they come for one or two days and then drop out. "If they need an extra dollar, they will work. Then they quit. They claim we don't pay enough on the farm. But they don't turn in seventy-five cents of work in an hour, even if we pay. They're gettin' wiser and wiser all the time."

Before the war, according to him, "A local man could chop two to three acres of cotton in nine hours. Now you can't find a man who can chop even one acre of cotton in a day. This is the difference." It is hard work, he admits. Roy, however, thinks that "they won't do it because they've learnt to make easy money. They've lost their dignity and pride. Nobody wants to do hard work no more, even if it makes good money, because they don't have to. They can go on relief."[12]

He blames it on welfare. "Government has taken away people's ambition to work. That's what leads to communism. When you take away a man's ambition, what's he good for?"

4

Elio Cruz, dark, young, and stocky, is a much bigger operator than Roy.[13] He owns 320 acres, of which 210 acres are in fine long staple cotton.

"In cotton we started mechanizing five years ago." He first bought a small picker and hired a man to work it. "But that hurt me. He just went through the field and made a mess of it."

Then Elio purchased a second, larger picker and learned to operate it himself. "If adjusted properly it can pick even this cotton without spoiling. You've got to learn." He admits, however, that this year they are having a problem selling the crop.

"Every year we buy something new to replace hand labor." For weeds also, he is using chemicals now. Till 1959, his weeding was done manually. It required ten men. He thinks the switch from labor to machine is going to work out all right in cotton. "It is my vegetable program that has been hurt most by shortage of labor. Vegetables are still handled by hand. But prices are down, and labor is up 60 percent."[14] Even at that, it is not available.

Till four years ago he was cultivating onions and lettuce on a large scale.[15] He processes the chili peppers himself—powders and sells them directly to the store. Last year, he had forty acres in vegetables. "I needed fifteen men. I got only six. We got by only by working ourselves sixteen to eighteen hours a day, my two brothers and dad. No, not the wife. Women do not work in the field. We picked all day long and packed at night." This year, he has thirty acres in vegetables. "We'll need about twelve hands. I'll get them, I hope." He is dubious. "We didn't use to have any problem at all."

Yes, he has tried local labor, "lots of times." There is a little village nearby, and according to him, it has plenty of unemployed, purely agricultural workers. He used to depend on them. "I would get about 20 hands from that village—even women, to work in onions and lettuce." But not any more. They stopped coming about six years ago. "Can't rely on them. Two or three will come out; but they leave as soon as they get their money. It is really serious now. I have had to pay locals a dollar an hour, but they are not worth 25 cents."[16] Like Roy, he blames it on welfare.

Cruz purchased this farm from his father in 1948. But since then, "we have not been able to buy any more land," although he has been "very up-to-date. Everything that comes out new, we buy it. That is why we are bust. I am so mixed up."

His two-row cotton picker cost him $18,000. "I have

just bought a new tractor also. It is a little fancier but does no more work. Yet, its price is 37 percent more than of the one I purchased five years ago." The price of all equipment has gone up; but "on our prices, on everything *we* sell, we are losing every year."

His investment in machinery is more than $50,000. It would be too large a unit to manage, he thinks, but "I should really have 800 acres to pay for the investment I have in machinery, and I could do with the income." Over the past decade, "My net income has decreased actually, although we are producing at least a third more than we did prior to 1955."[17] Cost of production has risen higher than the additional income. Capital expenditure has increased likewise.

"Why then would a young man like you stay in farming?" I ask him, returning to an earlier theme. "You know you could earn more elsewhere with less investment and effort?"

"I don't know" is the reply. "But I wouldn't want my boy to be a farmer." He would like to see his son go to college and do something else—go into medicine or law. He would discourage him very much from farming: "Simply because I don't think it is profitable any more, to invest more than is invested already. It don't pay. Even if he could make the farm bigger, I wouldn't recommend it. It is still risky. We have insurance against hail and bugs, yes. But you can't make money on insurance."

For himself, however, "Frankly, I don't know why I've stayed in farming. I thought it was good when I got into it. I like farming. We are independent. It means a lot. I've seen people working for salary. They're still working for another man." He likes this way of life. "The family has always done it."

CHAPTER IX

The Lord's Acres

1

Once again, except for Sam Nakamura, all these farmers are white. They are of European descent, though Chavez, DeCoste, and Cruz may have an admixture of American Indian blood. But none of them is socially or economically at any disadvantage. The level of their formal education is not disparate. And their techniques of farming are in tune with the commercial scientific-technological ethos of the nation.

Underlying the impressive application of science and technology in agricultural production, however, there is a distinctly medieval flavor, fervor, and pervasiveness of religious faith and tradition in America's farm society that merits mention. For example, few community functions in the rural areas are held without an opening prayer or invocation. It would be inconceivable to speak of religion, in public or in private conversation, in a light vein. A question frequently asked of me in a farmer's home was: "To which church do you belong?" Or: "What is your faith?"

Ritual conformism is stronger in some regions than in others. Certain denominations are seemingly more secular. The variation in this respect, however, between and within denominations, depends mainly on the local church —to what extent it deems it proper and within rights to intervene in the life and behavior of its congregation. Among sects that frown on birth control, for instance, a large number of children, at times with less than annual spacing, are common among farm families. The decision to limit or not to limit the size of the family is not taken by them on grounds of personal preference, health, or economic circumstances.

Similarly, Carl's family is not singular in observing Sunday. His neighbors do the same, and not all of them are Roman Catholic. Mary, wife of another dairy farmer, denies the popular notion that Catholics are more orthodox than the rest. "We are not praying all the time," she protests. After a brief pause, she continues earnestly: "We pray once in the morning when we wake up and dedicate the day to God. Then we pray before and after each meal. And then, once again at night before going to bed."

Sunday mass is a *must*. But then, so is Sunday service for Protestants as well, be they Methodists, Lutherans, Disciples of Christ, Baptists, or whatever else. Catholics at least relax after mass. They may not do any work, but Sunday night is often the dance night. To enjoy is not to sin. Not so with many Protestant sects. Dancing, drinking, or indulgence in any form of entertainment is forbidden to them on the holy day. In parts of some states it is forbidden by law. Taverns are closed, ball games must be finished by a certain hour, and dancing is prohibited. An Amish dairyman will not even sell the milk on Sunday. Some denominations are more fundamentalist than others, but most of them consider observance of the Sabbath fairly fundamental. Whatever is done is on grounds of necessity with the explicit concurrence and sanction of the local clergy.

There are exceptions of course, as always. Max, for example, owns 540 acres in the state of Washington and raises a hundred bushels an acre of irrigated wheat, along with corn, onions, melons, and potatoes. Max, however, is a Japanese immigrant from Hiroshima. He came at the end of World War I, at the age of fourteen. Though a Christian and an American now, old and balding, he has not been able to shake off his ethnic obsession with weeds.

"If you let a weed stay for one day," he says in a thick accent and shaking his forefinger, "it will grow double the size. A weed will not observe Sunday or any holiday." Therefore, nor does Max. "We work on Sundays and every day."

Other regular exceptions to the rule belong to sects that do not consider Sunday to be the true Sabbath. Seventh-Day Adventists, for example, will not work on a Saturday. According to Max, even if cattle were to break loose and wander all over their fields on that day, they will do nothing. There are some Adventists in his neighborhood.

Hurlbut is one such, in Tanana Valley in Alaska. He is cultivating mostly carrots, cabbages, and potatoes. He has 160 acres cleared. He observes Sabbath from Friday sundown, although, "I know I sin often by being impatient and standing at the window there, waiting for it to be over, so I can get to work." Throughout the summer in Alaska, every quarter hour of daylight is critical because the season is very short. The growing season is only about a hundred days. No farmer, therefore, can afford to lose an entire day, especially at the time of sowing and harvest. Hurlbut, however, is very strict. He sins only mentally.

Before he settled in Alaska, he was farming in southern California where farmers were given water for irrigation once every ten days. The question arose as to what he should do if it came on the Sabbath. Hurlbut was down the line, and he had to take his turn whenever the water came or wait for another ten days.

So, "I talked it over with God. We talk with Him like a father, you know." He decided to continue to observe the Sabbath and not let in the water even if the crops should suffer. "But nothing happened. The crops did not die." However, he could not make a success of it and left California to homestead in the forty-ninth state.

2

Farmers' devotion is not limited to an observance of the Sabbath ritual. It expresses itself in considerable monetary donations also. Church buildings, for example, are constantly remodeled, extended, and embellished and new ones are often constructed, despite the decreasing farm population. Since the consolidation of schools, the church is about the only rural institution that is still growing and surviving on an each-to-its-own basis.

Mississippi is one of the more predominantly agricultural states. Alcorn County in northeast Mississippi, designated as a low-income problem area, is typical of a large section of the state and of the South, except that it is almost entirely white. Its nonurban Negro population is negligible.[1] In the two decades following 1940, however, rural communities, or neighborhoods as they are called here, declined from forty-five to thirty-seven. Half of them had under eighty households each.[2] A hamlet-centered neighborhood that used to have three physicians has none any more. The last of them died in 1957. Instead of ten rural post offices, by 1958 the county was left with five. As for rural schools, originally located on a neighborhood basis, they had dwindled to nine, as against sixty-nine in 1910. Yet, in fifteen years, as many as sixteen *new rural* churches had been established in Alcorn County.[3] Contrary to every other trend, and against a 23 percent decline in the rural population, churches had increased by 31 percent. Less than 4000 households supported sixty-four church establishments in 1960.[4]

In Palmetto, another small Mississippi community, a typical rural church has been enlarged recently. Five more rooms and a kitchen have been added. "My husband did that. I wish I had as good a kitchen," says a farmer's wife without a trace of envy and with a great deal of pride.

Rarely does a community have just one place of worship. Normally, there will be as many churches in each place as there are denominations. Often, there are several to a single sect, catering to different income, racial, and ethnic groups. At Holdingford, Minnesota, for example, there are two cathedrals—one for the Germans and one for Poles. Fergus Falls, with a population of only 13,000, has seventeen to twenty churches; nobody knows quite how many. They are Lutheran, or almost all, catering to different ethnic groups. Fergus Falls is a farming town with no industry, little traffic, and mostly aging people.

Almost everywhere, at intervals of a few miles the slim steeple with the cross dominates the rural skyline. Apart from the communities that do not worship in a conventional church, the house of worship is normally the most costly structure as well. Expenditure for new construction of religious buildings in the nation may approximate or exceed a billion dollars a year. The cost of a single church may run to several million dollars. Methodists have spent around three million dollars building one on the campus of an agricultural university in the Midwest.

"To us it is important and significant," a member of the faculty and his wife inform me. Reverently, she points out: "That single stained glass window up there cost twelve and a half thousand dollars!" The community around the campus is mainly rural. It contributed generously toward the cost of the building.

3

"We do not understand it. But in fact, all that we give to the church comes back to us. We do not really give it away," according to Lester Peterson. He is a devoted Lutheran, farming some 900 acres in Eldred in the region of the Red River Valley. This belief in a contract, the concept that whatever a man may sacrifice or give in the cause of Christ is made good by God in ample measure, is widely held.

A Catholic priest in the rural township of Gentilly, Minnesota, dismisses Max Weber's theory of the Protestant Ethic—the supposedly greater propensity of puritans to make money—in terms of this contract. In fluent French he explains: "It is stated in the Bible that if you give, you get back a hundredfold." In his view, Protestants give more to God. Therefore their returns also are higher.

In pursuance of the belief, and despite the grumblings of the church hierarchy of various denominations—they all grumble—donations to divinity, in money, labor, and time are generally willing and generous among farmers. In the South, there is what is called the Lord's Acre Movement, "taking hold in literally hundreds of communities, many of them in the mountains, with the people working together to till acres dedicated to the Lord or tend stock devoted to Him. Religious services are held to bless the seed and the land."[5]

In many denominations a farmer will try to contribute the Biblical tithe regularly and give extra for special occasions and purposes. "Yes, I think so," confirms an elder of the Church of Jesus Christ of Latter-Day Saints, in Salt Lake City. "A devoted member will pay 10 percent of his gross income to the church and make other contributions besides."

One purpose that is considered worthy of special support in all sects is the work of missionaries in spreading the word of the gospel. Among Mormons, merely a prayer and monetary contribution for this purpose does not suffice. It is customary also to send sons, and often a daughter as well, to serve in a mission, for a period of two to two and a half years. Between the ages of nineteen and twenty-one, boys are expected to leave their home, friends, family, studies, and whatever they are doing, to go wherever in the world the church may send them, to convert people of other persuasions, Christian and non-Christian, to the Mormon faith.[6]

This often involves considerable sacrifice for the parents. For one thing Mormons usually have large families. This means that several children may be sent. Moreover, parents are required to bear the cost. It comes to about a hundred dollars a month per child, all the while that he or she is out. They must also pay half the cost of travel. The church contributes only the return fare. Many parents in the rural areas, therefore, begin to save for this obligation soon after the child is born. It becomes a goal in life. "The faith convinces them that the Lord will bless them for their effort and sacrifice."

The Hendersons, for instance, have a hundred acres, thirty cows, a daughter, and three older boys. All their three sons are on missionary duty. The parents send them three hundred dollars each month. "Yes, we had planned and hoped they would go." Father is still paying for the farm, and mother must work a great deal more and help in the barn since the boys left home.

Hawkins, another farmer, owns only twenty acres, rents eighty-three, and milks twenty-eight cows. He earns a gross annual income of $11,286 from the sale of milk and livestock. The farm is in three separate pieces, and they are short of water. The house is extremely modest. Untidy too, with children's things scattered all over.

Forty-three years old, Hawkins has eight children living. The oldest is nineteen, and the youngest, a baby of a year and a half. Hawkins also has a debt of $28,000, on his farm, house, and machinery. Last year the family did not have a dime left after paying the bills and dues on the loan. She is "terribly" worried. If *only* they could get rid of the debt and have just ten more cows and fifty more acres, "We would be perfectly happy."

Yet, their oldest son is out on a mission in Nebraska. They have to send him ninety-five dollars every month. He is costing them twelve hundred dollars a year, and they could do with his help on the farm. When I asked why then had they sent him, the mother's face lit up. All the woes she had been moaning about seemed to drop away. According to her, he had wanted to go; but so had they wanted to send him. "He writes *such* nice letters."

Sometimes, even if a boy is not inclined to go, his parents will push him. "It is the thing to do. They will scrub floors or borrow to pay for it—they are so keen about it."

It happened to Warren. On finishing high school he

wanted to continue his studies at the university. He thinks he could have won a scholarship. But Warren's father insisted that he go on a mission first. When the boy called on the college dean for advice, the latter also was doubtful if the scholarship would be given until he did his term in a mission.

So, Warren went to preach. By the time he returned, however, his father's health was failing. He died shortly after. Warren never went to college. He had to start working on the farm instead, which he has been doing ever since.

CHAPTER X

Spiritual Secularism

1

Warren is sorry that he could not acquire a university education because of prior claims of the mission. Nevertheless, he is a devoted and active member of the church.

Forty-seven years old, he has served as ward bishop for several years.[1] Every morning before breakfast, the family kneels around the table, on a bare floor, as the father prays in a loud, unfaltering voice. At dinner, grace is said with heads bowed and folded hands. Extracts are read from the Book of Mormon every night before going to bed, and the entire book is read through once every week.[2]

Church attendance is strict and regular for adults and children alike. Precepts are observed faithfully. No one smokes or drinks—not even tea or coffee.[3] In conversation, constant emphasis is laid on nonmaterial values, and it is reflected in the quality of their living. A farmer owning 300 acres and milking seventy-six cows, Warren grosses some $40,000 in a year. His dairy herd is the largest in the county and one of the best in the state. In 1962 he obtained an average yield (rolling basis) of 16,140 pounds of milk per cow. Yet the house they live in is old, with only a basement and one floor, and indifferently furnished.[4] It was built by his father. There are two small shelves of books. Most of the books pertain to religion.

2

What is more, even if Warren had had the opportunity and benefit of university education, it is unlikely that he would have been stricken with skepticism.

Among the Mormons in fact, emphasis on schooling is second only to the importance attached to religious observance and morality. It is a part of their religious doctrine. The level of their education, therefore, is generally high.[5] But at no level is there a conflict between the two. Higher education does not weaken faith. "On the contrary," explains Leonard J. Arrington, at the university at Logan, "as education increases, there is a tendency for religious activity and participation to increase."[6]

It is so perhaps, because there is little or no formal separation between material and spiritual values.[7] Far from everyday life having been secularized, the tendency has been to spiritualize secular activity, "to exalt economics and economic welfare into an important, if not indispensable, element of religious salvation."[8] And so, by working hard, being cooperative and thrifty, accumulating, staying out of debt, an individual is working essentially for nonmaterial goals and benefits to build the Kingdom of God—for the Millennium.

The Church of Latter-Day Saints also admits a deep and live faith in revelations, prophecy, and miracles.[9] Yet, there is no apparent contradiction in the typical Mormon mind between science and theology.

"We have no fear of any scientific development, or that truth will be in conflict with church dogma," is the categorical comment of ex-Secretary of Agriculture Ezra Taft Benson. "We believe that Mormonism *is* the truth. We do not believe that there can be a conflict between truth as revealed by religion and as proved by science. The two are one and the same."[10] According to him, whatever scientific enquiry has discovered to date, "and all that it is likely to discover in the future, is already there in the Bible."

3

At the mass level, the devotional bias is clear from the pattern of people's participation in their community's life and activity. Mormons have a highly organized society. Yet a survey of two rural communities, Ephraim and Escalante in Utah, revealed that "there is relatively little participation in organizations that focus on economic, civic, and educational problems, while there is relatively high participation in social and especially religious organizations."[11] As against 93 percent of the adults who did *not* actively participate in any formal economic organization, 81 percent were actively involved in associations of a religious nature. Only 2 percent gave their time to education-oriented associations, while 86 percent did not hold membership in any civic organization. The proportion of leadership positions found among sample adults by type of organization was 2 percent educational, 8 percent economic, and 73 percent religious.[12]

Ephraim and Escalante were not exceptional communities. At this period, throughout the country, and not only among the Mormons in fact, churches constituted *the* central factor in social organization, providing one of the most important forums of participation for the rural population. "In general, more rural people are affiliated with churches, either as members or active constituents, than belong to any other single organization."[13]

A survey in North Carolina indicated that 78 percent of social participation of a sample of rural people was through churches. Only 22 percent were involved in any manner in all the other community agencies combined.[14] The Farmers Federation of Western North Carolina maintained a separate department for religion. "Economic (organization) was least likely to be included in participation patterns for household heads" in a rural community in central Pennsylvania; in Seward County in Nebraska, there was "relative inactivity of distinct farm organizations."[15]

A survey of a sample multidenominational population of rural whites in four counties in Mississippi revealed
that all but 2 percent of the adults who belonged to any
organization belonged to a church group. Religious group
participation was predominant over all other forms, and
only one-fourth of the population had membership in any
other type of organization. Furthermore, the higher partici-
pant generally had had more formal schooling, so that "the
rising education level would indicate that participation rates
would tend upward rather than downward. . . ."[16]

4

Obviously, Mormons were not alone in their success
in blending educational procedures and secular practice with
religious dogma and even plain superstition.[17]

"Oh, no, we are not taught the theory of evolution,"
is the repeated statement of high-school children in several
states.

Early in April 1963, Martha Powell, a twenty-one-
year-old teacher in a school at Messick, Tennessee, arranged
for a class debate on the subject because, she said, of student
interest.[18]

The principal of the school, Radford W. Rosebrough,
Jr., promptly intervened and ordered a halt to the plans on
the ground that discussion of Darwin's theory in the class-
room is forbidden under the Tennessee law of 1925. The
statute made it a misdemeanor to teach "any theory that
denies the story of creation as taught in the Bible."

"I don't think the young lady was forcing the theory
on any student, but we objected to the debate," explained
the local city school superintendent, E. C. Stimbert. "We
feel at this grade level (high school) biology should be
taught and not debated." The debate was never held, and
the incident was closed with its cancellation.

"If I thought it would do any good, I would be willing
to go to court to have the law repealed," Miss Powell stated
in a press interview. Thirty-eight years earlier, another
young biology teacher, John Scopes of Dayton, did go to

court. He lost the case and was fined a hundred dollars and costs.

5

The principal of a public high school in Starkville, Mississippi, frankly approved of and endorsed the Tennessee approach to education. "We believe that science and religion agree; that whatever we may discover in science endorses religion. Even if we did accept Darwin's theory, we would say that it is so because it is God's plan. No, we don't teach anything that conflicts with religious belief."[19] Evolution therefore was not taught here at school level. Bible was.

Bible was *not* taught in public schools in Illinois.[20] Religious topics were touched upon only in the social relations class. "But," explained the administrator of a high school in a rural community, "a teacher dare not deviate from the local level and climate of faith and beliefs. The school cannot lead in social change."[21]

The staff is hired and fired locally, and "the community determines what is to be taught in its schools. Teachers cannot be radically different."[22] After a moment's pause he adds bluntly: "We would simply lose our jobs. . . ."

Products of schools, therefore, cannot be expected to be radically different. When I mentioned the Tennessee-Powell incident to a young agronomist at a state agricultural experiment station, he did not see anything amiss with it. Engaged in plant breeding, he accepts the Biblical version of divine creation of man without reservation. A Baptist and a university graduate, Craig was born and brought up on a five-hundred-acre cotton farm.

"I think the Bible story of creation is correct," he asserts gravely, in a low, earnest tone. "It conflicts with Darwin's theory of evolution, yes. But it does not conflict with what I know—with genetics or science. I am here in the practical field. I do not see any conflict between Christian belief and scientific knowledge as I know it. I have generally kept them apart, as I think most people do."

73

The subject is never discussed really, according to him. It would be very controversial if it was. The average person would be violently opposed to Darwin's version. "Generally, it is simply not talked about."

Donald, the son of a Methodist farmer, age twenty and training in electronics, accepts similarly without any questioning "that Darwin must be wrong." He also believes in the physical resurrection of Christ and when the appointed hour comes, of all dead humanity.

CHAPTER XI

Milestones

1

And so, in the countryside of one of the world's most modern and literate societies, large billboards along the highways proclaim: "Seek thy Creator while He is still around." Or, "Jesus is soon coming."[1]

This display of certitude concerning the Creator stands out in sharp contrast with the uncertainties, doubts, and hesitation in the minds of farmers about their own little secular problems and choices.

"I . . . don't . . . know . . ." is the halting but constant refrain, in reply to some of the most critical questions, as to why a farmer did what he did. Afterthoughts follow; attempts at rationalization, to find a reason. Often, the professed reason differs with farmers making an identical choice. Not always is it the obvious or the most rational in economic terms.

Only Charles Kingston stated categorically that he chose to farm on purely economic grounds. He thought he could make more money at it. Many more, including the larger operators, such as Verl Daniere and Elio Cruz, denied that economic returns had much, if anything, to do with their choice and pursuit of agriculture. The Danieres knowingly rejected the economic opportunity—literally in their backyard—to produce much more than they were doing

75

with less risk, on irrigated land, because they felt "It is much harder work." On the other hand, Anderson works extra hard, he thinks, for mainly a noneconomic reason—because he has been taught to believe that land being God's most precious gift, he must take good care of it. Even Albert, the farmer in Utah, who believed that he produced the most he could, "irrespective of returns," was anxious to make it clear that he did not believe in making "money for the sake of money." He did it so that he could educate his children and earn that vacation in California or Florida. With fifteen acres in wheat, Wallace in Pennsylvania voted against the government's offer of a higher support price for the grain, because he believed that it was meant to favor the large producer. But a large producer like Harvey, with an allotment of 220 acres in wheat, also voted against the same proposal because, "I would rather have less and be free. . . ." Harvey continues to work very hard, however, because, "We've got to . . . we can't help it. We are heavily mechanized." Moreover, like Anderson, "I was always told work is good for you."

It is interesting how often these farmers denied that they were influenced in their decisions by what their neighbors had or did. Some of the wives felt that it was a factor. Except for Whitman in Mississippi, the men usually stated that it did not affect them personally. They did not care. Again, only Wallace, who in the first instance had purchased the farm to be independent, said that he was prepared to quit if he could find an alternative. He was not the only one faring poorly in the squeeze of rising costs, declining profits, and mounting debts besides. Not even Ralph Fick, who did not own an inch of land and had no prospect of ever doing so, was prepared to consider leaving agriculture. And he was still young and had worked in a factory.

Their goals, targets, values, and priorities varied. Wallace chose to purchase a new automobile that he clearly could not afford. Robert did not want running water in his house. The Hendersons and Hawkins preferred to send their sons to serve in missions although they were hard pressed and short of funds for their farms and living expenses. Carl and Warren were both milking seventy-six cows, and each earned about the same income. But there was a vast difference in the quality of their homes and living. Furthermore, none of the farmers in the sample hit the heavens, even when they were indulging in the game of wishful thinking. Almost invariably, they desired as much as they already had or just a little more. Only if compelled to, would Anderson purchase the five hundred acres he was renting. Philip Brooks in Illinois wanted two hundred acres with some stock, although at the time, he was actually operating ninety acres that he owned, plus 264 acres that he rented. "I would be perfectly happy and content with that much," he insisted. Ralph would like to own only as much land as he was renting. Joe Brown was amply "content with what we have." Ray found his hundred acres sufficient. "No, no—not more" was a frequent refrain.

Though the soil on some farms might be poorer than on others, none of them was situated in any of the so-called "poverty" pockets of America. All farmers in the sample, therefore, had about equal access to the admirable network of private and public agencies that so amply provide education, technical know-how, credit, equipment, various inputs, and the multiple services that a modern farmer needs. They represent different regions and types of farming. But, except for Robert in Wisconsin, none of them had a gross farm income of less than $5000 a year. Nor did any of them have off-farm employment or income. They are typical of the full-time, professional, white commercial operators in the mainstream of American agricultural production in the early 1960's.[2] However, as with Robert, John, Ray, and Carl, they were at different milestones on the same highway. Their incomes and level of efficiency in farming varied widely. Some had reached their final destination, not because it was the end of the road, but because they had *wanted* to go only that far. It was far enough for them. Others may, and probably will, travel farther, but not necessarily for the same reason, or the same distance.

2

It is not that I did not meet and interview farmers in the subsistence group, with lower incomes. I visited with them in Appalachia. I met them in the cut-over counties of the Lake states. I met them in the north of New Mexico and many other places in the Midwest, South, and East. I met them in distant Alaska. I found them fascinating. Their replies and reactions were of interest; often they were very different from the usual farmer. They would have made a more colorful story.

Nevertheless, they have been excluded from this study, because its primary concern has been with the farmer who produces commercially and in the manner that makes American agriculture what it is. Therefore, also, I have not cited examples of any of the racial minorities, such as the Negro and the American Indian. Nor have I described farmers belonging to special religious sects, such as the Old Order Amish, who do not use *any* power-driven machinery, or even electricity on their farms because the Bible does not authorize them to do so. They still work with horses. They are American, white, and excellent farmers. But they are not typical.

Far more striking than the individual or group disposition of subsistence farmers in America is the fact of their simple survival: that they should still be there, in such numbers in proportion to the total. In 1965 the *majority* of them were like Robert, with a gross annual farm income of less than $5000. This was surprising in view of not only the fabulous resources and prosperity of the country's postwar economy, but more so in light of the history and pattern of land settlement and its development. Rarely in history have farmers enjoyed such unfettered freedom and extraordinary measure of patronage and equality, of acquisition, choice, movement, and opportunity in the midst of such an abundance of resources, economic, natural, and the rest.

In the colonial period, European monarchies did try to transplant in their respective territories in the New

World their native and largely feudal tenurial systems. The attempt, however, was feeble, shortlived, and even while it lasted difficult to administer. With virgin land unoccupied, extending to the limits only of his imagination, and available virtually for the taking, no immigrant escaping from the oppressive constraints of Europe of the seventeenth and eighteenth centuries could be expected to remain a serf to another—to a master or manor.

In any event, to the extent that European systems in land tenure did get established on American soil, they were destroyed with and after the Revolution.[3] Crown properties and large estates of the loyalists were everywhere confiscated. They were divided into smaller parcels and sold. And so, "in the United States during and after the cataclysm a host of groundlings fresh from the plow and counting house surged over the domains of the Jessups, De Lanceys, and Morrises."[4] Quitrents, entail, and primogeniture were abolished. Even in the South, which later came to be known for its extensive plantations, the majority of the white settlers were small farmers.

Furthermore, land outside the original thirteen states was declared public property. In theory its settlement was based on the twin principles of "free" and "equal." Federal land disposal policy deliberately encouraged owner-operatorship, seeking to give the individual unrestricted right of private property in agricultural land—of acquisition, control, and disposal in family-size units. It was assumed that a country of freeholders would assure maximum utilization and conservation of resources, efficient production, and a wide distribution of wealth and income. The generally accepted adage was that of Arthur Young, that the "magic of property turns sand into gold."

Terms for acquiring land became increasingly cheap and liberal. From 1862 on, any adult could homestead 160 acres, and later 640 acres, free of charge, simply by filing a claim to it, residing on it, and cultivating it for five years.[5] Alternatively, he could pay $1.25 an acre after only six months of residence. Earlier, two horses or eight head of cattle sufficed to purchase a quarter (160 acres) section. An unskilled laborer might save enough in a year to own eighty acres. A mechanic or school teacher could do it in less time.

The "frontier" is supposed to have vanished in 1890.[6] But plenty of land was still available. Three times as much land was homesteaded after 1890 as before. In the half century following 1860, new areas almost as large as Western Europe were brought under cultivation. In 1960 the process was continuing in Alaska.

For three centuries in fact, settlement and development of agricultural land had been a primary preoccupation and concern of the American people. Moreover, at no stage in the country's history, barring the most recent decades, when land prices rose sharply, was it not possible for a farmer to acquire easily and cheaply as much land as he wanted and to use it as he willed. Except for some irrigated tracts, as in the Columbia Basin, there has never been any restriction on the acreage that an individual could hold. And since land always has been and still is the most basic and key resource in agriculture, sheer abundance of its supply and easy availability has given the vast majority of Americans who wished to farm a starting equality that has few parallels.

3

Aside from land, from earliest times farmers in America have received also every incentive, facility, and perquisite, such as education, research, extension, credit, equipment, and communications conventionally considered essential for good farming.

"Scientific farming" had both an early start and state patronage soon after the Revolution. The first agricultural society was founded in 1785, and the first agricultural fair was held in Washington in 1804. By 1858, there were nine hundred societies for the promotion of scientific agriculture. The first weekly paper devoted to the same end was started as early as 1819 by John S. Skinner at Baltimore. The first stage in mechanization of farms developed most rapidly in the half century after the Civil War. Value of farm machinery more than doubled between 1860 and 1890 and increased from $500 million to $3.6 billion between 1890 and 1930.

Columbia University was the first to institute a course in agriculture in 1792. On July 2, 1862, the Morrill Act was adopted. It provided funds to support, endow, and maintain in every state "at least one college where the leading object shall be, without excluding other scientific and classical studies . . . to teach such branches of learning as are related to agriculture. . . ."[7]

This "land-grant" act constituted the first and most important piece of legislation to promote agricultural education.[8] It was followed by the Hatch Act in 1887, which provided funds for experiment stations in the state colleges, so that research was added to teaching. In addition, the U.S. Department of Agriculture has all along done a great deal to provide protection, credit, experimentation, education, and dissemination of information on problems pertinent to farming.[9]

For more than a century, therefore, the American farmer has not lacked for government's attention and assistance. On the contrary, invested with an aura almost of divinity, he has held a very special position in the nation's heart, mind, and philosophy as a repository of special virtues. As Thomas Jefferson put it: "Those who labor in the earth are the chosen people of God, if ever He had a chosen people, whose breasts He has made His peculiar deposit for substantial and genuine virtue."[10] Farmers and nonfarmers, politicians, and several economists as well continue to subscribe to the underlying philosophy, though by implication it reduces the virtuous in American society to a hopeless and rapidly declining minority. On January 9, 1956, in a special message to Congress, President Dwight D. Eisenhower stated: "In America, agriculture is more than an industry; it is a way of life. *Throughout our history the family farm has given strength and vitality to our entire social order. We must keep it healthy and vigorous."* (Italics mine.)

In any event, agriculture has always been too important a sector in the nation's economy to be ignored. More important perhaps, the farmer in the U.S. has long enjoyed a preponderant influence in the legislatures of the country, sufficient to command attention and at times practically dictate policies favorable to himself.

4

Yet by 1968, despite the munificence of God, government, and countrymen toward farmers and farming throughout America's brief history, on two-thirds of the farms, the fences were down and virtually beyond repair.[11] Some two million farm operators and their families were slipping down and under the agricultural ladder with the inexorability of fate. And these did not include the wage hands, who had yet to step up on to the first rung off the ground.[12]

Furthermore, these farmers were not on the way out because they wanted to quit. It is not that they had rosier prospects in steel, electronics, General Motors, or any place else. There was nothing voluntary about their pending exit except their mental and technological obsolescence—to the extent they had allowed themselves to become so in a free society and an economy replete with resources and opportunities.

To cite only one random example of a farmer who had actually gone under: Unlike Robert, he was not biding his time to retire. He was younger and had young children in school.[13] However, until not so long ago, he was farming in Tishomingo County in the northeast corner of Mississippi.[14]

The country is hilly, pretty—plenty of woodland. Dogwood is in bloom; some pine and hardwood. The man is under fifty years of age—white. Says he is sick—does not know of what. Mainly nerves he thinks and that affects his heart. He looks all right. Wife is younger. They have three daughters—fifteen, thirteen, and three.

He still owns forty acres of land, of which at least ten used to be planted by him to cotton and corn—could be more. And it had good pasture when they first moved in, fifteen years ago. The rest was in timber.

The pasture is gone now. The fence is broken at several places. The posts are lying on the ground. A well near the house has caved in. It has a winch and a bucket. But no water. They get their supply from a nearby spring.

He is not growing any crops now. They do not grow any vegetables either. The man says he is sick, and she does not care. She has an old hen. They have a dog. They do not have a car. An old pickup truck is parked—cannot say if it works. He used to have a mule, but not any more.[15]

He purchased this farm in the first place. He used to work it himself. He cannot recall, however, exactly how much cotton and corn he produced or how much fertilizer he used. Or didn't he? He says he did.

The house, too, is caving in.[16] Of boards, unpainted, it has two rooms and a kitchen. A pile of laundry lies outside the front door. Water is heating in a big black cauldron in the yard for the washing. There is an electric cook stove and a very old refrigerator in the kitchen. A radio is playing full volume. Chairs are rickety. The kitchen is dirty and untidy. So is the yard. Junk is scattered all over.

Clothing is of the poorest. The man is dressed in blue overalls; edges frayed. The fifteen-year-old wears striped flannel slacks. She is pretty, in the seventh grade. She is thinking of leaving school, "Because I get discouraged." She does not know what she wants to do. The little girl has a red tricycle—the only touch of color.

The land adjoining his farm has been purchased recently by a businessman from town. For the first time, Bob Miller and his family saw a bulldozer working to level and clear the ground. He describes its operation at length, with a momentary touch of animation. But he does not know the name of the machine. He had never seen it before.

They are vague about their church. Children do not go to Sunday school. They know nothing about community clubs, home agents, county agents, or even the Farmers Home Administration—have never seen or heard of them.[17] He only knows that there is an office where he could get information if he wanted to. He has never wanted to.

Even the famed TVA he at first confuses with something else. And then: "Oh, is that the place electricity comes from?" He knows nothing more about it.[18] He couldn't care less. He doesn't seem to care—not about *anything*.

CHAPTER XII

Silk and Mud Walls

On the other side of the earth, across oceans east from Tishomingo County, Mississippi, where Bob Miller lives, there is another farmer. He too is practically on the bottom rung of the agricultural ladder.

In Gumma Prefecture, on the central island of Honshu in Japan, he owns and cultivates in all 0.8 hectare. The land is poor. Nearly 60 percent of it is planted to mulberry; only 20 percent is in paddy; the rest is in upland unirrigated rice.[1]

He has a couple of pigs in an open shed, the floor of which is not very clean. In spare time he weaves baskets of bamboo strips to supplement his income. A motor scooter is standing in the yard. He owns a power tiller. But no television set or anything "fancy."

Thirty-two years old, Susumu is slight, nondescript, average; unmarried. He lives with his parents. But he is the operator. Father is not home. Mother is in work clothes— navy blue slacks and blouse. Her skin is like wrinkled parchment. Hair, almost the color of the skin, is pulled back in a small tight bun. She is short and very thin.

She raised a family on 0.4 hectare of land. They got as much again after the postwar land reform. The most cherished ambition in her life has been to have a son, see him married, and then retire. "Not from work," she hastens to add. Only from the compulsions and responsibility of work—"to have the freedom of working as and when *I* want to." She has one more son. "But he has taken another family's name."[2]

They live in a single room, which they share with thousands of crawling silkworms in wooden trays filled with mulberry leaves. Worms occupy most of the space. The family's share of it is exceedingly small, at the kitchen end. The room is piled with stuff and overhung with cobwebs, thick and old. The walls are of mud. There are more silkworms in a new shed in the yard that he has built recently.

The house is only a couple of hundred yards from the office of the local experiment station. No agricultural extension officer, however, visits him. He does not expect him to do so.

Nevertheless, this farmer is producing nearly half a ton more rice per hectare than is the average for the prefecture. He is applying a great deal of chemical fertilizer—more than is recommended—in addition to the compost he gets from the hogs. He read about it in a journal.

Even so, all the paddy rice he can grow is consumed at home. But for upland rice this year he has sown a special variety that is used in making New Year cakes.[3] He expects to sell that and earn some cash. "It fetches a good price," his mother adds, nodding her head hopefully.

"Oh, no," he is not planning to give up agriculture. He might have considered quitting if he still had only 0.4 hectare. Prospects of his purchasing more land are nil. But now that he owns 0.8 hectare, "I believe I can make it," he says. He is confident. Besides, he is supporting his parents. "They would not want me to leave."

On the contrary, Susumu is looking forward to getting married soon. "Then we'll have two more hands and I can enlarge my cocoon production. It takes a lot of work."

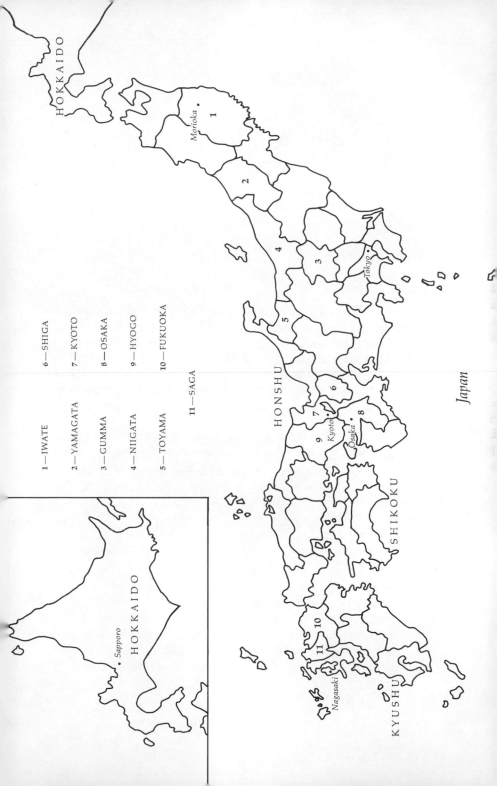

Japan

HOKKAIDO

HONSHU

SHIKOKU

KYUSHU

Morioka

Tokyo

Kyoto
Osaka

Nagasaki

Sapporo

HOKKAIDO

1—IWATE   6—SHIGA
2—YAMAGATA   7—KYOTO
3—GUMMA   8—OSAKA
4—NIIGATA   9—HYOGO
5—TOYAMA   10—FUKUOKA

11—SAGA

CHAPTER XIII

Mini-Millionaires

1

There are not many rungs to the agricultural ladder that a farmer in Japan can climb, however ambitious or efficient he may be. There is a very low ceiling on the amount of cropland that a farmer can own. Little land is available for lease or purchase even to those having less than the legal limit.[1] And furthermore, no one can own land and not cultivate it himself except under special circumstances.

Only the neatly terraced fields, therefore, rise to the summit of the mountains, into and at places way above the clouds. As a Chinese visitor observed once: "Cultivation culminates unto hilltop." But never the fortune of the farmer.[2]

2

Takeo Kamikawara, for example, has practically reached the summit. He has a farm in Iwate Prefecture, in northeastern Tohoku. The region used to be known as the Tibet of Japan—it was so backward.

Forty-nine years old, Takeo wears a gray jacket over an open-collar shirt and gray trousers. He has several gold teeth, a ruddy complexion, and black hair receding from the forehead. He started farming almost three decades ago. In an area noted for inferior volcanic ash soil and a harsh climate, Takeo owns 2.5 hectares of paddy; an upland field of 0.7 hectare; 5 hectares in forest; and 1.0 hectare of pasture.[3]

His oldest son Tadayoshi, twenty-nine years old, lives and works with him. The son is the main operator. Together with their wives they are eight hands on the farm, though Takeo's wife has not been feeling well for the past year. He has two more sons. But they left home in search of jobs. One is in Tokyo. The other works in Morioka.[4]

Their house is large and comfortable. A garage is under construction. The yard is weedy, but it has an interesting collection of cacti in pots. Also some flowers. He has invested around 200,000 yen in plant and machinery and earns a gross farm income of 1.5 million yen in a normal year.

According to Takeo and his son, however, "Our income has never been enough." They do not think it is sufficient now. They are not satisfied. They would like to make at least two million yen from the farm. But they are unable to figure out how to do it.

They cannot get more land. And since Iwate is situated in the snowy and cold zone of Japan, they can raise only one crop in a year. Tadayoshi goes south every winter from October till March and drives a tractor for a daily wage of 1300 yen.[5] Of this he saves about half to invest on the farm. They have no other off-farm income. They have added a dairy enterprise. "It means more work, yes; but it brings in more cash." They are milking four cows. "Well, what else *can* we do?"

As for rice, their main crop, Takeo is already producing 570 kilograms per *tan*, which is well above the average. Moreover, he believes that is as high as the yield can be under the existing techniques and know-how. Ten years ago he was getting 420, and twenty years ago only 270 kilograms per *tan*.[6]

Nevertheless, he and Tadayoshi are trying very hard to improve the yield of rice. "But we are not succeeding. We do not know how we can do it." They are using all the chemical fertilizer they can, as well as stable manure. They think they are doing everything right; exactly as it should be. They keep in close touch with the agricultural extension worker and with the experiment station in Morioka. They are hoping that scientists can offer yet a higher yielding strain of rice or suggest some new cultural practices that will be more productive.

Since for the time being at least they are not able to increase their output of rice or expand the acreage, they are debating whether they should have more cows. Takeo, however, is not very confident that they can handle more cows with the labor at their disposal, unless either rice cultivation or dairying gets more mechanized. He does have a mechanical milker, and he hires a thirty-five horsepower tractor from the village cooperative for plowing the land. He also owns a truck, electric motor, tiller, and thresher. But transplanting, part of weeding, and harvesting of rice with a blade sickle are still done by hand. It takes a lot of work and time—on an average here, a total of 181.9 labor hours per *tan*.

3

Similarly, but farther south in the village of Mukai-zima, in Kyoto Prefecture, Kyuzo Doi also earns a gross farm income of about 1.5 million yen a year. The size of his farm is 1.9 hectares of reclaimed land. It is in two separate pieces. That is all.

The climate here is warmer than in Tohoku. Multiple cropping is feasible. Kyuzo cultivates rice and vegetables. He juggles with the space, time, and labor at his disposal with the precision of a conjurer.

In order to stagger the work load he cultivates three varieties of rice. He plants 0.4 hectare to an early strain; 0.8 hectare to medium; and 0.7 hectare to a late maturing variety. After harvesting the early rice, he drains the field and puts in radishes in 0.2 hectare, cabbage in 0.1 hectare, and spinach in the remaining 0.1 hectare. On the area vacated by the second crop of rice he puts in two varieties of cabbage.

Kyuzo also rents 1.5 hectares from a part-time farmer

for cultivating rice. He provides labor and machinery, while the owner of the land pays for fertilizer, seed, and irrigation water. From the rented land Kyuzo earns 15,000 yen per 0.1 hectare on a contract basis.

The family's labor force consists of himself—in a jacket and khaki pants, tallish for a Japanese, brown and slim, forty-three years old—and his wife—stocky, bright, and talkative, in the usual dark blue polka-dotted work clothes, short waved hair, thirty-eight years old. They have four children, but they are not old enough to help. For transplanting rice he hires three women for ten days, and for harvesting, two women for twenty days. No labor is hired to help with the vegetables or any other operation.

His mother lives with them as well. She is too old to work in the field, but she takes care of the house and relieves the daughter-in-law for full-time work on the farm. She also manages the poultry in a barn adjoining the house. They have five hundred layers this year.

In all, and in this manner, they earn a net annual income of about 800,000 yen, not counting family labor, interest, or rent. They have a debt of 500,000 yen. The house they live in is on the edge of the village. It was built by his father, about twenty-five years ago. Of traditional design, it is neat and well furnished in Japanese style. The kitchen has running water, an old-style tiled stove burning rice straw, and a gas stove. They have several electrical appliances including a refrigerator, an iron, and a washing machine. In the central room there is an elaborately gilded Buddhist shrine. They do not know how old it is: "Could be five or six generations old." There is also a framed but faded photograph of the Emperor and Empress on the wall, a television set, and an electric fan. Straw mats cover the floor; fresh yellow and white chrysanthemums are in a large ceramic vase in a recess in the wall. There are Chinese lanterns and neon tubes. A bunch of onions hangs in the doorway.

Kyuzo does not own an automobile and does not want to. He would rather have a bigger pickup truck because though the eggs are sold to individual customers in the neighborhood he has to take the vegetables to the wholesale market in Kyoto. At present he has a three-wheel one-ton truck. He also has two small power tillers and threshing, husking, and drying machines.

"No, the income is not sufficient," according to Kyuzo. Last year he ended up in the red, because his sister was married. They cannot say exactly how much more they could do with—a million yen net perhaps. "The more the better," the wife says blithely. The question again is: "How?"

His rice yields also are as high as they can get in this soil and region. He would very much like to purchase the land that he is leasing and have 3.4 hectares of his own. "That would be one way to increase my income." But it is not for sale; nor any other land in the neighborhood.

He might be able to rent perhaps another 4.5 hectares and specialize in rice cultivation only. "It would be profitable." But whereas rice requires a great deal of labor at the time of transplanting and harvest, there is little work the rest of the time. He does not relish the idea of so much idle time. Also, in that case, he would have to hire more help at peak periods. Wages, however, are high and rising, and labor is difficult to get. He is not certain if he would be left with much profit. "No," he has never tried direct seeding of rice. "That *would* reduce labor and cost substantially," he admits. He does not think, however, that irrigation and, more so, the drainage here are good enough for him to dispense with transplanting. He is afraid his yields may go down.

Alternatively, he could devote a small fraction of his land purely to vegetable production and reduce the area under rice. "But that too may not work out, because vegetable prices fluctuate a great deal, while income from rice is assured." Its price is controlled and set by the government.[7] Whatever the proportions, a rice-vegetable combination appears to him to be the most profitable proposition for his farm under the circumstances.

"How about enlarging the scale of your operation by cooperative farming? You could use bigger machines then.

Would they not be more efficient and lower the cost of production? Couldn't that be one way of increasing your net income?"

He does not agree. "Now every farmer has his own tractor, be it of three, five, ten, or thirteen horsepower. If we purchased one big tractor of thirty horsepower or more, and used it cooperatively, it would plow deeper perhaps, but efficiency would not be as high. Besides, we would have to sell our machines at a discount."

They held a meeting in the village to discuss whether they should form a cooperative. The bigger farmers agreed with Kyuzo that individual farming and ownership of equipment, however small, is more efficient. The smaller farmers felt that not only would they be required to pay more for the big machines, but being labor-saving devices, they would render at least part of their family labor underemployed, or even totally unemployed. To them that would be doubly costly, since off-farm jobs are not readily available, and generally they are not well paid. They would therefore much rather utilize their labor more fully on their own little farms and work with smaller labor-intensive and cheaper equipment. Since neither the big nor the small farmers wanted a cooperative, the proposal fell through.[8]

"What about livestock?"

Of hogs he has no experience or knowledge. He hesitates therefore to experiment with them. But he did keep two dairy cows in 1953. "The returns were not too good." Moreover, not only did they require a great deal of work, but they also required his presence every single day in the year. "I couldn't leave the farm for even one day."

"I tried to persuade some other farmers to cooperate with me in the dairy venture. Then we could all have had cows and also some free time." But he was not successful. As it is, he works through the week, Sunday and all. "I like to rest whenever I want to, and not just on a Sunday." Their normal waking day stretches from the crack of dawn till ten at night, when they go to bed, and they work generally from seven in the morning till six in the evening. For harvesting they start an hour earlier. "At the time of transplanting rice, we wake up at four. We are in the field by five."

Kyuzo takes a vacation twice a year—goes to Arima hot springs in the neighboring Hyogo Prefecture. Once he goes for two days, with other men in the village. On the second trip, which is for one day only, the whole family goes. The wife would love to make three more such one-day trips with the family, away from work. To the Buddhist temple, husband and wife go only once, on New Year Day. Mother goes four times.

"No," he does not invoke any divine assistance in his farming operations. "I don't believe God has anything to do with the fate of my harvest or my fortune." He does not perform any religious rites at the time of sowing rice, either. "But I do try to sow on the day traditionally called 'lucky.' It is known as *hachijn-hachiya*, or the eighty-eighth night. Personally, I do not think it has anything to do with luck. It was found, I suppose, to be the best day for sowing in this climate, and was made 'lucky' to serve as a reminder to farmers." If it rains on that particular day, Kyuzo does not sow. "But I try to make it as close to it as possible."

"Yes, indeed! I would very much like to own and operate a big farm, like the ones in America." He has heard about them. He is confident he could. "But then. . . ." They both laugh and shrug their shoulders, hands outstretched.

CHAPTER XIV

Pigs, Poultry, and Cattle

1

Not many farmers in Japan, however, have or can aspire to have as much land as Takeo Kamikawara and Kyuzo Doi. The majority are more akin to Susumu in this respect. Many have even smaller holdings. Although on a national average a farmer is permitted to own up to about three hectares of cropland, the area of arable land available per farm household in 1960 was 0.88 hectare. Cultivated land per person employed in agriculture was a mere 0.38 hectare.

Furthermore, most farms in Japan are fragmented. The average is five separate plots per farm, each an infinitesimal 0.51 hectare.[1] The economist Seiichi Tobata once counted "250 individual terraced fields in one area covering only three *tan* (0.74 acres). The smallest field contained four stubs of planted rice (at Noto Peninsula, Japan Sea Coast)."[2]

In 1961, 38 percent of all farm households had less than 0.5 hectare (21 percent had less than 0.3); 32.6 percent of the farmers had holdings of between 0.5 and 1 hectare; and 24.7 percent owned between 1 and 2 hectares each. Only 4.3 percent of all farms were of more than 2 hectares each.[3]

As to crop also, the scale was exceedingly small. In rice, 86 percent of the farmers worked a holding of less than a hectare. More than half had paddy fields of less than half a hectare. In potatoes, wheat, barley, beans, green vegetables, and so on, the area was mostly less than 0.3 hectare per farm. In fruit, such as apples and tangerines, 80 percent of the orchards had 0.3 hectare or less.[4]

2

Aside from field crops, therefore, a tremendous national effort has been under way to open new avenues for increasing farm incomes by encouraging large-scale enterprises, in livestock for example, on modern American lines.

The following description of a commercial chicken and hog outfit appearing in *Nihon Keizai Shimbun—The Japan Economic Journal*—bears witness to the earnest effort:

Mr. Soda ushered the writer to his poultry farm with 100,000 chickens in the suburbs of Tachikawa City in the Tokyo Metropolitan Area, telling that he had invested some 200 million *yen* in the farm. At the right pole of the gate, there is a sign announcing "Gold Eggs—Green Farm," and at the left, another sign, "The Tokyo First Chicken Factory." The farm is definitely named the Factory. Every visitor has to put on a white coat, a white cap, and a pair of boots, all of which are to prevent the invasion of contagious chicken diseases from outside. For the same purpose, every car coming in has to pass a ford at the entrance to have its tires sterilized. Inside the gate, a green turf and a flower bed attract visitors' eyes. On your left-hand side you will see a mess hall of Scandinavian style for employees. The chicken house is built of light steel bars, and its roof is in the saw blade shape like that of the ordinary factory roof.

The number of chickens raised here amounts to 100,000 adults plus 50,000 broods. This tremendous number of the former is attended by only twenty persons, that is, 5000 chickens per employee. The daily production of eggs accounts for 70,000 pieces which can fill up a ten-ton railroad wagon.

Similarly:

In hog raising, a giant enterprise has been opened with the purpose of achieving the production target of 10,000 pigs in five years in Adachi-*ku* (ward) of the Tokyo Metropolis. This was organized by sixteen hog raisers by profession with equal capital investment of two million yen each. It took the cooperative form and commenced business in May this year (1961). The present hog population of only 3000 will be increased to 10,000 in five years, which figure will constantly be maintained, though 25,000 pigs are to be shipped per year. If the present price level is maintained for another five years, the proceeds then will be as much as 400 million yen, an extraordinarily enormous amount of money if viewed from the current average size of hog raising enterprises. In the case of the above enterprise in Adachi-*ku*, pig houses are independently built each for meat hogs, young hogs, pregnant hogs at their time, mother hogs at the weaning time, and breeding hogs. These houses are all built of light steel bars. One for meat hogs has the capacity for 1000 heads and looks like a hangar. If you take a glance inside it, it is full of pigs as far as the eye can reach.

They are fed with commercial feedstuffs through automatic feeders designed by an expert. One worker can attend to 1000 pigs and this labor saving will make the business profitable even when the market price goes down by 20 percent of the current level. This hog raising cooperative is now planning to construct a slaughterhouse and a large refrigerator.[5]

These are impressive and unexceptionable models of modern techniques, scale, and efficiency within the crowded metropolis of Tokyo. Out in the more spacious countryside, however, there were still only 18.9 poultry birds per producing farm household in 1961; 80 percent of the farmers were involved in raising them.[6] The average number of hogs was less than three per farm. This, after a growth "nearly unprecedented in the history of our agricultural commodities."[7]

Moreover, 70 percent of the hog farmers had no sows for breeding. They confined themselves to fattening the piglets that they purchased or took on contract; 72 percent fed only one or two heads, while close to 90 percent fed less than four. A notable achievement of 1962 was that "increase in swine population outran the comparable figures in the number of swine farmers."[8]

3

Unlike pigs and poultry, cattle require much more land. Scarcity of land and the absence of an indigenous tradition and experience have been serious factors in restricting cattle raising in Japan. They have not, however, deterred the authorities from making a determined effort to promote cattle farms and dairying. The story is interesting.

Till less than a century ago, neither beef nor milk formed a part of the regular Japanese diet. There were some native breeds of cattle in the country. But they were used as draft animals, mainly in transport. There is documentary evidence of cows having been milked in the seventh century A.D. and on subsequent occasions. But milk was not taken as food, only as a drug by the nobility. It would be evaporated until dry and given to patricians suffering from tuberculosis or syphilis.

The first three "white" cattle of milking breed were brought into the country, in 1728 probably, by a Dutch animal husbandry expert, Hendrik Kesselrink. He was hired to teach horsemanship to Shogun Yoshimune. The cows were kept at a ranch at Mineoka, fifty miles from Edo—now Tokyo.

The next milestone appears in 1857, when a farmer offered cow's milk to Townsend Harris, the first American consul at Shinoda. This, however, came from a local breed called Izu, which has since become extinct.

Then in 1862, after first learning to milk a cow from a Dutchman named Bellow, one Tomekichi Maeda established a dairy in Yokohama. All the milk was sold to foreigners, who had come in increasing numbers after 1854, when the country's shores were thrown open to the Western world under the "persuasion" of Commodore Perry.

It was not until after the Meiji Restoration, in fact, that a systematic attempt was made to develop animal husbandry in Japan. In 1869 the Japanese Navy recognized beef as a nutritional food. In 1887 it was designated to form a part of the naval rations. Subsequently, the Army began to produce canned beef in its own factories. With a section of the civilian population as well, consumption of meat and dairy products became now a symbol of civilization and progress. And so, for the first time, there was a substantial domestic demand for beef. Milk, too, began gradually to find a more common usage than as medicine for the nobility.

To meet this demand and, more so, to implement the larger national policy of developing all branches of agriculture on modern scientific lines, with special emphasis on livestock, the Meiji government imported a number of European and American experts and animals.[9] Aside from a variety of hogs, horses, and sheep, from 1868 onward came a steady stream of pure-bred Devons and Shorthorns, Ayrshires and Jerseys, Simmentals and Brown Swiss, Holsteins and Guernseys, on both government and private account. Very special attention was bestowed on stud bulls. The purchase of these could not be entrusted entirely to private entrepreneurs. They were inclined to buy them cheap. Official emissaries, therefore, would travel all through Europe and the United States to select with extreme care a blue-blooded pedigreed bull.[10]

The government established several stock-breeding farms in different parts of the country, and enacted the Bulls and Studs Leasing Regulations of 1877. It would lease the animals in pursuance of it. By 1885, 230 official bulls had been distributed in different districts, including Tohoku and Kyushu, where cattle had not been raised traditionally.

An attempt was also made to improve indigenous cattle by cross breeding. But for various reasons, it proved a failure. The scheme was abandoned in 1916, and the prefectural breeding stations set up for the purpose were abolished. Most of the imported breeds also failed to flourish, even to survive.

After a century of such vicissitudes and effort, however, there is now an established and growing demand for beef and milk products in Japan. The population of dairy cattle had risen to over a million by February 1962, while milk production exceeded two million tons. All told, there were 3.3 million head of cattle, of which 657,000 were slaughtered for beef. Even so, 70 percent of the livestock farmers owned only one or two animals each. Moreover, it has meant a heavy dependence on imported concentrates for feed. Only 10 percent of the farmers graze their animals even in summer. They are mostly stall fed and subsist on straw, field residuals, and wild grass, as not much of the forest and grasslands are available to livestock breeders. There is a scheme to develop grasslands. But the land that could be used for pasture is dispersed and situated in remote, inaccessible, and largely infertile areas.

Shortage of land, therefore, continues to pose a serious problem. According to Mr. Yamamoto, president of the National Federation of Dairy Farmers' Cooperatives, "dairy farming in Japan is mostly carried on pin-points of land. . . . Milk cows are raised on fragmentary land without adequate grass."[11]

The grass is collected from ridges dividing the paddy fields. The area planted to feed crops is 1.7 *tan* of the poorest land per milk cow. Storage facilities also are nonexistent or very inadequate. A silo is a rare sight on the Japanese landscape.

CHAPTER XV

Fierce Windes and Stonie Soils

1

Whatever the enterprise, be it rice, poultry, hogs, or cattle, an acute limitation of scale persists in Japanese agriculture. The individual farmer is able to do little or nothing to overcome it. Also, factors such as the lay of the land, soil, and climate leave the peasant with no say or choice.

Called "the Kasai Islands" sometimes, which means a garland archipelago, Japan is composed of a string of several islands. They run north to south for over a thousand miles, off the eastern edge of Asia. All the islands except four— Hokkaido, Honshu, Kyushu, and Shikoku—are very small. They are also very mountainous. As much as 75 percent of the land has a gradient of more than fifteen degrees. Generally, nothing is flat for any distance the eye can see, except the man-made paddy fields.

Only about 16 percent of the total land area is arable. All of it is cultivated.[1] Terraces with a slope greater than fifteen degrees moreover, make up more than 9 percent of the acreage under paddy rice. Of all paddies outside Hokkaido, 3.9 percent are more than 500 meters above sea level and 5.2 percent lie between 300 and 500 meters. The altitude makes the crops susceptible to damage from cold.

Furthermore, a considerable portion of the arable land is composed of thin, acidic, inherently infertile soil. Japan has two hundred volcanoes, old and new; forty-five are still active. They account for 10 percent of the volcanoes in the world and are distributed all the way from Hokkaido in the north to Kyushu, the southernmost island. Volcanic debris and ash has been widely dispersed throughout the country. It covers approximately two out of the five million hectares of the cropped area; 1.5 million hectares of grassland; and another 1.5 million hectares of forest land. Concentration is highest in southern Hokkaido, the Pacific side of Tohoku District, and in Kanto and Kyushu. Volcanoes in Japan make pretty pictures but very poor soil. Natural productivity is low for field crops and rice, unless special measures are taken to ameliorate soil conditions.[2]

Farmer Yamayasu in southern Hokkaido, for example, plows with a horse because he cannot afford to buy a machine. Out of a total annual expenditure of 150,000 yen on his farm, however, he spends 50,000 yen to purchase chemical fertilizers to grow one crop of rice on less than two hectares of land. Besides, he spends the winter carting special earth to mix with and dress the topsoil in his fields in order to remedy its mineral and structural deficiencies.[3] The density of volcanic ash is high here. The related problem of erosion also is severe, both from wind and the water of the melting snows. The worst time is from April to June—in the midst of the sowing season.

2

Aside from poor soil, the temperature and rainfall vary a greal deal and can be very eccentric. Although the islands are in the North Temperate Zone, abnormal climatic conditions are fairly "normal" in Japan. Extensive damage to crops by floods and typhoons, and from cold and dry spells, is a common occurrence.

Rainfall is good. It ranges from forty to eighty inches and is generally distributed over the year. But it is heaviest from the southeasterly monsoon, especially in the southern region, which is also exposed to severe late summer typhoons.

No district has an average temperature of more than twenty degrees centigrade. But whereas the northern extremity is close to the subarctic, the south is subtropical.[4] The sowing season for rice ranges, therefore, from mid-March to late May; that for transplanting, from early May to early July; for earing, from early July to mid-September; and for harvesting, from late August to mid-November.[5] The growing season in Hokkaido is limited to 110 days in the year. In Kyushu it is 195 days. In both, however, the prospect of a secure harvest is about equally remote. The solitary crop that can be cultivated in Hokkaido is liable to certain damage from cold and outbreaks of rice blast should the harvest be delayed into autumn. In the warmer southern tracts the choice appears to lie between early transplanting in spring and risking an attack by the rice stem borer, and transplanting later and losing a ripe crop to devastation by typhoon.

Arthur Hatch, an English preacher aboard the ship "Palsgrave" which reached Hirado in 1620, gives a graphic description of the country and its climate. On his return to England, in a letter dated November 25, 1623, he recorded his impressions as follows:

> The Countrey of Japan is very large and spacious, consisting of several Ilands and pettie Provinces; it is Mountainous and craggie, full of Rockes and stonie places, so that the third part of this Empire is not inhabited or manured; neither indeed doth it affoord that accomodation for Inhabitants which is needfull, or that fatnesse and conveniencie for the growth of Corne, Fruit, and small grayne as is requisite; which causeth the people to select the choysest and plainest parts and places of the land both to till and dwell in. The Climate is temperate and healthie not much pestred with infectious or obnoxious ayres, but very subject to fierce windes, tempestuous stormes, and terrible Earthquakes, insomuch that both Ships in the harbour have been over-set, and driven ashore by the furie of the one, and Houses on the land

disjoynted and shaken to pieces by the fearefull trembling of the other.[6]

Clearly, if there was a divine purpose or design, neither the topography nor the climate of Japan was fashioned to favor pastoral pursuits such as agriculture.

3

It is not as if in the absence of divine favors the farmer in Japan were compensated by a particularly lavish or even adequate supply of the conventional man-made resources. With minor exceptions, these too have been meager, despite the extent of industrialization and the phenomenal growth of the country's economy in the postwar years.[7]

For a farming population of 13,030,000, the total fixed capital assets in the agricultural sector in 1961 were valued at 345.9 billion yen.[8] Of this, 44 percent was invested in land and buildings. Annual earnings of a farm household averaged 459,466 yen, of which 236,623 yen came from agriculture, the rest from nonfarm sources.[9] Farm operating expense per household came to a modest average of 154,935 yen, while working capital per *tan* worked out to 10,993 yen. And if indebtedness of the producer is a measure of plentitude and solvency in a modern economy, the agricultural sector in Japan is primitive. Against cash deposits and savings of 409,112 yen per farm household in the fiscal year ending 1961, outstanding debt was 59,556 yen per family.[10] Not only had the deposits doubled since 1958, but 50 percent of the surplus cash (400 billion yen) of the agricultural credit associations and another 240 billion yen held by the Central Co-operative Bank for Agriculture and Forestry had been used for nonagricultural purposes.

The outflow of farm savings into other sections of the economy, together with the cash on hand, amounted to 500 billion yen in 1961, as against rural borrowings of 50 billion yen. Obviously, the Japanese peasant was borrowing and spending much less than he was earning and saving—a wholly obsolete notion and practice.

4

Aside from capital, there has been great progress reportedly, in recent years, in the mechanization of Japanese agriculture. The nature and design of the implements is determined almost entirely by the cultural requirements of rice, since more than 40 percent of the total arable land—largest for any single crop—is planted to it, and 90 percent of the farm households are engaged in its production. Rice amounts to more than one-half of the total agricultural output.

Anyhow, in every year since 1957, expenditure on farm machinery exceeded every other form of investment in agriculture in Japan.[11] Yet, four years later, usage of power was 13.3 hours per *tan* per annum as against labor inputs of 427.5 hours.

After a seventy-fold increase in a decade in the number of households using power for traction, only 22.5 percent of the total cultivated land was being plowed with power cultivators or tractors on 35 percent of the farms in 1960.[12] Tractors of more than nine horsepower numbered less than 7000 in the whole country. Besides, there were the small two to five horsepower, often multipurpose power tillers, more suited to the average-size holding.[13] Even these, however, were owned by only about one-tenth of all the farm households. In many small fields the soil was still prepared by hand digging, with a long-bladed mattock.

Similarly, 26,000 farmers used a power machine for weeding in 1960. Another 67,000 used an animal-drawn mechanism. More than five million households weeded manually. Electric motors had become popular and commonplace. But only 1,124,000 were in use, plus 1,696,000 petroleum engines. They did not add up to one unit per farm. In a country, moreover, in which over 55 percent of the arable land is irrigated, cultivated by 5,223,000 households at the time, the total number of power pumps came to 283,000.

Of the various cultural operations, threshing—of all grains—is the most mechanized in Japan. The thresher was about the only machine used widely before World War II also—on about 4 percent of the farms. By 1960 nearly half the farms were using a total of 2.5 million power threshers, in the range of 0.5 to 3.0 horsepower each.[14]

About the only manufactured inputs that the Japanese farmer uses liberally in fact, are pesticides and chemical fertilizer.[15] He uses more fertilizer per unit of land than the farmer of any other country in the world except the Netherlands.[16] And so, whereas per acre consumption of nitrogen in the U.S. in 1961, was thirteen pounds as against 111 pounds in Japan, the labor input of an American farmer for the production of a hundred kilograms of rice was only 5.8 hours even way back in 1910. That of the Japanese farmer half a century later was 49.0 hours. By 1950 the American farmer was spending 1.3 hours of his energy to produce one hundred kilograms of rice, and since then it has been reduced further. In the case of wheat and other farm commodities also, disparity in labor productivity between the two countries is as great or greater.[17]

CHAPTER XVI

Rice God, Inari

1

Notwithstanding the scarcity of most of the resources used in agriculture, and the relatively low labor output, farming in Japan is one of the most highly developed and productive operations in the world, not excluding the United States.[1]

For example, rice has been grown as a *commercial* crop in the U.S. since the latter part of the seventeenth century. Trial plantings were made in Virginia in 1609. By 1690, however, its cultivation was firmly established in South Carolina. About 1899 Seaman A. Knapp, in the Division of Botany in the U.S. Department of Agriculture, introduced ten tons of Kyushu rice from Japan that was distributed in southwestern Louisiana and eastern Texas. Several other varieties were tested on farms, and cultural methods were demonstrated. By 1960 America was a leading rice-producing country, second only to Brazil in the Western hemisphere.[2] It was one of the world's important exporters as well.[3]

Moreover, since acreage is controlled by the government and it is never grown by farmers only for domestic consumption, wherever rice is raised in America the soil and climate are close to the text-book ideal. No marginal soils are planted to it. Nor is it cultivated as a subsidiary crop.

All of it is irrigated—by flood irrigation. There is no "up-land" rain-fed rice.

Furthermore, all cultural operations are mechanized. The major rice regions—in Arkansas, Louisiana, California, and Texas—have been described as the most highly mechanized farming areas in the world.[4] In 1962 the equipment required for a rice farm of three hundred acres in California cost about $80,000. Thus, the soil is prepared by large "rice-special" tractors with ten, twenty, maybe more times the drawbar than the little walking-type garden tillers used in Japan. Much of the seeding and most of the fertilizing and spraying are done by airplanes that cover several hundred acres a day. No transplanting is involved. Weeds and pests are controlled entirely by chemicals.[5]

The grain is harvested and threshed in a single operation by high-powered self-propelled combines. It is then dried artificially in a drier or aerated bin before storing or milling. These harvesters are especially designed for rice and equipped with crawler tracks that enable the machine to cross wet spots, small ditches, and low levees. Or they are equipped with large tires with mud legs so that they can be operated over the sloping levees. Commonly, they have twelve-foot to sixteen-foot headers that can be operated under extremely muddy conditions. Most of them are equipped with choppers, which cut up the rice straw as it leaves the combine, and with a distributor, which spreads the straw particles uniformly over the stubble to facilitate plowing under.

Not a single acre under rice in America is double-cropped. In most areas the crop is under two to three years rotation. The most modern technology is applied to seed breeding and selection and to every other aspect of cultivation. There are special rice experimental stations in each producing state. Research in rice breeding is conducted cooperatively by the U.S. Department of Agriculture and the state institutions.[6]

When I asked Russell Carrino in Yuba County in California why he cultivated rice, his reply was: "Rice is an easy crop. It does not take constant care—only a few busy days in spring and fall. All summer it is flooded and requires only spraying and supervision."

Tall, youthful, married, Russell is a tenant. He does not own any land. He rents 252 acres. It is all in rice. The Carrinos are hoping to own a farm one day, "provided we can find rice land that we can pay for."

Russell prefers rice, though he had no prior experience of cultivating it and went broke learning. "I grew up on a farm." His father, however, had forty acres in row crops—barley and prunes. "Believe me," says Russell, "growing rice is much *much* easier than picking prunes."

Despite the technology, mechanization, and scale of operation, not only does the American farmer not produce a ton of rice very much cheaper than the Japanese, he does not produce as much.[7] On a national average, the Japanese peasant obtains 1100 kilograms more per hectare than does an American.[8] He obtains an average yield of 5280 kilograms from one hectare in a considerably worse climate and on nearly five times the acreage of much poorer soil.[9] Moreover, 5 percent of the rice land in Japan is not irrigated; a great deal is double-cropped; and all of it has been sown to rice at least once every year for hundreds of centuries before the American soil was first plowed.[10]

Japan produces more rice per unit of land than not only the United States; it produces more than almost any country in the world that has a sizeable acreage under the crop. The island's agriculture is thus able to support a population more than half that of America, with production from roughly twice the number of farms on a total land surface smaller than California.[11]

It has been calculated that Japan produces roughly 13,000 potential food calories per cultivated acre per day. At the rate of 3500 original calories—that is of plants eaten directly rather than processed through livestock—one cultivated acre in Japan feeds 3.7 persons. If the Americans were to crop six hundred million acres of their farmland as intensively as do the Japanese, to grow cereals for direct human consumption, they could feed more than two billion people.[12]

2

Rice is the basic foundation diet of the Japanese, but not because the grain was native to the land. Nor were the people restricted by a taboo on other foods. Owing to Buddhism, there was a bias, but no cult of pure vegetarianism in the country. In recent years the government has been trying to wean the people to more "modern" diets, and it is having its effect, especially on the younger generation.

Hitherto, however, rice has been predominant primarily because it was nationally relished. It also enjoyed status. Traditionally, to eat rice three times a day was a cherished ideal—one of the highest goals of life on earth. Of all the food crops, therefore, rice has been supreme throughout the recorded history of agriculture in Japan—above considerations often of comparative costs and returns.[13] And like every good thing on earth, it has divine associations. There is a rice god, Inari. Shrines consecrated to him are to be found in every town and village and in many private homes.

3

So strong has been the attachment to rice in the past, that but for it, several parts of Japan—Hokkaido, for instance—should not be cultivating it at all. It is like growing this, originally a tropical plant, in Massachusetts or southern Ontario.[14] Yet, Hokkaido produces more rice than any other farm commodity, in terms of acreage, volume, and value. And it is not even as if it was established there unaccountably in the prehistoric era by some process of oriental mysticism.

Rice came to Japan via Kyushu in the southwest, from the Yangtze River basin in China in the first century B.C. It spread to and over the main island of Honshu, reaching its northern district of Tohoku in the eighth, and Aomori by the thirteenth century.

Till a hundred years ago, however, but for a narrow coastal strip on the Oshima Peninsula in the extreme southwest of Hokkaido, this, the northernmost island and territory of Japan, was mostly uninhabited except for a small and primitive tribe of Ainus. They lived by hunting and fishing. There was no settled agriculture in Hokkaido. Neither rice nor any other grain was being cultivated.

The island began to be colonized and developed systematically only after the Meiji Restoration with the primary purpose of settling the displaced and unemployed samurai—the warrior class from Tokugawa times. In 1871 a Colonization Commissioner's Office was set up in Sapporo to administer the program.

The commissioner, who was chief of the administration, felt not unreasonably that Hokkaido was much too far north and too cold for growing rice. He took the precaution also of inviting and consulting with several distinguished foreign experts from Western countries. At the time, a dozen of them were concerned exclusively with the problem of developing agriculture in Hokkaido. One of them, an American agronomist, Thomas Anticel, surveyed the Ishikari region in 1871 and reported to the commissioner that "Paddy field making is the last thing to do."

Horace Capron, an ex-secretary of the U.S. Department of Agriculture and at the time chief adviser to the Hokkaido Colonial Government *(Kaitakushi)*, also rejected rice on the ground "that it is expensive and inferior to other cereals in nutritive value."

William S. Clark, director of the Sapporo Agricultural College (established in 1876) and on leave from Massachusetts State Agricultural College of which he was president, was of the same opinion as his compatriots. Clark reportedly taught his students the Christian Bible and hymns. But under his direction Sapporo College was modeled after the Massachusetts State Agricultural College, and it tried to teach American agronomy and develop large-scale farming. Machines and implements for the College farm—it covered an area of 100 hectares—were ordered from the United States. Seeds were purchased in Massachusetts. And a model barn was constructed for which plans and specifications were furnished by a Professor William Wheeler. According to Clark, "Our barn has abundantly demonstrated its utility in the matter of saving labor, three men now taking all the care of twelve horses, thirty-two neat cattle and ten hogs besides doing some outside work, in winter time."[15]

In pursuit of the same philosophy, "The Kaitakushi (the Colonial Government) by advice of Capron, established a large and very expensive intermediate station at Tokyo practically of no value in connection with the colonization and development of Hokkaido. All kinds of most expensive agricultural machinery—threshing machines capable of threshing one hundred bushels of grain, self-binding reapers that could cut twenty acres, mowing machines, gang plows, corn planters, and innumerable machines and implements, the greater part of which were useless as a fifth wheel would be to a wagon," were imported.[16]

Max Fesca, a German agronomist and soil specialist, also surveyed Hokkaido at the request of the minister of Home Affairs. He too pointed out the obvious unsuitability of the region for rice cultivation. Under the weight of such prestigious consensus, official attitude could not have been anything but negative.

The farmers, on the other hand, all immigrants from the mainland, whom Clark in another context describes as "ignorant and half-civilized," were not impressed. They were so addicted to rice that they refused to heed the advice of experts or authority. Some were even imprisoned for cultivating it secretly. Besides, and as was to be expected, they suffered repeated crop failures.

Nevertheless, acreage under rice kept growing. The first break came in 1873 when a farmer experimented with *Akage,* a strain that proved to be more resistant to cold than the one they had been using. With it began the northward expansion of the grain.

Akage was improved upon by another diligent farmer in the village of Shinkotoni in Sapporo County, when in 1895 he selected another variety called *Bozu*. It, too, was bred from *Akage*. But it was beardless, more prolific, earlier-maturing, and more resistant to disease. Just about this time, experiments were made with direct sowing in order to save precious hours of daylight on various cultural operations. A seeding machine was designed for the purpose. Along with the direct sowing method, *Bozu* and its progenies held the field in Hokkaido till 1938 as the most popular and successful strain of rice.

It was not long before the government capitulated and also began to experiment with rice. "Experience in Rice Cultivation" was published in 1883. Four years later the Sapporo Breeding Farm was established for seed production. In 1889 an experimental farm was set up in Kamikawa on Ishikari River. Shortly after, experiments were made near Asahikawa. In 1892, with the appointment of a Japanese agronomist, Tsuneaki Sakawa, as the chief of the Treasury Department of Hokkaido, rice began to receive active encouragement from the local administration.

By 1901 rice was being sown on 12,000 hectares on the island and production amounted to 25,000 tons. In a decade, the acreage doubled. By 1921 the cropped area exceeded 90,000 hectares, and production had increased to 210,000 metric tons of brown rice.

However, serious crop failures from abnormal cold spells continued, as in 1884, 1889, and on several occasions subsequently into the next century—in 1913, 1926, 1931, 1932, 1934, and 1935. Also, there was repeated damage from rice blast. In 1933 a bumper crop was destroyed by blast in the Sorachi area.

The extensive damage from cold and blast in the 1930's provoked fresh thinking and research. It gave an impetus to large-scale adoption of primitive but effective control measures of the disease. They included the following techniques:

1) Seeds should be sterilized;
2) In transporting rice straws, infected straws should not be dropped;
3) No straws should be left on the paddy field;
4) Straws in infected areas should not be placed in the paddy field unless they are well rotted;
5) The paddy field should be well drained;
6) Soil dressing should be made;
7) Bordeaux mixtures should be sprayed at one time.[17]

New strains and cultural techniques, as of sowing in *protected* nurseries and then transplanting as in the rest of the country, were further developed.[18] But typically, every disaster led to the breeding of better varieties and a more widespread adoption of improved techniques and practices tailored to specific needs of the new environment, which made a more northward extension of cultivation possible and also gave higher yields.

By 1961 production of rice in Hokkaido had increased more than two hundred times since the early Meiji period. From nineteen hectares in 1883, area under rice had expanded to 200,900 hectares. Between 1931–40 and 1955–61 output went up by more than 300,000 tons on almost the same area.[19]

More important, not only had the yields per hectare become appreciably higher, but they had become remarkably stable despite the cold spells which, of course, continued. By 1960 yields were almost as stable in the far north as in the milder districts of Kinki and nothern Kyushu that were formerly famed for their high levels of productivity. But more than techniques, it was the sheer perseverance, or rather perversity, of the farmers that disproved expert advice and ultimately conquered the truly formidable limitations of climate and geography.[20] They risked and lost repeatedly. But for their obduracy, however, the techniques would never have been born.

CHAPTER XVII

Labor of Love

1

Aside from his traditional attachment to rice, the farmer in Japan has some other interesting "perversities" also. For instance, in the course of interviews and conversation, the country's economists and intellectuals betray a grievous statistical shame at the low labor productivity of their rice farmer.[1] It bothers them because it is the international mode now to measure modernity and progress primarily by how little work it takes to produce anything. They think poorly of the farmer who gives so much of his time and labor to the cultivation of rice.

On the other hand, the farmer apparently is insensitive to the issue. He pours his and the family's labor into the farm as if it were a matter of love and not of the market. Often, he appears to prefer crops and cultural practices that require more work. He exhibits a strange propensity for exerting more than is economic, and at times, even essential.[2]

His yard is usually weedy. But never the fields.[3] Yet, he knows full well that those last blades of grass that he pulls out of his paddy so laboriously do not affect his production by an ounce. Transplanting of rice seedlings is done with similar excessive care. It is neat, precise, and meticulous, like an embroidery on silk.

The type and extent of labor that cultivation of rice in Japan involves would appall the most hardworking farmer anywhere in the United States. It merits a brief description.

Rice is first sown in special nursery beds that have been prepared with great care. The seeds are pressed with a wire-net roller or wooden trowel so that half—under no circumstances the whole—of a seed sinks into the soil. Sometimes, instead of pressing, the seeds are simply covered lightly with burnt chaff mixed with upland soil.

The nursery is then irrigated slowly and submerged. As the primary leaves emerge the bed is drained several times to expose the sprouts gradually to air and daylight, each succeeding time for longer hours. A warm and windless, but cloudy day is preferred for the purpose. If the temperature is low, however, and there is danger of frost, the nursery is submerged deeply. In the colder regions, the bed is covered with vinyl sheet or oil paper for warmth and protection. Sometimes it is electrically heated.

About forty days after sowing the seedlings are removed and replanted in the main field. There are three methods of doing this, as follows:

1. *Transplanting with the aid of a crosswise stretched rope:*

(i) A stretched rope supported by the side levees serves as base line for planting rows. The rope has marks at regular intervals to ensure uniform spacing between hills;

(ii) Several planters line up along the rope;

(iii) Each planter, moving crosswise, plants a certain number of seedlings on each hill along the marks on the rope;

(iv) When one line has been completed, the rope is moved to the next row and each planter steps backward and repeats the operation.

2. *Transplanting with the aid of lengthwise stretched ropes:*

(*i*) Several ropes are stretched lengthwise at appropriate intervals of 1.5–2.0 meters in the paddy field. The field is thus divided into several even panels;

(*ii*) One planter is in charge of a whole panel, which contains several rows;

(*iii*) He (or she) transplants seedlings in each row, maintaining the uniform space between hills and between rows simply by the eye;

(*iv*) When seedlings have been transplanted in one row, the planter steps backward to transplant in the next row;

(*v*) When he has completed a panel, he moves to another.

3. *Transplanting with the aid of rules or markers:*

(*i*) The points at which seedling are to be planted are marked on the field by a rule or marker;

(*ii*) The planter puts in the seedlings exactly at the marked points (5–7 in number), always stepping forward, so that no seedlings are transplanted in anyone's footprints.[4]

In this manner, to each hectare of land, as many as 200,000 separate clusters or hills of rice seedlings are planted. When ripe, these are harvested by hand. The plants are cut at the base with a short blade or saw-edged sickle, the reaper in a squat position.[5] The sheaves also are bound by hand. They are then dried on the ground if it is dry. If not, they are hung up on racks made of bamboos or logs that are erected in the field. Threshing is done after the grain has been dried to 15–16 percent moisture. It is dried again for a second time before husking.[6]

2

About 1960 experiment stations, extension workers, and agricultural economists were all making an earnest effort to persuade farmers to give up the practice of transplanting and to sow rice directly in the field mechanically. The immense potential of the technique for improving labor productivity was very much to the fore.

It could not be recommended in the cold regions in the north where rice cultivation is really forced or semi-forced by being sown early under cover in special protected nurseries. In the rest of the country, however, experiments had shown that yields per hectare need not be significantly lower if rice is sown directly,[7] while it would save hundreds of hours of backbreaking work, make it more productive, and rationalize its distribution—spread it out more evenly through the year. Moreover, it would make further mechanization possible.

Under the prevalent cultural techniques, on a national average, 1819 hours were required to cultivate one hectare of rice. To mention a few of the items: labor spent on transplanting took 261 hours; weeding, 307.3 hours; and reaping, 388.8 hours. Seed-bed operation consumed 91.6 hours; and tilling, fertilizing, and harrowing, another 263.2 hours.

With direct sowing and even the small-scale mechanization that it would make feasible, seeding time could be reduced to 13 hours; tilling, fertilizing, and harrowing to 62.1 hours; weeding to 50 hours; and reaping to 70 hours. The ninety-one hours spent at the nursery stage would be eliminated altogether. Total labor input per hectare would be cut down to 465 hours—almost a quarter of the requirement in 1960.[8]

Considering how much work of the most strenuous type (and expense) the suggested technique of direct sowing would eliminate, one would have expected the recommendation to catch and spread like bush fire. Instead, three and even five years later, it was proving difficult to keep a few embers alive. The farmer was not rushing to switch from intensive to extensive techniques of cultivation, despite rising wages and increasing shortage of labor.

Experts, economists, and planners in Tokyo, at the provincial universities, and at the prefectural experiment stations, shook their heads sadly.[9] They spoke of it regretfully as a pattern of the future when the farmer will be forced into it by sheer necessity, more compelling than when the suggestion was first made. Or, when a new generation of cultivators with different values of work and leisure takes over.

A study by the Institute for Agricultural Economic Research at the University of Tokyo made a different prediction—that transplanting of rice will persist even if labor becomes more scarce. The farmer will simply lengthen the period of transplanting. He will spread out the work load by raising seedling in special *protected* nurseries instead of, as hitherto, in the ordinary open ones.[10] So far, protected nurseries were confined to the cold regions and were used only to attain a more stable yield of rice.[11] According to this study, they would be utilized more widely in the future in warmer areas as well to serve a different need and purpose. It could well be, therefore, that rather than abandon the practice and save labor, farmers would adjust the technique of transplanting to the dwindling manpower. The study projected that in the near future forced and semiforced cultivation methods will be used on 1.5 million hectares, or about half the total acreage under rice.

3

To return to the fall of 1963. Specialists at the agricultural experiment station in Kyoto had been experimenting with direct sowing of rice for more than three years. They had found no appreciable reduction in yields. The climate here is suitable, and pests and weeds could be controlled effectively by chemicals.

"Ideally, there should be no need to enter the field once it has been sown and flooded till the paddy is ready to harvest," says Yoshio Hayashi, director of the experiment station. "The problem of keeping a watch on the young shoots over a larger area is mainly psychological."[12]

Moreover, intensive multiple cropping is the norm in this region. Like Kyuzo Doi, many farmers produce as many as seven crops in a year. Any suggestion for saving labor, therefore, should have been eagerly sought and accepted. Yet, for miles around it is difficult to see a standing crop of rice that has not been transplanted.

Hatta is farming literally under the shadow of the experiment station in Kameoka. He owns one hectare of paddy land and cultivates another 4.5 *tan* in cooperation with two other farmers. Forty-five years old, he has been farming for nearly thirty years. He has four workers in the family—his parents, himself, and his wife. His gross income hovers around a million yen from the farm. He has no off-farm income.

On his own land he is growing rice, and in winter barley and wheat. Besides, he raises seedlings of parsley and other green vegetables. An excellent farmer, he has won a prize in rice culture. But he does not sow his rice directly. Nor does he intend to. At first he claims that he does not do it because he is cultivating vegetables as well. Then he explains that he did try it about twenty years ago, but the yields were very low. He has not tried again more recently. Finally, it emerges that "land productivity is still the most important consideration with me and with other farmers. That is why the practice is not spreading."

On the land farmed cooperatively, for example, "We use more chemicals for killing weeds in order to save on labor. But not on my own farm. I am too nervous to experiment." He weeds manually. According to him, the yields on the cooperative farm are lower than on his own. But so too is the cost of production.

On his farm Hatta pays 200,000 yen in wages for help hired for transplanting and harvesting rice. He realizes also that the return on his and the family's labor is dismally low. It is very much lower than in other professions, especially in this, a highly urbanized and industrially developed area.

"But I do not mind," he insists. "Money is not of prime importance to me. I enjoy the work. I like to work hard. I *do* work very hard. But then I like it."

Shigeru Fujita is another excellent farmer in the neighboring Shiga Prefecture. He owns 1.5 hectares of paddy, and 2.3 hectares of upland fields of which 2 hectares is in pasture and 0.3 hectare is sown to fodder crops. He is milking fourteen cows. His net farm income comes to about a million yen a year.

Fujita's family consists of three men—himself and his two sons—and his wife. He is forty-seven years old. They hire help for harvesting and transplanting rice for thirty man days in the year.

"No, I have not tried direct seeding," although the cows and rice compete for his time and attention. He is afraid that if rice is sown directly fertilization of the seed may not be 100 percent. Moreover, "it will be difficult to take care of the seedlings in the field. They may not all survive. Also, my fields are very wet and cannot be drained completely. They are terraced and in thirty separate plots. Mechanization would be difficult."

All of which adds up to his neither trying, nor having any intention of trying to sow his rice directly. "Yes, a farmer in the neighborhood did try on a very small plot. He got almost the usual yields," Fujita admits. "But there were many weeds in that field," he complains with pointed disapproval.

4

Similarly, in Fukuoka Prefecture in Kyushu, the experiment station and extension workers have been recommending direct sowing of rice for more than three years. At the end of it, however, according to their estimate, less than 0.3 percent of the paddy land in the prefecture had perhaps been seeded directly.

The new technique should have appealed to a farmer like Shigeo Yamada. He owns 1.26 hectares of paddy and 4.6 *tans* in upland fields, which he irrigates also by pumping water. He raises rice, wheat, rape seed, white potatoes in spring, white potatoes in autumn, sweet potatoes, ordinary cabbage, Chinese cabbage, three crops of radish, and sweet corn—all in a year.

There is only him and his wife to do all the work. Their three children are too young and his father is too old. Shigeo is forty-one years old. He hires labor for twenty-five man days to help with transplanting and harvesting rice. There is also an exchange labor system for transplanting rice. He knows all about the direct seeding technique. He is interested. But only vaguely. "No, I have not tried it." He believes that fertilization of the soil and pest control are the more important factors in increasing yields. They continue to be his primary preoccupation.

Yoshio Matsunaga, a farmer in the adjoining Saga Prefecture, feels the same way. He owns 1.35 hectares of paddy land. He too has not experimented with direct sowing of rice and does not want to. He is not even interested. He explains: "True, it would save labor. Transplanting rice *is* hard work. But production by the transplanting method is good. By sowing directly the yield of rice per *tan* may not get less. But then," with puckered eyebrows he says slowly, "it will not be any higher." That dismisses it.

CHAPTER XVIII

In Freedom and Feudalism

1

"By sowing directly the yield of rice per *tan* may not get less. But then, *it will not be any higher.*" Therein perhaps lies the clue, the true reason why Matsunaga, Hatta, Fujita, Yamada, and most of the other farmers were so reluctant to adopt the direct sowing method.

If the technique had promised *higher* yields, they would have taken to it immediately with enthusiasm; possibly, even if it had involved more instead of less labor than transplanting. In the case of higher yielding strains of seed, for instance, according to Katsunao Iwasaki, director of the Tohoku National Agricultural Experiment Station, "New varieties are in use in the farmers' fields at times before we have classified them."[1] Since the nontransplanting method promised merely *not* to lower the production per *tan*, they were not interested immediately. They did not consider it worth their while even to try it out on an experimental scale.

What is more, this supreme anxiety of the farmer in Japan to increase his output at almost *any* cost, is not a recent phenomenon, peculiar to the postwar period of "enlightenment." It clearly predates the 1960's and such incentive-weighted policies of the government as offering the producer higher than black market price for purchase of rice.[2] It predates also the country's "liberation" in the

123

1940's, when Japan was instructed in the mysteries of *demokurashii* and ordered by General MacArthur to "establish respect for the dignity of man, and destroy the economic bondage which has enslaved the Japanese farmer for centuries of feudal oppression."[3]

On the contrary, whatever the circumstances and resources, in the absence of any discernible economic inducements and patronage as well, the peasant in Japan appears to have done his best to produce the most he could, and continually to better his performance. And if prices fell, as in the depression years before the war, he did not cut back on production. According to R. P. Dore: ". . . farm families switched to barley, millet, and buckwheat at home and sent more rice to the market."[4]

2

Japan has a long history. Early in the seventeenth century, however, when the first permanent English settlements were being made in America, Ieyasu, the first of the Tokugawa Shoguns (1603–16), succeeded in subduing the hitherto warring provincial barons and unified the whole territory of Japan under a centralized feudal form of government.[5] The event is significant politically. But also, this was the period when was laid the foundation of an agrarian structure and organization, essential features of which have survived into and past the middle of the twentieth century.

The Tokugawa economy was based on the village. It produced the staple food and revenue—rice. Power of the government *(bakufu)* lay in overlordship of all the land in the country. Nearly a quarter of the total area was owned and administered by the Tokugawa family. The rest of the land was divided among nearly three hundred fiefs *(han)*— their number kept changing. Each fief was headed and administered by a lord (daimyo). He lived in a castle town with an army of soldier (samurai) retainers. The daimyo were vassals of the Shogun. They held their fiefs at his pleasure and were obliged to govern in accordance with his orders and direction.[6] The structure was held together by oaths of loyalty and reciprocal grants of fief or hereditary stipend certificates.

Not unnaturally, the Tokugawas wanted to reign over their domain forever. They did so with remarkable stability, holding together in tolerable peace a population of about thirty million people for an uninterrupted stretch of two and a half centuries. In order to perpetuate their rule, however, they sought to establish a state social system and morality, in which status was fixed by birth, absolute authority held primacy, and any change was frowned upon, and in fact, was forbidden. The attempt was virtually to freeze society into a hierarchy of unequal ranks, rights, and opportunity. Its principal constituents were the throne, the feudal baronies, peasants, artisans, and traders. Unlike medieval Europe, "The Buddhist Church was no longer an estate of the realm, and the Shinto establishment in the seventeenth century was lacking in political influence."[7]

In principle, no one could rise above the rank and class in which he was born. Everyone, including the emperor, was under the control and at the mercy of the Shogun. Even marriage could not be contracted privately. Sons were not equal and status of daughters was lower.[8] There did not exist in the language, terms for "popular rights" or "liberty." An early translator of Mill's essay "On Liberty" had great difficulty, "because of the lack of proper words in the Japanese vocabulary."[9]

According to one historian, "The Tokugawa Japanese lived out his life with his head constantly lowered to higher authority."[10] The lowliest was that of the peasant, though in theory, he was considered to be the foundation of the state. He was ranked next to and below the samurai, but above the artisan and the merchant. Statements such as, "A farmer is worth two samurai," are common in Tokugawa literature. In numbers also, peasants were the most numerous—about eight-tenths of the total population. Rice, their major produce, dominated the national economy and polity. Wealth was measured in measures of rice. It was the basic food, the main source of revenue, and the virtual medium of exchange. The stability of the government depended upon it. A shortage could deflate the currency. Every grain of that rice, however, was a harvest of feudalism.

The peasant was not a free agent. He was fettered to *a* piece of the earth. Though secure in the plot registered in his name, he was forbidden to sell or mortgage the land till in 1720 Shogun Yoshimune curiously reaffirmed the ban on alienation but permitted land mortgage. Nor could a peasant change his occupation to engage in trade or industry. He was not permitted even to travel beyond his native district except for pilgrimage to Ise Grand Shrine or the Zenkoji Temple. To abscond was a major offense for which the whole village was liable to be penalized. Until another suitable cultivator was found to till the abandoned land, the village or the *Gonin-gumi* (the Five-Man Group) could be required to cultivate it and pay the taxes.[11]

This was the time when across the Pacific on virtually an empty continent, about the only limit to a pioneer's horizon was his own vision and initiative. In Japan, on the other hand, the boundary of a peasant's field was generally the outside limit of his legitimate frontier. For most it measured one or two *tans*. The land produced less than five *koku* of rice. After tax it would not suffice to feed an average family at the normal rate of one *koku* per head per annum. There were owners of larger holdings as well, rich farmers known as *gono*. But they were not numerous.

Within the spatial limit of those couple of *tans* even, the farmer's freedom was severely restricted. He was not free to choose his crop or the variety of seed to sow. Though rarely enforced in practice, an infinite number of regulations prescribed his daily chores, duties, dress, food, and recreation. An order known as *Keian no Furegaki*, for example, was issued to all villages in 1649. It listed a number of injunctions, some of which read as follows:

—Farm work must be done with the greatest diligence. Planting must be neat, all weeds must be removed, and on the borders of both wet and dry fields beans or similar foodstuffs are to be grown, however small the space.

—Peasants must rise early and cut grass before cultivating the fields. In the evening they are to make straw rope or straw bags, all such work to be done with great care.

—They must not buy tea or saké to drink, nor must their wives.

—Men must plant bamboo or trees round the farm house and must use the fallen leaves for fuel so as to save expense.

—Peasants are people without sense or forethought. Therefore they must not give rice to their wives and children at harvest time, but must save their food for the future. They should eat millet, vegetables, and other coarse food instead of rice. Even the fallen leaves of plants should be saved as food against famine. . . . During the seasons of planting and harvesting, however, when the labour is arduous, the food taken may be a little better than usual.

—The husband must work in the fields, the wife must work at the loom. Both must do night work. However good-looking a wife may be, if she neglects her household duties by drinking tea or sightseeing or rambling on the hillsides, she must be divorced.

—Peasants must wear only cotton or hemp—no silk. They may not smoke tobacco. It is harmful to health, it takes up time, and costs money. It also creates a risk of fire.[12]

3

Aside from freedom and status the Tokugawa peasant lacked the resources, factors of production, and the prospect often of simple survival.

Thus, not all peasants had a house of their own. "Of 33 holders actually residing in a Bizen village in 1609, only six owned homesteads; in a Kawachi village in 1594, the proportion of resident holders who owned homesteads was 14 out of 36."[13] Seventeenth-century land registers of the major regions show that from 40 to 80 percent of the cultivators were without a dwelling of their own.

An average peasant did not always possess a draft animal either. In most villages they averaged less than one per family, and usually the larger landowners would have more than one. In a village in Shinshū in 1679, for example, there were thirty-nine cultivators and thirty-four work ani-. mals. But two families owned four animals each.[14]

Credit too was difficult to obtain, and interest rates were exorbitant. In any event, most loans originated in and went to meet the more pressing needs of consumption. Despite the official ban on sale and alienation of land, there-fore, thousands of peasants lost it because of their inability to repay a loan.

Furthermore, with increasing urbanization during the eighteenth century, a market in the conventional sense developed in agricultural products in Japan.[15] Cultivation of cash crops such as cotton, mulberry, sugarcane, tobacco, and indigo also became fairly widespread. In their case, price was the key factor in determining the fortune of farmers. The key crop, however, price of which determined all other prices and the general state of the economy, con-tinued to be rice.[16] Its price fluctuated wildly, depending on such uncontrollable and unpredictable factors as demand and supply. Often, a farmer would be ruined in the midst of a bumper crop, just as millions could die with money in their pockets in times of shortage.

In 1715 rice was fetching 230 *momme* of silver per *koku*. By 1717 its price had fallen to 130 *momme*. In the following year, thanks to a bumper harvest, it was down to thirty-three. In 1730 "The price fell to two-fifths of what it had been in the days when rice was precious. People looked on it like dirt," writes Dazai Shundai, in his *Keizai Roku* ("Treatise on Political Economy"). When peasants "come to sell it the price is not enough to pay for carrying it away, so that they make no profit from what they do not eat themselves."[17] Only two years later, however, in most of central and western Japan, a standing crop was attacked and destroyed by pests. Price of rice rocketed. But millions suffered and over ten thousand people starved to death. In several towns there were food riots known as *uchikowashi* or "smashings." In 1734 there was again an excellent harvest and storehouses were crammed with rice. Price slumped to forty *momme* and less. Government fixed a floor and passed a law forbidding fluctuations in market quotations. Osaka merchants were ordered not to pay less than forty-two *momme* a *koku*. If they did, they were liable to a fine of ten *momme* per *koku*. But no one paid any attention to official fiats, and they proved wholly ineffective.

In the quarter century after 1710 the price of rice fluctuated between a maximum of 230 and a minimum of thirty *momme*. But generally it tended to fall. The story was repeated in the second half of the century, except that the crisis was more or less of continuing shortages because of a series of grim natural disasters. First there was a prolonged drought. It was followed by extensive floods. In 1778 there were more floods in Kyoto and in parts of Kyushu. Several volcanoes erupted causing great devastation. Later again, rains were incessant from spring to harvest. Famine stalked almost every province for about five years running —into 1787. A witness describes the scarcity conditions as follows:

> Although the shortages in the Kantō did not amount to a great famine, the loss of life through starvation in the northern provinces was dreadful. There was nothing to eat but horseflesh or, when this ran short, dogs and cats. Once these were consumed, people died of sheer starvation in great numbers. In some villages of thirty, forty, or fifty households not one person survived, and nobody could say who had died or when, for the corpses were unburied and had been eaten by beasts and birds.[18]

It is estimated that in the decade of 1780–90, population fell by over a million. There was a period of reasonable normalcy between 1790 ad 1830. But all gains and a large number of people were again wiped out by another severe famine in 1834. There were three great famines in the Tokugawa period: the *Kyōhō* famine of 1732–33, the five-year famine of *Temmei* which began in 1783, and the *Tempō* famine of 1832–36. At the end of it, in Sir George Sansom's estimation, the total population of Japan "was rather less than it had been a hundred years before."[19]

Apart from these spectacular calamities on a national scale, suffering was frequent and shortages could be just as severe in smaller pockets because neighboring daimyo would not always send relief and share their surplus even if they had any. There was no free flow of food and goods between fiefs. A year before the *Temmei* famine started in 1783, Tsugaru fief had a bad harvest. Its daimyo, however, compelled the peasants to pay their taxes in kind as usual, and sent 400,000 bags of rice for sale to Edo and Osaka markets. The resulting shortage of food alarmed the daimyo's officials. They borrowed 10,000 *ryō* from the central government to purchase rice from neighboring fiefs. But they were unable to purchase any, and the people and peasants of Tsugaru fief starved.

CHAPTER XIX

The Sesame Seed

1

Catastrophes left their scars. But they were interspersed with good years. Price cycles too included bad as well as good spells; though with increasing monetization the cream of the profit, when prices were high, went to merchants, rice-brokers, and moneylenders rather than to peasants.

Whatever the fate of harvest and prices, however, one factor was relentlessly constant—the cost-price squeeze. According to Thomas C. Smith, "Throughout the Tokugawa period the costs of production—the meals provided tenants on workdays, fertilizer and agricultural implements, the wages for hired hands at the planting and harvest—were constantly rising. . . ."[1] It was the most important reason probably, for debt and foreclosure on a scale that ultimately wrought a significant change in the class of landownership and pattern of production. According to one commentator (*circa* 1800): "For one man who makes a fortune there are twenty or thirty reduced to penury."[2]

Writing in 1721, Tanaka Kyugu states that a spade that used to cost three hundred *mon* was now selling at three times the price. Everything the farmer needed—horses, farm implements, fodder, straw, rope, leather—was up and cost more than the price fetched by whatever he sold. Again, according to Tanaka, where one *ryō* used to purchase fifty to sixty bales of dried fish for making fertilizer, it now bought seven or eight. And so, it cost two *ryō* to fertilize one *tan* of land. There is frequent complaint that peasants were being ruined by ". . . the high cost of fertilizers in recent years."[3]

Cost of labor was another major and ever-increasing burden on the farmer's pocket. Whether due to voluntary control by abortion and infanticide, or natural calamities and epidemics that were so frequent during the eighteenth century, population does not appear to have increased, or barely, in the second half of the Tokugawa period. After 1720 it is estimated to have remained almost stationary at about thirty million people. In the number of people engaged in agriculture there was a decline, resulting in an acute shortage of farm hands—a phenomenon that proved to be neither temporary nor tractable.

Clearly, part of the rural population was being drawn or driven into other occupations and sectors of the economy despite official strictures and restraints. In 1712 government decreed that all farmers must return to their villages. The decree was repeated several times. In 1843 rural immigrants into Edo were sent back forcibly to their respective provinces.[4] Abortion and infanticide, known as *mabiki*—literally it means thinning a row of vegetables by uprooting—was forbidden by state edict in 1767. "Conversely, in order to secure a supply of children for work in the fields without the expense of bringing them up, farmers were known to buy children kidnapped in the large towns by regular traffickers known as 'child merchants.' "[5]

But nothing worked. Shortage of labor continued to grow. Being scarce, it became ruinously expensive. There was an outcry that agriculture was being ruined because of the high cost of labor. A typical village document states: ". . . there are many villages which suffer year after year because, owing to want of labor, they are late finishing the planting."[6]

A village headman from Shinshu writes in the early

nineteenth century that wages equalled the return on labor. So on every *hōkōnin* employed there was a loss equal to the cost of his keep. "In recent times," states a petition for relief from another village in Musashi in 1802, *"hōkōnin* have become exceedingly short, and wages *(kyūkin)* are consequently so high that . . . large holders have recently been unable to make a living from farming alone."[7]

According to an agricultural treatise from Sado Island: "Those whom we call superior farmers have a surplus at year's end, because they have enough family members of working age to cultivate properly and therefore get high yields. Those whom we call inferior farmers have no surplus at year's end, chiefly because they have too few family members of working age to farm satisfactorily and therefore get poor yields."[8]

2

The most inflexible item of cost, however, was the tax that every peasant was required to pay. He alone in the country paid regular dues that sustained the state and a pyramid of two million or more elite, vassals and retainers, who produced little but culture and glory. The state maintained them mainly from the revenue derived from agriculture.

Revenue was assessed in measures of unhulled rice. The basic annual levy that was common throughout the country was called *nengu*. It was based on the productivity of land; to determine it every field was surveyed and graded. Tests were made by sample crop cutting, or *"tsubo gari,"* that is, by harvesting and examining the quality of the grain from selected squares of one *tsubo* (six feet square). Size times grade gave the estimate of the normal yield of a field, on the basis of which tax was assessed. Customary ratio for dividing the crop was generally *"shikō roku-min"* or "four to the prince and six to the people."[9] Sometimes, however, it was two to the prince and one to the peasant. Normally, the tax varied from 40 to 60 percent of the gross produce.[10] Besides, there were several local levies. And in the fall, after harvest was over, farmers would often be required to work on roads and embankments and render a miscellany of services for which they received no wage.

On rice, the payment of tax was in kind. On upland crops it could be settled partly in cash. In effect, the arrangement would leave little rice for the family's consumption but more of inferior grains and vegetables.

Furthermore, though assessment was supposed to be made annually, or at least at set intervals of three, five, or seven years, from about 1700, land ceased to be surveyed regularly. Often, therefore, tax was based on an assessment several decades old and bore little relation to actual yields at the time. An official of the Matsuyama *han* wrote of a peasant whose "holding is smaller and its yield less than registered, so however hard he works there is never profit but only bitter suffering."[11] Apparently, there had been no resurvey of land in this *han* between 1592–95 and 1673–1680. This large a time lag was exceptional. But that of a decade was common. Enterprising farmers exploited the opportunity to beat the static tax by constantly improving their yields. For the poor or marginal farmer, on the other hand, rigidity in the amount of tax he was charged could be an unsurmountable threat to solvency.[12]

Failure to pay, or even to complain, could evoke serious retribution. The classic case is of Sakura Sogōrō, a village headman who dared to appeal to the Shogun against the local daimyo's maltreatment of peasants. The appeal was granted. But according to legend, Sogōrō, his wife, and their children lost their heads for having approached the Shogun's palanquin directly. Similarly, headman Matsumoto Chōsō, in Obama fief, appealed somewhat stubbornly for reduction of tax imposed on his village. The tax was reduced. But Matsumoto was executed. Even so, although many must have suffered imprisonment, torture, and death, taxation was oppressive enough to goad peasants into open revolt and violence.

From early in the eighteenth century, the frequency and scale of peasant uprisings increased. They were sporadic and unorganized. But after 1811, hardly a year passed without an outbreak—"a continual protest against the economic distress in which the peasants found themselves."[13] Often, several thousands participated. In 1739, eighty-four thousand peasants demonstrated in one province against a particularly heavy tax on rice. In 1764 two hundred thousand farmers marched to Edo to protest against emergency levies that had been imposed upon them to meet a special expense account of the *bakufu*. In 1842 there was a large-scale demonstration in Ōmi against corrupt officials who had been sent by the government to resurvey the land for tax assessment. In the north and eastern regions large tracts were abandoned by farmers because they could not produce enough to meet their dues.

The principle underlying Tokugawa tax policy was straightforward and simple. "It is right that the peasants should be so treated that they have neither too much nor too little," wrote Honda Masanobu, a trusted adviser of Shogun Ieyasu. The manner of doing it also was simple: "Each man must have boundaries of his fields clearly marked, and an estimate must be made of the amount needed for his consumption. The rest must be paid as tax."[14]

Again, according to Kamio Haruhide, an official appointed by Shogun Yoshimune (1716–45) to improve the falling revenues of the *bakufu*: "Peasants are like sesame seed. The more you squeeze them the more oil you get." The statement expresses more than the harshness of a stray eccentric, who, incidentally, did succeed in collecting more revenue.[15] It reflects the attitude of the times and the tax treatment meted out to the peasantry in Japan for a period of more than three hundred years. Toward the end of the Tokugawa regime when the *bakufu* and most of daimyo were in severe financial straits, it was not unknown for the lord to appropriate 80 percent or more of what was supposed to have been the peasant's produce.

3

Finally, a stage was reached when the combined cost of fertilizer, wages, and tax was likely to exceed income, especially on larger farms of three *chō* (7.35 acres) or more that used more wage labor. Or at least, the farm would not yield sufficient income to meet the cost of living of the better-to-do farmers who had an expensive position to maintain.

Peasants were not a homogeneous group at this period, but a hierarchy ranging from the *genin* (hereditary servant) to small, medium, and large landowners. Economic disparities were sharp and clear. The following extract from *Contemporary Observations and Hearsay (Seiji kemmon roku*, 1816) gives a glimpse into the life and tastes of this wealthier class of rural gentry:

> Now the most lamentable abuse (of the present day among the peasants) is that those who have become wealthy forget their status and live luxuriously like city aristocrats. Their houses are as different (from those of the common folk) as day and night or clouds and mud. They build them with the most handsome and wonderful gates, porches, beams, alcoves, ornamental shelves, and libraries. . . . Moreover, village official and others of wealth entrust cultivation to servants; they themselves wear fine clothes and emulate the ceremonial style of warriors on all such occasions as weddings, celebrations, and masses for the dead. . . . They keep masterless warriors around them and study military arts unsuitable to their status; they take teachers . . . and study the Chinese and Japanese style of writing and painting.[16]

Cost and income factors, however, made deep inroads into the original intent and order of unchanging status, stability, and security of peasants—of the class and of the individual. Holdings changed ownership frequently, although there was no increase in the number of people

engaged in agriculture. Toward the latter period of Tokugawa rule, it would be a rare farm to stay intact, the same
size for a generation.

In fact, to survive at all, farmers had three choices:
to cut down their standard of living, to save on wages by
using their own and the family's labor free of cost, and to
increase their output continually to meet the rising cost of
production. Efficiency became the most critical factor in
determining whether a holding could be cultivated with any
profit. *There was a decisive shift, therefore, in the economic
and technical balance, in favor of a small holding that could
be worked efficiently, mainly or entirely with family labor,
to yield a modest surplus.*

In a village in Shinshu, for example, holdings of less
than five *koku* of rice increased from 59 percent in 1595 to
72 percent in 1870. Large landowners did not necessarily
liquidate or reduce the size of their estates. Many continued
to expand them. There were cases, as in Tōtōmi Province,
where the hereditary headman held 70 percent of the cultivated area in his village in 1868.

But large landowners also were compelled to seek
the benefits and efficiency of small-scale farming. As opposed to the principal mode in the seventeenth century, of
working a large farm directly through hired labor—called
"tedzukuri" or hand-cultivation—increasingly it was found
more profitable to rent all or most of the land to tenants in
several small family-size units.

"Landlords were breaking up their entire holdings
among tenants, except perhaps for what they could work
with family labor and servants, and substituting rent in kind
for labor services."[17] Those who did not suffered. Thus, of
four large holdings in a village in Tajima Province in 1728,
three were cultivated mainly by their respective holders, and
of the fourth, 80 percent was given out to tenants. By 1783,
of the three holdings cultivated directly, one had disappeared altogether and its owner been reduced to the status
of a tenant. The other two had dwindled to an insignificant
size. The holding worked by tenants, however, had ex-

panded from 8.3 *chō* to 10.1 *chō* of arable land. Income of another family in Tōtōmi Province from rents increased from 181 to 335 bales of grain between 1776 and 1881, while that from the land worked directly by the family fell from ninety to forty-seven bales. Its tenants increased from twenty-two to sixty-two (1788–1864). Proportion of the land worked by the owner himself dropped from 66.6 percent in 1821, to 27.7 percent in 1830, and to 19.7 percent in 1844. "Such was the swiftness of adjustment once the fact was recognised that the small farming unit was more efficient."[18]

A tenant was more successful for the same reason that made any small peasant more competitive. Like him, he worked himself and as much land as he could cultivate efficiently on a meager margin. He *had* to. For only if his yields were considerably higher and costs lower could rent be added to tax and still leave the cultivator with a surplus.

As a writer toward the end of the eighteenth century says: ". . . the tenant by extraordinary diligence will cultivate twice as much land as hired labor, and he will provide his own fertilizer by the bitter work of gathering it. Thus he can make a bare living from a very small plot, even though he has no additional land of his own and no income from work outside his home. . . . Hence all large holders have adopted tenant cultivation."[19] At times a landowner might even reprove his tenant for producing too much rice because his tax liability would increase proportionately.[20]

And so, to the limited extent that the *bakufu* decrees succeeded in binding the peasant to the land, they failed to keep the land inert, bound to the same peasant, or often to any peasant at all. To quote Thomas Smith again: ". . . there was a general economic competition among peasant families, with changes in land ownership merely the most sensitive index of individual success and failure."[21] Depending on whether a family acquired or lost land it went up or down the ladder in the village social and economic system. In the course of the reshuffle, a new class of landowners emerged —city merchants and rural moneylenders. Also, a new class of landless peasants came into existence. It was called *mutaka*, meaning a person without *taka* or yield.

Despite the polarization in ownership of the land, however, the *operational* unit steadily became smaller and more uniform. Whereas it used to be common to have farms of three and four *chō* alongside others a tenth or even one-twentieth that size, by the middle of the nineteenth century, units of more than a *chō* and a half had become rare. Differences of scale ceased gradually to have much significance. Few families now owned more than one draft animal—if they owned one at all. There was roughly the same area of land and capital per adult worker on each holding. Eventually, it became the permanent pattern of Japanese agriculture and organization, and its most striking feature.

CHAPTER XX

The Aristocratic Revolution

1

And then, after a brief civil war the Shogunate was abolished. On January 25, 1868, occurred the celebrated Meiji Restoration. The whole country, including the fifteenth Tokugawa Shogun, submitted to the rule of the emperor— a youth fifteen years old. Though it restored a king who had never been dethroned, the event is considered historic for ending two hundred and fifty years of feudalism.

The name of Edo was changed to Tokyo (Eastern Capital). It became the seat of the government in March 1869. The emperor's residence moved into the city from Kyoto. Modernization of Japan thereafter has been likened to the bursting of a dam. Aside from its political transition from a feudal hegemony to a centralized monarchy in less than a decade, sweeping reforms had transformed the agrarian and tax structure.[1]

In August 1871 a brief decree abolished the feudal domains. The daimyo and their samurai retainers were pensioned off. Henceforth, the fiefs were to be units of the local administration (prefectures) under the central government. The daimyo were ordered to take up residence with their families in the capital. The former four estates of society—the samurai, farmer, artisan, and the merchant—

also were abolished. In 1874 conscription was ordered to create a national army.

Feudal proprietory rights were swept away, and with them the foundation of the old land revenue economy. All cultivated land was declared to be the property of peasants, though it was not specified "which peasants." A complete resurvey of fields was undertaken, and new land registers were compiled. Agricultural land was divided into a hundred million plots and each was measured and graded according to its fertility. From 1873 it took fourteen years to complete the survey.[2] Title deeds were issued for each and every plot to those deemed to be in customary possession, though many small cultivators were overlooked in favor of the larger and more influential landowners. All restraints, including the never-too-effective ban on alienation of agricultural land, were removed, and full and unrestricted right of private property was vested in the owner. Although there were many shortcomings in the nature and implementation of the reforms, erstwhile serfs now became independent proprietors, free to cultivate any crop they wished, to dispose of their land at will, and even to give up farming altogether and leave the village.

A unified revenue system was created in July 1873. The old harvest tax was converted into a land value tax—a fixed annual cash levy of 3 percent on land values assessed at 8.5 times the crop yield determined at the time.[3] It was reduced by half a percent in 1877.

2

Yet, "emancipation" opened no floodgates of opportunity to those engaged in farming. The mass of them had neither political influence nor organization. And though agrarian discontent had been one of the factors in undermining the Tokugawas, farmers (or the common man) played no active role in the Restoration or subsequent reforms. They did not even rejoice in it. On the contrary, peasant uprisings increased in the first decade of the new regime.[4]

For collapse of the *bakufu* was not the result of a popular uprising or revolution. It happened because of a civil war between two factions of the ruling community. Inevitably therefore, although many of the leaders and reformers of the Meiji Restoration were exceedingly capable individuals, they were of the same class, antecedents, upbringing, and tradition as those whom they displaced— the feudal lords and their samurai retainers. Smith has described it as "Japan's aristocratic revolution."[5]

After the Imperial Proclamation of June 1868, the supreme organ in which all authority—executive, legislative, and judicial—was vested, was the *Dajōkan* or Council of State. The highest offices in the administration were given to princes of the royal family and members of the court nobility, "because due affection should be shown to relatives of the Sovereign and due respect to persons of rank."[6] But real power lay in the hands of advisory officials. These were samurai from western clans who had engineered the downfall of the Shogunate. Most of the lower-ranking officials also were initially ex-*bakufu* servants and retainers, for the simple reason that they were the only trained personnel available. The country could not have been administered without them. But neither could it have been administered with them in a fashion radically different from the past.

Consequently, there was no sharp break with political tradition. Much of the feudal spirit and authoritarian procedure of the pre-1868 era continued to inform and govern policies of the new government and its institutions. There was no serious ideological cleavage between the new and old—revolutionaries and conservatives. "The leaders of the victorious party stood for no new political theory . . . the abolition of feudalism was mainly an afterthought."[7] When they seized power, they had no revolutionary grand design for reconstructing the state, society, and economy. Primacy of an elite class remained. Furthermore, whereas after the Satsuma Rebellion of 1877, a conflict between conservative and progressive schools of political thought did develop, it did not materially affect the policy and approach of the new rulers toward the problems of the farmer.

Writing at the time of an agricultural depression in 1885, Saigō Jūdō exhorts the peasants to work harder to make up for nature's deficiencies: "They should weed fields five times where they only weeded them thrice. They should work from 4 A.M. until 8 P.M. instead of from 6 to 6, and they should cut out useless breaks at midday."[8] Generally, the assumption continued to be that if farmers were poor, they had only themselves to blame for not working hard. Hard work could overcome all difficulties.

The Meiji government's fiscal policy discriminated *against* agriculture. For a considerable period, it was governed by the earlier Tokugawa principle of extracting the maximum possible revenue—as much as the peasant could possibly pay. Aside from the principle, financial realities of the situation did not leave the new administration with much choice. It was hard pressed for funds. As a report of the Financial Affairs Bureau in 1868 stated: "The finances of this bureau exist in name only. In reality our coffers are empty, and our sole function is to negotiate loans. Even day-to-day requirements are met with great difficulty."[9]

In its very first year in office the government was obliged to borrow twenty-nine million yen. By 1881, the debt—domestic and foreign—had mounted to forty-six million yen. By 1897, however, the loans together with their heavy interest dues had been repaid. Funds came primarily from agriculture. For over a generation it continued to be the state's most important source of income, as under the ancien régime. In the early 1870's, land tax furnished 94 percent of the total revenue. Twenty years later it still accounted for 60 percent, and at the turn of the current century, for more than half of all national and local revenue receipts.[10]

Moreover, even after the reform and revision of the land tax in 1873, it appropriated as much of the peasant's produce as the feudal dues in Tokugawa times. The method of evaluating land on the basis of which the new tax was assessed was deliberately designed to ensure that there was no decline in the revenue.[11]

3

There were other drawbacks to the new system. Every peasant, for instance, who owned any land was under an obligation now to pay a fixed sum of money every year irrespective of the fate of his harvest. Valuation of land and the tax remained constant.[12] Previously, the tax had been a fixed percentage of his produce.

Moreover, as long as he paid his dues in kind he did not *have* to sell his produce in order to raise the cash.[13] He sold only if and when, and to the extent he had a surplus. Cost and risk of marketing, especially of rice, was borne in the main by receivers of rent and tax. Not by small peasants. Under the new dispensation, however, tax was due in the harvest months. In order to pay cash, the farmer was forced to sell his crop immediately after harvest when markets were flooded with rice and its price was low. And then perhaps, he would have to repurchase it for consumption at a higher cost before the year was out and take a loan for the purpose. Only the richer peasants and landlords could withhold their produce until prices improved. In parts of the country, moreover, in the early decades there may not have been a local market where the small peasant could sell his produce. In such a case he would have to turn it over to an itinerant merchant—at his price.

In this manner government's income from the land tax was stabilized and freed from price fluctuations. The government received the same sum of money every year irrespective of price or volume of production. The farmer, on the other hand, even the pure subsistence farmer who had no marketable surplus, was exposed now to the vagaries of a free market economy. The proportion of his produce that he gave in tax even, depended henceforth and was determined by the price rice and other crops fetched at a given time in a given year. And it varied accordingly. Also, the government levied new consumer taxes and appropriated monopoly control over the brewing and sale of saké (rice wine) in 1898, production and distribution of tobacco (1904), and of salt (1905). It meant that farmers *had* to sell more of their produce in order to purchase these popular and essential items of consumption.

This forced and unregulated commercialization, together with unconditional rights of private ownership of land bestowed by the new system of title deeds, drove masses of the smaller and less efficient peasants into irretrievable debt and tenantry. "Indebtedness, the mortgaging of land, and eventually the transfer of ownership was a recurrent pattern."[14]

Cultivation of land by tenants had been a growing feature of Japanese agriculture since early in the eighteenth century. Not only did the Meiji reforms not reverse the trend but they accelerated it. By 1891 a third of the farm families were owner-cultivators. By 1910, forty-five percent of the acreage was being worked by tenants, frequently the same plot of land that had once been theirs. Some 30 percent of the cultivating peasants did not own any land. Even initially, in the case of mortgaged land, title had been given to the mortgagee and customary rights of permanent tenancy did not receive legal recognition, though generally they continued to operate.

Not only did tenancy increase rapidly in the early years of Meiji rule, but there was no reduction in rent. And it continued to be paid in kind.[15] Typically, it was a fixed and not share rent. It amounted, as before, to 50 to 60 percent of the produce in paddy rice. On upland crops, it would be somewhat less. The tenant normally provided the farm implements, seed, and fertilizer and bore the cost of threshing and hulling the rent rice and transporting it to the landlord's granary or a commercial warehouse. He was responsible for maintaining the land and irrigation ditches in good repair as well, though there was no provision for compensating him in case he was ejected.[16]

The tenant would have to seek also the landlord's

permission if he wished to change his cropping pattern, and often—as in Tokugawa times—he might be threatened with dispossession if he used too much fertilizer. Though higher yields did not affect the landowner's tax liability any more, it meant greater risk now because higher inputs of new organic manures made the crop more susceptible to disease and lodging. Many landlords preferred lower but more secure yields.

Distinctions of social status continued to be rigid. A tenant would uncover his head in the presence of the landlord and would remain in the formal kneeling position throughout an interview. When addressing his tenant the landlord would omit the normal *san* suffix used between equals. His house would have three entrances. One was used by the master and distinguished guests. The second, by less distinguished visitors, such as village officials. The third and lower one was reserved for women, servants, and tenants. Some of the landlords did not reside in the village. There would be often three intermediaries between them and their tenants—the manager *(bantō)*, submanagers *(shihainin)*, and the tenant's representatives *(kosaku-gashira)*.

The high level of rent was maintained in part now by pressure on land. There were close to 2150 people to a square mile of *cultivated* land in Japan in 1880, as against 245 in the United States in 1940. Over the next sixty years, population of Japan doubled while the area under cultivation increased by about 25 or at the most 33 percent.[17] Most of the new growth of the population was absorbed in the rural sector.[18] At the end of the Meiji period, therefore, the average size of an agricultural holding was about the same as it was at the beginning, that is 1 *chō* (2.45 acres).

4

And so, after more than half a century of a modernized and reformed administration of the Meiji rulers, 5.6 million farm families shared a net agricultural product worth 1883 million yen. Two-thirds of it was absorbed by taxes, interest on farm debts, and rent. More than half of the dues were paid to the government, absentee landlords, banks, and other nonagricultural interests.[19]

The average peasant, cultivating a holding of about 1 *chō*, had at his disposal 1038 yen for capital, excluding the price of land. Of this, one half accounted for buildings. It left him five hundred yen for working expenses and for investment in animals, implements, and other miscellaneous items needed on a farm. Net product per farm operator principally engaged in agriculture was less than four hundred yen in a year. There were another 9.1 million persons, mostly family members, who also worked part-time on farms. Per capita output, therefore, would be less. Of the acreage 90 percent was still devoted to the cultivation of food crops.

At the time of the Meiji Restoration, any kind of vehicle on wheels, including the humble rickshaw, was unknown or uncommon. By 1937, when Japan was the most industrialized nation in Asia, the total capacity of all power-operated equipment in the agricultural sector came to 623,000 horsepower, or 0.11 horsepower per farm household.[20] Almost all of it was used for pumping water or processing grain.

The average peasant continued to plow essentially a poverty furrow much as before, on an income of less than three yen a day, and as in the seventeenth century, often without the assistance of a draft animal. A small 350-pound tractor was being tried on a cautious scale in Okayama. But less than one work animal was available to every two farmers. Of 5.6 million farm households in 1937, 3.6 million owned neither cattle nor horses.

CHAPTER XXI

Treasure of a Family

1

Yet, apparently, Kamio Haruhide was right. With a draft animal or without, and however tight the squeeze, the Japanese peasant did produce more and more just like the sesame seed.

In the two and a half centuries following 1600, there was a remarkable growth in agricultural productivity. Output increased substantially in this period in range and quality. In the seventeenth century alone, area under rice cultivation was extended from 1,600,000 *chō* to 2,900,000 *chō*. Production is estimated to have increased from eighteen million to twenty-five million *koku*. In the absence of national statistics, records of individual farmers can perhaps give a better indication of average yields and also of the magnitude of growth.

The journal of the Imanishi family in Kawachi Province (present Osaka Prefecture), for instance, shows yields of paddy rice to have averaged 2.31 *koku* per *tan* (about 11.75 bushels per quarter acre) over a period of fifteen years —from 1798 to 1812.

Successive generations of a family in Aki Province maintained a journal faithfully for a century from 1787. It gives the annual production for five fields of constant size.

Increase in yields was significant on all the five fields. On three that were planted only to rice through the entire period, the ten-yearly average of production rose between 50 and 71 percent. On one of the remaining two fields the increase was higher. It also was planted to rice every year from 1787 to 1856. With 1787–97 as the base, its decennial average ran as follows: 100, 148, 168, 203, 212, 195, 195.

Again, in the village of Kebuyama, in what is now Iwate Prefecture, land was resurveyed in 1864 after an interval of sixty-nine years. Increase in its productivity during the period presumably resulted in a corresponding increase in tax assessment by 52 percent.

Furthermore, and as noted earlier, crop yields were generally higher on tenants' plots than on those worked directly by the owner through hired labor. Yet, rents were exorbitant, and the tenant did not enjoy any of the public rights and duties of the *hyakushō* or landholder. He was not even listed in the village land register. His economic dependence on the landowner tended to be one of intense personal subordination. One of the landlords laid down the following not untypical list of admonitions for his tenants in 1725:

> Tenants were not to leave the village on a visit or to put up relatives for more than five days without reporting the reasons to the landlord; they were strictly forbidden to lodge wandering priests, pilgrims, and other strangers even for a single night. They were to avoid ostentatious and expensive things. Specifically forbidden were *zōri*, *haori*, and *wakizashi*. They were not to put new roofs on their houses or otherwise repair them without the landlord's permission. All "luxurious" things in their houses, such as *shōji* and mats, were ruled out, but gables, which had been forbidden in the past, were now allowed. They were to show due respect at all times to the landlord and his family and servants and to the *hyakushō* of the village. They were not to wear footgear in the

presence of the landlord, nor to adopt a family insignia resembling his, nor to use a character in a name that was in use in his family, and so on.[1]

2

In an unsigned treatise on agriculture, published in the last decade of the seventeenth century, however, its peasant author exclaims: "If on land yielding 10 *koku*, 11 can be harvested: that is the treasure of a family!"[2]

It was not an empty exhortation of a reformer. The author was probably voicing a current and widely prevalent belief that underlay the effort of successive generations of a vast number of peasants, each trying to produce that one extra *koku* of rice despite—or was it *because* of—the difficult conditions of life and work. They often did it by devising simple improvements in traditional techniques. But mainly, it was by doing more of the same operation better— by paying closer attention to the minutiae of husbandry. It involved more labor which was increasingly in short supply and expensive since the turn of the seventeenth century. However, they chose to cut down the scale of their farming to dispense with hired labor and wages and worked harder.

For example, peasants began to pull out the weeds in their fields more thoroughly and more often. In the diary of the Ishikawa family in Musashi Province there is no mention of weeding in 1728. By 1867, however, it is recorded to have been repeated several times.

Similarly, an increasing number of farmers selected the seed more carefully—from sturdier plants. And they tested it in salt solution. By soaking the seed in water to sprout before sowing they lengthened the growing season. They also made a substantial reduction in the quantity of seed sown per unit of land.

Sowing of rice in a nursery bed and then transplanting the young seedlings was an old practice. But like weeding, transplanting used to be done haphazardly. By the nineteenth century, however, seedling were being planted in the field with greater precision in evenly spaced rows. It took more time and labor. But it ensured the maximum number of plants to each field without overcrowding and permitted more efficient weeding.

There was also a substantial shift from dry to wet rice cultivation in this period. Irrigation facilities were expanded greatly by the construction of thousands of small wells, tanks, ditches, and canals. Funds for the larger works were probably provided by the daimyo, merchants, and rich peasants. But at the cultivators' level there was a marked improvement in water management practices. Paddy fields were leveled more carefully to ensure that all rice plants stood in the same depth of water. This made irrigation more effective. The same water was used to protect young plants against low temperatures, while oil came to be used widely as an insecticide.

None of these practices was new—innovations of one or several remarkable men working in a laboratory. It could be, however, that not all of them were practiced or were even known of in every part of the country.

Aside from improvement and efficiency in the practice of existing techniques, therefore, their greater spread was a significant achievement of the times also. How exactly the spread occurred is not known, for not only were peasants not free to choose their crops or the varieties of seed to sow, but many feudal lords prohibited the export of improved techniques from their territories. Even within the territory of a daimyo diffusion was not always free. A village called Maesawa in Toyama Prefecture placed a guard on its border to prevent the seed of a certain strain of rice developed in the village from being taken out.[3]

However, a number of factual and practical treatises on better ways of farming bear witness to the interest in the subject. They must have been written and published, because there were readers, by those who felt it an obligation to instruct fellow cultivators.

As Miyazaki Antei, author of one of the earliest and best known of these agricultural treatises states: "I had lived and farmed for forty years in a village, and having learned much, I deeply regretted the ignorance of the peasants. Thus it was that I forgot my own stupidity and thought to write a book the peasants could go by." He makes it clear in the preface that "this book is intended for use by farmers and (therefore) needs no literary embellishment."

Called *Nōgyō zensho* and completed in 1697, Miyazaki's work was based on much more than his personal experience. After farming for four decades, he spent several years in collecting data from different parts of the country. Everywhere he traveled "on foot through the villages noting local soils, crops, and tools, relentlessly quizzing the older men and taking down what they said."[4] He discussed practically every aspect of Japanese agriculture in ten old-style volumes.

Many similar general works followed. Also more specialized ones that dealt with only one particular aspect of farming. By the middle of the nineteenth century there were authoritative treatises on almost every major crop, and on climate, soil treatment, irrigation, farm implements, and so on.

3

And so, for all its manifold faults, restraints on freedom and mobility, and the excessive tax and rent rates against which peasants revolted so frequently, the Tokugawa agrarian system was not inefficient in terms of production. The agricultural sector was producing a surplus above subsistence, and the total as well as per capita product was rising all the time. So too, evidently, was the general standard of living.

Thus, a shopkeeper in Ōi village in Okayama *han* in 1813 is reported to have been selling the following commodities: ink, paper, writing brushes, *herasaki*, cauldrons, cutlery, needles, smoking pipes, tobacco, tobacco pouches, teapots, casserole dishes, rice-wine bottles, oil containers, vinegar, soy sauce, bean paste, salt, matting, noodles, kelp, hair oil, hair strings, hair pins, cotton cloth, socks, towels, bamboo trellis, carrying baskets, *zōri*, straw sandals (*waraji*), wooden clogs, tea, teacups, lucifers, wicks, incense, fire pots, lanterns, oil, candles, rice wine, timber, hot water bottles, cakes, *sembei,* trays, funeral requisites, grain, *and other every day necessities.* Other dealers sold agricultural implements, fertilizer, *tōfu,* dried fish, fruit, vegetables, etc.[5]

In 1857, when the end of the regime was only a decade away, according to Townsend Harris, the American consul, people of Kawasaki "are all fat, well clad and happy looking, but there is an equal absence of any appearance of wealth or of poverty." Of the populace of Edo he observes that "The people all appeared clean, well clad and well fed; indeed I have never seen a case of squalid misery since I have been in Japan."[6]

Similarly, in the estimation of Sir Rutherford Alcock, another European eyewitness in Kanagawa in 1859: "The evidence of plenty, or a sufficiency at least, everywhere meets the eye; cottages and farm houses are rarely seen out of repair—in pleasant contrast to China where everything is going to decay. . . . The men and women, now they take to their clothing, are well and comfortably clad—even the children. . . . There is no sign of starvation or penury in the midst of the population—if little room for indulgence of luxury or the display of wealth." At Mishima he observes, "the impression is irresistably borne in upon the mind, that Europe cannot show a happier or better-fed peasantry."[7]

These accounts could be exaggerated. Others can be found that are not so flattering. And certainly, conditions were not uniform in all parts of the country. In south Kyushu for example, they were then, as they still are, relatively more backward. Nevertheless, the observations are interesting because at the time, for over a century, Japan had managed ". . . to support a population approaching thirty million on a farming area not much greater than that of European countries which supported only five or ten millions."[8]

CHAPTER XXII

Growth and Incentives

1

Growth in agricultural production continued after the Restoration of 1868, though the majority of peasants gained little or no benefit from the subsequent reorganization of the agrarian and land tax structures. Until the 1890's Japan was a net exporter of agricultural products. Even in the decade of 1882, despite a sharp deflation—the price of rice was cut almost in half—cultivated area under rice expanded 7 percent. The average crop yield rose 21 percent.[1]

It was in the quarter century following 1889, however, that growth was outstanding. According to official estimates, there was a 40 percent increase in output of rice between 1889 and 1914 and a 25 percent gain in yield per acre. Similar improvements were achieved in other crops such as wheat and barley. There was a much greater rise in the production of silk cocoons and tobacco.

Growth was higher for the total Meiji period, though yields of rice more or less leveled off after 1920, and the country began to depend increasingly on imports from its colonies of Korea and Formosa. According to William Lockwood: ". . . food and raw material production rose persistently and rapidly through this period. It outdistanced the growth of population by a wide margin." His estimate is that physical volume of agricultural production rose at least 75 percent from 1895–99 to 1935–39. The area under cultivation grew by only about 20 percent, and the number of farm families by 10 percent or less. "At the end of this period, in other words, the average peasant family operated a farm little larger than at the beginning. Yet it was able to produce at least 75% more food and raw materials, with no greater expenditure of labor, perhaps even less."[2]

However, there are scholarly differences of opinion as to the exact volume of production and rate of growth during the period. To mention some of them:

According to the Nagoya index, in the twenty-five years prior to World War I, total production of food and industrial materials doubled. Between 1910–14 and 1930–34, the series show an increase of 45 percent in food production at an average annual rate of 1.9 percent; and a 75 percent increase in the output of raw materials at 2.8 percent per year. The aggregate growth of the two combined came to 50 percent in these twenty years, as against a 34 percent rise in the country's population.

According to an FAO study, "notwithstanding the institutional limitations," gross output of agriculture increased by 121 percent between 1878 and 1912 at an annual average rate of 2.7 percent. Per hectare yield of rice in the same period rose 42 percent at 1.2 percent per year. Between 1913 and 1937 also, according to this study, agricultural production continued to expand by about 40 percent, though the pattern of cropping and growth varied.[3]

According to yet another estimate, of Bruce F. Johnston, there was a 77 percent increase in agricultural production in the thirty years between 1890 and 1920 at an annual average rate of 1.9 percent. The physical output of six major crops—rice, wheat, barley, naked barley, and sweet and white potatoes—doubled in fifty years between the 1880's and the decade of 1931–40. Increase was due mainly to higher yields. The acreage under these crops expanded by 18 percent, while yields rose 66 percent.[4] But whereas the six major crops increased at an annual (compound) rate ranging from 1.4 to 2.4 percent prior to 1920, in the next ten years, their output went up by only 0.1 percent per year. In the decade of 1930 it improved to 0.9 percent. But it was still very much less than the lowest in the pre–1920 era.

Two other economists, Ohkawa Kazushi and Henry Rosovsky, on the other hand, claim that production of agriculture in Japan increased by 136 percent between 1882 and 1917, that is at 2.4 percent per year. According to them growth rate of agricultural net product per worker at this time ranked among the highest of any nation, including countries where farming was highly commercialized and supply of land virtually unlimited.[5]

James I. Nakamura, however, questions these rosy estimates, especially of the period between 1880 and 1920. He does not believe that the spurt in agricultural growth was or could have been so very sharp and impressive. It only seems so, according to Nakamura, because estimates of acreage and yields per acre were grossly understated in the Tokugawa and early Meiji years.

"Undermeasurement was an institutionalized practice in the Tokugawa period," according to him.[6] And when land was surveyed for tax assessment under the revised levy system of 1873, landowners substantially underreported the area under cultivation and, much more so, their yields per *tan* in order to minimize the tax. The incentive and opportunity to underreport continued till the end of the century, after which there was a gradual decline. Also, "One probable reason for the sharp rise in the reported paddy rice production per *tan* of about 20 percent that occurred in the late 1880's is the establishment of new statistical regulations, procedures, forms, and detailed instructions by the Ministry of Agriculture and Commerce from 1883 to 1886, following the creation of the Ministry in 1881."[7]

Nakamura assumes median paddy rice yields of 1.6 *koku* per *tan* in 1873–77, and of 1.95 *koku* (4.96 bushels) per *tan* in 1918–22. His estimate for the years between 1875 and 1920, therefore, lowers the range of growth rate from 0.8 to 1.2 percent a year. It gives an annual average increase of 1.0 percent over the period—less than half the rate claimed by

Ohkawa and Rosovsky. However, in terms of value of production (at 1913–17 prices) at the beginning of the period, Nakamura's assessment for 1878–82 "is actually 76 percent higher than the Ohkawa value of the same period."[8]

2

The statistical debate does not, however, invalidate or detract from the fact that whatever the rate, there was a substantial and sustained growth in agricultural production during the Meiji-Taisho-Showa (1868–1940) period.[9] Increase in the output of food grains outstripped the growth rate of population. And on the eve of World War II, as at any corresponding period in the preceding century, yields of rice per hectare in Japan were higher than in the United States.[10]

Also, there is no disputing that in the first four decades after the Restoration, this growth in the farm sector accounted for the bulk of increase in the national income and of tax revenue and savings.[11] Aside from providing livelihood for over half the population, it was agriculture initially that financed the industrial and commercial expansion and the costly military enterprises of the Meiji rulers.[12] "High rents, interest on farm debt, and government taxes channelled a large share of agricultural income into the possession of financial institutions, city landlords, and the State treasury."[13] Consumption levels of the farm population ostensibly increased at a slower pace than the rise in farm productivity. Moreover, the latter was achieved with small capital outlays and a very modest increase in purchased inputs.

Even Nakamura's downward revision of the pre-1920 rate of growth does not reverse the trend. He admits that the increase took place and that it was substantial—comparable to that in Western countries and at a much higher rate than in the Tokugawa period. He questions simply the assumption that the 1868 "revolution" had a revolutionary or magical impact on agricultural technology and development. According to him, therefore, "the so-called early spurt of the Japanese economy was not as remarkable as previously believed." But then he supports the thesis that levels of productivity achieved during and by the end of the Tokugawa era were very much more than is generally assumed. He agrees with Thomas Smith that "Japanese agriculture . . . underwent notable technological (though not mechanical) changes long before the modern period. Between 1600 and 1850 a complex of such changes greatly increased the productivity of land. . . ."[14]

In 1880, therefore, before the spurt in agricultural production had even begun, according to one estimate, Japan had higher yields of rice per hectare than all but three of the world's thirteen major rice-producing countries did in 1965.[15]

In any case, conditions were not uniform throughout the post-Restoration era. Nor was there a single monolithic and purposeful, or at times even a coherent state policy on agrarian affairs to which increase in production could be attributed. The range of variations was wide: ". . . of boom and depression; of food shortage and surplus; of unrestricted landlordism and secure land tenure; of *laissez-faire* and price stabilization; of traditional and of scientific agriculture. There were times when agricultural development slowed down. . . ." But taking the period as a whole, the main trend was unvarying: ". . . always tending towards increasing productivity."[16] Development of agriculture and its progress were continuous even when conditions were less than optimum.

3

At no stage during the seventy years after the Meiji Restoration could conditions for development of agriculture be described as optimum. They varied from bad to worse.

But if maximum growth occurred prior to 1920—on this there is no disagreement—then curiously, it was precisely the period when government policies and conditions for farming generally were the least favorable.

Though a section concerned with agriculture was created in the Ministry of Interior soon after the Restoration, a separate Ministry of Agriculture was set up jointly with

Commerce in 1881. Even a decade later, however, it was staffed with fewer than ninety ranking officials. The total budget for the Ministry of Agriculture and Commerce in 1890 came to less than a million yen. It was a third of the allocation for the Imperial Household. Five-eighths of it was spent on administering national forests.

Besides, the usual bureaucratic weariness and complacency set in very soon. As an official in the department, Yanagita Kunio, says in 1909:

> The fact that officials rarely issue memoranda and suggestions (for improvement) may be because the volume of business they have to deal with has increased, or because the boundaries of each person's authority have been fixed and no one likes to take the risk of treading on another's territory. Anyhow, the fact is they have ceased.[17]

As stated earlier, there was no decline in the tax burden of landowners from Tokugawa times. Nor in rent.[18] Terms of trade between agriculture and nonfarm goods did not change till World War I, when there was a sharp rise in food prices. Agricultural prices in the decade 1911–20 were on an average thrice as high as in the 1880's. But nonagricultural prices also increased nearly as much. However, it is doubtful if price levels per se had much effect on the volume of production—especially of staple products like rice.

The orthodox Confucian view that "agriculture is the base of the country, if agriculture flourishes then the country prospers," still held. The Meiji village, however, was starved for capital, neglected, and discriminated against in matters of tax and public expenditure. Industry held unquestioned primacy in official policy, while agriculture carried the main burden of its development in the early decades.[19] It was not permitted to compete for any scarce resource required for industrial expansion. For the enormous contribution it made to the rest of the economy, agriculture received back 4 percent of the total public expenditure. For farmers of this period, therefore, taxes were high. Price of land was high. So also was the cost of credit, if it was at all available.[20] Usury flourished and commodity prices fluctuated freely, depending on the vagaries of the market and the weather.

Curiously, even the weather was more wayward in these decades than subsequently.[21] There were severe cold spells in the north in 1884 and again in 1889. There was extensive damage from drought in the region west of Kinki in 1883 and 1886. There was a recurrence of serious damage from cold in 1902 and 1905, and again in 1913.

In the first twenty-five years after the Revolution there was a steep rise in distress sales and mortgage fore-closures. Masses of small cultivators lost their land and were never able to regain it. This was the period when tenancy grew at a gallop. By 1903, of the total land under cultivation, 44.5 percent was farmed by tenants. In 1913 the proportion was 45.5 percent.[22] In 1941 it was still only 46 percent, though of a larger acreage. Regional variations were within the limits of 33 percent in Nagasaki and 59 percent in Kagawa.

4

In fact, "Once the initial reforms affecting landowner-ship and taxation were carried through, the issues of land tenure and distributive justice in the countryside were largely left aside, despite their importance for technical moderni-zation."[23]

In particular, the new government showed no concern for the small peasant or for millions of tenant operators who were on the lowest rung of the income ladder but cultivated most of the land. For them, it took no ameliorative measures, provided no institutional or fiscal assistance such as cheap credit, and enacted no protective legislation. There is no in-dication that it considered alienation of land to be un-desirable.

The Ministry of Agriculture did suggest a tenancy law for the first time in 1884. But as frankly stated in an official memorandum, its aim was neither to prevent the spread of tenancy nor to protect tenants. It was to make agricultural land a more universally valid mortgage security to ensure that price of land was maintained at a high level.

For the rest, an innocuous Industrial Cooperatives Law was passed in 1900, nine years after its presentation to the Diet. It laid down conditions under which farmers could form various types of cooperatives. As a result, there were 9274 credit associations by 1914. Many of them undertook marketing as well. Their transactions in rice and wheat, however, accounted for 10 percent of total sales. The loans made by them amounted to 3 percent of the total debt of members.

In 1899 an Agricultural Association Law was adopted. It sought to give a small measure of financial assistance to village agricultural associations for improving farming techniques.[24] In effect it strengthened the organization and power of the landlords in the village. It was customary at this time to take measures meant to favor landowners under the pretense of "prevention of insect damage, improvement of rice cultivation and the like."[25] Nothing was done that would go against their interests or interfere with property rights because landlords had sufficient political influence to prevent it.

According to Dore: "The 'problem of the villages' went on being discussed, and continued to be tackled only peripherally in successive amendments to the Industrial Co-operatives Law and the Agricultural Association Law, and in such measures as the Sericulture Law of 1911 establishing special-purpose Co-operatives for cocoon producers. But it was not until the 1920's that it really began to be considered a matter of urgency."[26]

5

The cause for urgency was the growing discontent among peasants, and the rising number of tenant-landlord disputes. They could not be ignored any more.[27]

In 1920 the minister of Agriculture and Commerce stated in the Diet that the growth of tenancy "affects not only the interests of landlords and tenants, but also the development of agriculture as a whole," that disputes between landlords and tenants are not simply local problems, "but a grave matter for our whole society."[28] He announced the appointment of a research committee to study what legal measures might be taken to deal with the situation.

A Rice Law was passed in 1921 to cushion the price swings. Taking the Tokyo average for 1914 as 100, price of rice rose to 274 in 1920, and then crashed in March of the same year. In twelve months it dropped by more than one half. Recovering to 257 in 1925, it declined again to 114 by 1931.

The Rice Law made state intervention possible both to control exports and imports, and to store, sell, and purchase rice in the domestic market through the official Japan Rice Company. Between 1921 and 1932, 185 million yen were spent by the government in a not-too-successful effort to stabilize the price of rice.

The law was amended and further strengthened in 1933. It imposed stricter obligations on the government to regulate price. In 1936 the Japanese farmer was given greater protection at the expense of the producers in the country's colonies. A similar policy was adopted to stabilize the price of the then all-important silk cocoons. It culminated in the Silk Price Stabilization Law of 1937. A 66 percent increase in the tariff on imported wheat also was imposed in 1932 to maintain domestic price at a high level.[29]

By 1935 two out of every three farm households were members of cooperatives, and low interest loans were available on a fairly large scale through several agencies. Also, the Debt Clearance Unions Law of 1933 attempted to ease the mounting burden of farmers' debt—of five to six billion yen since the beginning of the depression.

As for tenurial problems, proposals for a tenancy law were revived from time to time. The Tenancy Conciliation Law was passed in 1924 to settle disputes. Another measure adopted was the Regulations for the Establishment of Owner-Farmers of 1926. It provided for loans at 3.5 percent interest to tenants wanting to purchase the land they were cultivating—that is, if the landlord agreed to sell it. The loan was repayable in twenty-five years.

More radical measures, such as freezing rents (1939 level) and control of land prices (1941), followed only in the emergency created by the war. The last legislative attempt— an administrative order of 1943—attempted to alter the land system, because for the first time since the Restoration the rural population was showing an absolute decline. Even that, however, did not directly affect the landlord's interests. More effective from the tenant's point of view was the new procurement pricing policy. As the war advanced, it became imperative to secure the maximum deliveries of rice from peasants. It also became more difficult. In 1941 the government decided on a differential price system. Additional subsidies and bonuses were paid to owner-cultivators *and* to tenants— even for the rent rice delivered by tenants on behalf of the landlord. This was paid for at the higher producer's price while the rent payable in cash was based on the landowner's price. Since the food delivery system came into force in 1940, tenants (instead of landlords) were required to deliver their rental crop directly to the government, setting aside only a certain quantity for the consumption needs of the landowner. One important result of this was to change the hitherto rent-in-kind into a money rent in a period of considerable inflation. The second was that it automatically lowered the rent. Finally, for the first time in Japan's history probably, it was no longer profitable to be a landlord.[30] There was a sharp increase, therefore, in the number of landowners who took to working the land themselves. In less than a decade, between 1938 and 1946, noncultivating farmers declined by 87.5 percent.[31]

Judged by current standards, or by postwar reforms imposed by the Occupation Authorities, none of the above actions of the government was revolutionary. William Lockwood describes them as "a series of *ad hoc* measures which were palliatives at best." So they were. And deliberately. Their impact was also usually insignificant. As for example, the total area of land transferred to tenants in ten years under the Owner-Farmers Scheme of 1926 was eighty-six thousand *chō*. It was less than one-thirtieth of all the tenanted acreage.

Nevertheless, no such facility had been available to tenants at any time previously. However inadequate the measures, whether of subsidies, price protection, credit, or tenancy reform—even an articulate and public discussion of agrarian and social issues—they came into being and to the fore for the first time only *after* 1920.[32]

The first national peasants' union was founded in 1922. Universal male suffrage was granted in 1925. The fullest expression of constitutional democracy—the most Japan ever got in this era—was an interwar phenomenon.[33] The earlier Meiji governments by comparison were anti-democratic and steeped in the feudal-authoritarian tradition of Tokugawa times.

Yet, it was *after* 1920 that development of agriculture slowed down and the principal growth in the economy took place elsewhere. For the period as a whole, the impulse and momentum for growth in agriculture clearly lay outside the realm of state initiative, policy, action, or assistance—in the enterprise and energy of the millions of small farmers.

CHAPTER XXIII

Research and Education

1

There were two acts of the Meiji regime not yet mentioned that are widely believed to have had a considerable *causal* impact on the modernization and rapid growth of Japanese agriculture in this period. These were introduction of a secular system of universal and compulsory primary education, and the institution of a string of experiment stations for research in agriculture along with the requisite agencies for disseminating technical information and know-how to farmers.

Herein again, however, the time sequence does not correspond. Neither of these enlightened measures could have been the *cause* of agricultural growth in the quarter century preceding World War I.

Thus, a Ministry of Education was created in 1871. Schooling to the fourth grade was made compulsory fifteen years later. But it was not free. Tuition fee could be as high as fifty sen per month per child "at a time when the average annual income per employed worker was no more than about 21 yen."[1] A large majority of the peasants could not afford even a newspaper. Initially, therefore, the measure was unpopular and aroused widespread resistance.

Nevertheless, by the turn of the century, five million children—not all from farms—were receiving instruction of an indeterminate character in about 27,000 elementary schools. By 1907 more than 97 percent of the children were in elementary school as against 28.13 percent in 1873. And the four-year system had been extended to six years. But these youngsters had yet to grow up before they could replace their illiterate or semiliterate fathers on the farms as owners or tenant operators. The process could not have begun very much before 1920.[2]

Higher education—technical and general—at the secondary and university level was built up more slowly and in the earlier years was confined largely to boys from upper-income groups. Even "technical supplementary schools," open to students who had completed the four-year course of elementary instruction and the most numerous of all technical institutions, numbered only 221 by the end of the nineteenth century.

As for agricultural education, departments in the universities and professional schools developed substantially only about World War I. At the advanced elementary school level, also, it did not get organized till the 1890's because general education was given priority. In any case, few of the earlier graduates from agricultural schools and training courses went back to farming. Most preferred to take white collar jobs in the city, town, or village office. So also with university graduates. Chances of their returning to the village were remote. As a local proverb has it: "An educated child turns up his nose at the privy at home."[3]

Similarly, scientific research in agriculture and extension education did not begin to be organized until the 1890's. The first permanent national experiment station was established in Tokyo in 1893, with six branches in different parts of the country. Prefectural research stations were set up about the same time. Earlier, in 1874 the department concerned with agriculture began to publish a regular bulletin for farmers. In 1877 the prefectures were asked to appoint correspondents to report anything likely to be of value to the department. In return they received the bulletin and answers to specific queries. Three years later, private individuals—aside from prefectural officials—were permitted to correspond directly with the department by unstamped letter. By 1885, however, less than 2000 farmers were receiving the department's bulletin.

By this time many villages had organized voluntary associations of farmers *(Nojikai)* for improvement of agricultural techniques. Besides, the government began to employ a number of farmers to establish an Itinerant Instructor System—proven farmers being the instructors. Called the *Rōnō Gijutsu* or veteran farmers' techniques, the focus was on spread and exchange of existing know-how.[4] It did not, however, survive for more than a decade.

After the Sino-Japanese war, an attempt was made to increase production by compulsion—"extension by the sabre method" as some Japanese historians describe it. Between 1896 and 1904 twenty-four prefectures ordered that the rice seed bed should be oblong in shape and not more than four feet wide in order to facilitate weeding and to control pests, especially the rice borer. Eight prefectures imposed penal provisions ranging from a ten-yen fine to ten days' imprisonment for noncompliance. Several prefectures forbade the use of lime, believed at the time (but disproved later) to hurt the soil. Others ordered the spacing of rice plants in regular rows. In one district it came to be known as the "wine-bottle method," after an inspector, "having fortified himself on a *shō* of *saké,* charged into a field brandishing the bottle over his head and began to uproot irregularly planted rice."[5] Rice-grading regulations also were imposed. However, the policy could not last very long because of frequent clashes between farmers and the police and agricultural officers. By 1910 it too had lapsed.

Provision for regular extension education under the direction of agricultural experiment stations was made for the first time in 1899. It was to be through the village agricultural associations. These were given a statutory basis and every village was required by law to have one. Membership in the local association was made compulsory for all farmers in 1905. Only 3 percent of the budget of the experiment stations, however, was earmarked for extension work.

It was not until 1901 that the Imperial Agricultural Association was founded. Later, it recommended that full-time trained technicians be assigned to each village association for extension education. Measures for training the requisite personnel from among high-school graduates were taken subsequently.

Gradually, in this manner, there was organized a national network of schools, research stations, and a professional service for conveying the results of research to the farmers.[6] Neither education nor scientific research and extension, therefore, could have contributed, much less been the cause of the earlier phase of agricultural growth after the Restoration.[7] The measured technological progress in this period—before 1920—was very much greater than government outlays in agricultural research, extension, and rural education. Only as the rate of agricultural output decelerated or became stagnant after World War I did government outlays begin to increase.[8]

2

Nevertheless, improvement in agricultural technology in the Meiji period has been described by experts as "a chemical and botanical revolution." This refers to the impact on production of the introduction and intensive application of chemical fertilizers and varietal improvement of seeds.[9]

In these two fields as well, however, modern techniques could not have been operative prior to the organization of scientific research, which did not get going till more than half the era was over. Then followed depression and World War II, when the country's economy was completely disrupted.

Furthermore, there was nothing novel or radical about fertilizers or improved seeds. *Chemical* fertilizers were new when introduced. But not the principle and practice of fertilizing the soil. Only the ingredients varied. From the time that cultivation of rice began in Japan, it was never the custom to rest a field or rotate crops. Land was planted to a cereal every year, or even twice a year. Only the most intensive nourishment of the soil could have sustained its fertility. The farmer became aware of this very early in history.

Throughout the Tokugawa period soil was fertilized intensively.[10] At first, it was by compost made from household night soil and grass and leaves collected by the farmer from the common forest and wastelands. Report from a village in Kōzuke Province in 1780 states that one *tan* of paddy land required seventy to eighty horseloads of cut grass. The grass was piled up to make compost, or it was spread on the field and plowed under.

Although as late as 1890 wild grass was still in use, during the seventeenth and eighteenth centuries there was a steady shift from self-made natural fertilizers to the commercially available organic manures—mainly dried fish, oil cakes, and urban night soil. These were used in all parts of the country.[11]

These fertilizers cost money. However, as with family labor so with fertilizer, the Japanese farmer does not appear *ever* to have calculated its cost. It came to be treated as an indispensable item—part of fixed overheads. Neither price nor the marketable surplus of his produce determined the quantity of fertilizer applied. It was affected only by his financial ability to buy.[12]

And so, by the close of the eighteenth century, when farmers in the United States were merrily "butchering" the land, expenditure on *purchased* fertilizer was usually the largest item in a typical farm budget of the Japanese peasant. It accounted often for more than half of his total cash outlay. Its usage spread as sources of green manures dwindled due to cultivation creeping up the mountainsides and the government taking over communal lands. Rice straw too began to be used for purposes other than composting. According to one estimate, 45 percent of the fertilizers were purchased in 1890 and 53 percent in 1908. After the Russo-Japanese War (1904–5), soybean cakes began to be imported in large quantities from Manchuria. Their imports increased from 200,000 tons in 1903–7 to an average of nearly 1.2 million tons in 1917–21. Hokkaido fish cakes also were in great demand.

Ammonium sulphate (imported) appeared on the market after World War I. Domestic manufacture of chemical fertilizers began to develop only about 1930. In 1935 for the *first* time the consumption of ammonium sulphate exceeded that of soybean cakes. At this stage fertilizer accounted for 30 to 35 percent of the total cost of rice production—*the smaller farmers using more of it* (and labor) than those with larger holdings.[13]

War broke out soon, however, and there was a critical shortage of chemical fertilizers. Homemade composts and stable manures, wood and grass ash, and night soil staged a comeback both in the farmer's field and as a principal subject of research in paddy soil fertility.

3

Furthermore, the impact on cropping techniques was far greater with the switch to fish and soybean cakes than it was to chemical fertilizers.

Thus, green manuring could not generally sustain more than one crop in a year. Organic fertilizers raised yields and permitted a more intensive cultivation of the land. Double and even triple cropping became feasible.

Moreover, liberal application of organic manures made it necessary to plow deeper than the customary 7–8 centimeters.[14] This transformed the design of the plow. An animal-drawn plow invented by Enri Hayashi, a farmer in north Kyushu, came into use for the first time.[15] In turn, it required better drainage of paddy fields. In fact, the whole complex of tillage practices changed into what is known as the "Meiji method." Essentially, it is the same as the post-war technique of cultivating rice in Japan.

It was at this stage—in 1886—that the *first* variety of rice with high fertilizer response and high yield was also developed. It was called *Shinriki*. The heavy import of soybean cakes from Manchuria after 1900 was due primarily to the greater spread of *Shinriki* in southwest Japan, and to that of other similar strains, such as *Aikoku* in the Kanto District, *Kameno-o* in the Tohoku area, and *Bozu* in Hokkaido. They were selected on a one-region one-variety basis.

None of these varieties, however, was bred by scientists in government experiment stations.[16] The latter did not exist in 1886 when *Shinriki* was first distributed. On the contrary, all the new strains were selected from among the native varieties and were multiplied and popularized by the farmers. They started a movement to exchange seeds through *Hinshu Kōkan-Kai*, the society for exchanging seeds. Several strains would be collected from different parts of the country and the selection made through trial planting. New varieties were bred also by the laborious practice of picking up panicles.

Kameno-o was developed by farmer Kameji Abe in Yamagata Prefecture. Development of *Bozu* in Hokkaido has been described earlier. *Shinriki* was selected by Jujiro Maruo, a peasant in Hyogo Prefecture. The rapid propagation of the latter variety over wide areas also was due to the initiative of private rice seed growers in Hyogo Prefecture.

Some villages formed seed growers' cooperatives. Foundation seed fields and registered seed fields were established. All the paddy fields in a village would be used for the purpose of seed multiplication, while cultural operations were supervised by the cooperative. Careful attention was paid to seed selection before the seeds were packed for sale.

In Tokugawa times, principles of genetics were unknown. But the search for better seeds was continuous. A new variety was the result of a chance variation that a diligent farmer observed in a plant and set aside for seed and trial. But farm records show peasants planting four, five, or six varieties each year—some of them new.[17] It could have been because seed tends to deteriorate and yield less over time. Varieties of rice are estimated to have increased from about 177 in the early seventeenth century to 2363 by the 1850's.

Tailoring the seed to the kind and quality of fertilizer used was also an old practice in Japan. When wild grass or straw was applied, the rice varieties in use had a highly absorbing ability. With an increase in the nitrogenous component in soybeans, these plants began to suffer from disease and lodging. And so, disease-resistant, short- and strong-culmed, multipanicle type with a high fertilizer response came to be bred.

With the introduction of quicker-acting chemical fertilizers, these varieties were improved upon by the experiment stations—the short-culmed, profusely tillering or sprouting, and disease-resistant strains. Application of Mendelian principles to plant breeding in government experiment stations did not begin till 1910. Intensive experimental work on seed improvement followed later on the foundation of what had been achieved by farmers. The first stage was by mass and pure-line selection. There was a shift to crossbreeding from around 1925. And so, only around 1930 was *Shinriki* replaced by the experiment-station-bred strain of *Asahi*, and *Kameno-o* by *Riku-u No. 132*. In 1935 *Fukoku* began to displace varieties of *Bozu* stock in Hokkaido. As late as 1945, however, seventeen varieties selected by farmers were still being cultivated, the most famous of them on about 10 percent of the total rice area.

CHAPTER XXIV

Transforming Traditionally

1

As in Tokugawa times, so also after Meiji Restoration, impressive gains in agriculture were achieved primarily because tens of thousands of small peasants worked longer hours more efficiently to grow yet another extra *koku* of rice. Before 1920 they did so with little or no financial assistance from the state, almost entirely out of savings from within agriculture and within a rural organization inherited from the Tokugawa period.

Again, the early Meiji farmers did it by constant experimenting, inexpensive innovations, and modest improvement of farm implements. Though the scope must have been increasingly limited, there was yet a greater spread of known techniques and more efficient application of traditional practices, such as seed selection, preparation of seed bed, transplanting, weeding, timing of planting and placement of fertilizer applications, disease control, and storage. Mostly, old things were done in a slightly newer fashion or simply better.

Thus, irrigation of paddy fields was well developed by 1880. But water storage and drainage improved further, though irrigation facilities also were extended wherever possible. At the same time, land was cropped more intensively and double-grain cropping of paddy fields to grow

173

rice in summer, and wheat or barley in winter was developed. Seed varieties were improved. But so, too, was the quality of land by the farmers applying large quantities of manure continually over the years after digging or plowing deeply with the improved plow, along with better irrigation and drainage practices.

None of the innovations was spectacular. Nor were they radical enough to bring about a change in the structure or scale of the producing unit. Singly, the better techniques must have given a low, gradual, often barely calculable return in terms of increase in production or profitability on the five million or so holdings that averaged 2.5 acres each. They did not reduce unit costs; or very little.

On the contrary, some of the improved implements required as much work as the old ones or more. And greater skill besides. The new animal-drawn plow, for instance, had a short base (the part touching the ground) or no base at all. It plowed deeper—three to four inches. But it needed considerable skill to operate. It also needed a draft animal which not all farmers yet possessed. The new hand-rotary weeder was a labor-saving device. But it still required at least two weedings with the old *ganzume*—long-nailed rake-shaped hand weeder.[1]

Together and cumulatively, however, improved land, better seeds, and tools and tillage practices doubled the physical output per acre in about half a century. Most of the capital that the increase in production on this scale required came from the peasant's personal savings and use of his labor in spare time. "In good part it represented the sacrifice of family leisure. . . ."[2]

Fixed capital improvements, such as irrigation reservoirs that serve nearly 20 percent of the total irrigated area, were made mainly by local farmhands on a community basis. At the individual's level it took the form simply of improving one's own land, implements, and buildings. As there was practically no mechanization, cash outlay was required only for the purchase of seed and fertilizer.

2

On the eve of World War II agriculture in Japan had attained the highest production per acre in the world.[3] But modes of cultivation remained manual and traditional. A Westerner would have called them primitive.

Soon after the Restoration, Meiji governments did make a solemn attempt to foster a revolution in agriculture —as in industry—by introducing Western techniques and extensive farming methods with machinery. The lead was given by Lord T. Iwakura, one of the prominent figures of the new regime. He visited the United States and Europe in the early 1870's as envoy extraordinary and ambassador plenipotentiary. Several high officials went abroad after him and stressed the need for adopting Western-style mechanized farming. In 1871 an exhibition room was opened to display European and American agricultural machines. In 1875 they began to be manufactured domestically. Some of the other measures taken in this respect have been described earlier in another context.[4]

Several enterprising Western-returned ex-samurai also made bold experiments with large-scale "capitalist" farming. Almost invariably, however, they all failed. The sale of large areas to peers and high government officials in the less densely populated regions, such as Hokkaido, did not have the desired result of establishing large mechanized farms either. Even livestock ranches developed a tenancy system with breeding cows being leased out to tenants— thus conforming to the traditional form of agricultural organization. By the mid-1880's Japan had officially and otherwise reverted to her traditional techniques and tried simply to improve them and diffuse them more widely.

In agriculture, therefore, Japan has been primarily an innovator and not an imitator of the West. And she continues to be so. Since World War II there has been a modest increase in farm mechanization. Experiment stations —especially at the prefectural level—have been playing a very active and effective role in research, as has the government in pricing and subsidizing farm products.

And so, still better seeds have been evolved, suited to every locality and nuance of temperature and soil—at times a single small field will be sown with more than one strain of rice. Soils have been further improved and are better fertilized. Disease control has become much more effective. The price of rice has been high and stable. But cultivation has continued in the same tradition, the same style, and exactly the same scale of a family unit worked mainly or entirely by family labor, as in the Meiji era.

In three hundred years Japan has not known what might be described as a *revolutionary* change in technology or organization of its agriculture. If a Tokugawa peasant of the mid-nineteenth century or even earlier were to come alive and visit any average rice farm he would feel perfectly at home.

The power tiller, electric motor, and thresher would intrigue him. But little else would. In the north he would chuckle at the protected seed nursery perhaps—for not having thought of it himself. He would envy the ease with which in the 1960's farmers could obtain fertilizers and pesticides and would admire their great potency. He would think poorly of the number of weeds in fields where herbicides had been used because the family was short of hands to pull them out manually. He would appreciate the high yielding and early maturing qualities of certain varieties of seed. But from sowing to harvest he would be familiar with every cultural operation of growing rice. It was the same in his time.

3

On the other hand, if an American rice farmer of even the first decade of *this*, the twentieth century, were to visit a rice farm in California, that of Russell Carrino for instance, he would be bewildered. He would not recognize a single tool, technique, or operation.

Thus, in the low-lying coastal area of South Carolina

around Georgetown, rice had become the "grand staple" of plantation production in the nineteenth century. Here, on the farm of Elizabeth Allston—daughter of one of the state's outstanding ante-bellum planters—this is how rice was cultivated in 1903, and subsequently, according to the daily journal maintained by Elizabeth:

Cherokee, March 30, 1903.
March is the month when all the rice-field ploughing should be done. . . . The rice-field banks are about three feet above the level of the river at high water, and each field has a very small flood-gate (called a trunk), which opens and closes to let the water in and out. . . .

June 1, 1903.
One can plant from the 15th of March to the 15th of April, then again from the 1st to the 10th of May, and last for ten days in June. Rice planted between these seasons falls a prey to birds, . . .

Yesterday I went down to give out the seed rice to be clayed for planting today. . . . I took one hand up into the upper barn while Marcus stayed below, having two barrels half filled with clay and then filled with water and well stirred until it is about the consistency of molasses. In the loft my man measured out thirty-five bushels of rice, turning the tub into a spout leading to the barn below, where young men brought the clay water in piggins from the barrel and poured it over the rice, while young girls, with bare feet and skirts well tied up, danced and shuffled the rice about with their feet until the whole mass was thoroughly clayed, singing, joking, and displaying their graceful activity to the best advantage. It is a pretty sight. When it is completely covered with clay, the rice is shovelled into a pyramid and left to soak until the next morning, when it is measured out into sacks, one and one-fourth bushels to each half acre. Two pairs of the stoutest oxen on the plantation are harnessed to the rice-drills, and they lumber along slowly but surely, and by twelve o'clock the field of fourteen acres is nearly planted.

It is literally casting one's bread on the waters, for as soon as the seed is in the ground the trunk door is lifted and the water creeps slowly up and up until it is about three inches deep on the land. That is why the claying is necessary; it makes the grain adhere to the earth, otherwise it would float. . . .

I went down into the Marsh field, where five ploughs are running, preparing for the June planting. It is a 26-acre field, . . .

October 8, 1903.

The harvest has come and with it real harvest weather—crisp, cool, clear; and the bowed heads of the golden grain glow in the sunshine. . . . I had to cut on Thursday, for the rice was full ripe. . . . To-day the hands are "toting" the rice into the flats.

You see a stack of rice approaching, and as it makes its way across the plank which bridges the big ditch, you perceive a pair of legs or a skirt, as the case may be, peeping from beneath. Men, women, and children all carry, what look like immense loads, on their heads, apparently without effort. This is the gayest week of the year. Thursday the field was cut down by the hands with small reap-hooks, the long golden heads being carefully laid on the tall stubble to dry until the next day, when it was tied into sheaves, which the negroes do very skilfully with a wisp of the rice itself. Saturday it was stacked in small cocks to dry through Sunday, and to-day it is being loaded into the flats, having had every advantage of weather. . . .

I have sent for a tug to tow the two flats up on the flood-tide. . . . Flats are one of the heavy expenses on a rice plantation—large, flat-bottomed boats from twenty to eighty feet long and from ten to twelve feet wide, propelled in the most primitive way by poles and steered by one huge oar at the stern. They can be loaded up very high if the rice is properly stowed. . . .

October 31.

Spent yesterday in the mill threshing out my rice, most trying to me of all the work, the dust is so terrible; but the mill worked well, and so did the hands—and better than all, the rice turned out well, thirty-five bushels to the acre. . . .

November 6.

Threshed out the rice to-day. It made only twenty bushels to the acre. . . . The hands now are whipping out the seed rice, which is a tedious business, but no planter in this country will use mill-threshed rice for seed. . . . Here it is thought the mill breaks the rice too much, so the seed rice is prepared by each hand taking a single sheaf at a time and whipping it over a log, or a smooth board set up, until all the rice comes off. Then the sheaves are laid on a clay floor and beaten with flails, until nearly every grain has left the straw. . . .

1904.

On Monday, April 18, I planted the wages field at Cherokee. Here we cannot so well use the machines, so I have the field sown by hand. . . .

The women are very graceful as they sow the rice with a waving movement of the hands, at the same time bending low so that the wind may not scatter the grain; and a good sower gets it all straight in the furrow. . . .

May 9.

The April rice was very fine, . . . though Marcus told me it was suffering greatly from the need of hoeing, but he could not stop the preparation of the land for the June planting to hoe it out. This trouble is due to the moving of so many of the young people last winter to town. They were all good hoe hands and there is no one to take their place. The men now think it beneath them to handle a hoe; that they consider a purely feminine implement; the plough alone is man's tool. . . .

July 6.

I am anxious to get the field hoed out, for besides its being very grassy, . . . it is most important to get the rice clean of grass and the water put over it. . . .[5]

CHAPTER XXV

Footprints in the Snow

1

It becomes difficult to trace footprints in the snow after a fresh fall overnight. The endeavors and choices of millions of individuals over decades and centuries can be just as elusive to trace, identify, and assess. Yet, it is the quality of effort and multitudes of decisions of vast numbers of common people that cumulatively, and in a large and critical measure often, determine the design and destiny of development in any field of human enterprise.

To assess the performance and potential of a country's agriculture for instance, in terms only of land, climate, capital, technology, institutional arrangements, and government policy, would be akin to thinking of a marriage with a trousseau but without the bride. All these factors can remain constant within a region. But if one winter, many young farmhands decide to move to town, or men begin to think that it is beneath them to handle a hoe, a crop can suffer greatly. Eventually, the product can go out of cultivation altogether, as rice did in South Carolina. For Elizabeth Allston, by December 1906, "The rice-planting, which for years gave me the exhilaration of making a good income myself, is a thing of the past now—the banks and the trunks have been washed away. . . ."[1]

In another part of the world, in Hokkaido, rice is

being grown *only* because farmers insisted on growing it. And they succeeded in spite of tremendous odds and hostility of climate, soil, scientists, their own government, and its distinguished foreign advisers.[2]

To the extent possible, therefore, the focus of this study has been primarily on farmers in the United States and Japan. It has tried to describe their role, efficacy, and efficiency in deploying the given factors and opportunities in their respective environment. In recent years both these nations have achieved a remarkable growth in farm production. What did these countries and—more so—their farmers share in common that made the course and character of agriculture in the two countries similar in this respect?

2

Situated in different hemispheres, farmers of one country are all of an Asian race, physique, and culture. As Daniere said: ". . . they are a different people!"[3] He was referring to Japanese farmers settled in the United States. In Japan they are even more "different" from Americans. Their language is different. Their food consists mainly of rice. They are predominantly of "heathen" persuasions— Buddhist and Shinto with an overlay of Confucian ethic. And almost invariably they are alluded to as "peasants."

A majority of the farmers in the United States, especially in the top and middle income groups, are of European descent and culture. They speak American dialects of the English language. They eat a protein-rich diet. They are Christian; mostly Protestant. And they could be tenants and sharecroppers. But never "peasants."

Furthermore, the American farmer has known nothing but an egalitarian social structure, relatively free of sharp social distinctions, and a secular democratic form of government. In the belief that "all men are created equal," with respect to the white population at least, public policy in the U.S has been committed to and always upheld principles of individual freedom and equal opportunity. In economics (and agriculture) the principles underlie pervasive deep-rooted values and concepts concerning the nature of organization, efficiency in production, distribution of rewards (income), and control. John M. Brewster refers to them as the *work ethic, democratic creed,* and *enterprise creed.*[4] Aside from their role in determining the direction, goals, and content of the government's farm policy, the values are widely assumed to govern the preferences, beliefs, and behavior of the farm people as well. As for instance, the introduction to the 1960 Resolutions of the American Farm Bureau Federation, the largest and most influential of farmers' organizations, affirmed:

> We, as Farm Bureau members believe: . . . In the right of every man to choose his own occupation; to be rewarded according to his productive contribution to society; and to save, invest, and spend, or to convey to his heirs, his earnings as he chooses.[5]

Concerning *equal opportunity,* the same statement expressed the following belief:

> Americans' unparalleled progress is based on the freedom and dignity of the individual, initiative, *and equal opportunity,* sustained by our faith in God and our basic moral and ethical values. (Italics mine.)

In Japan, on the contrary, a great majority of the peasants were virtual serfs in a feudal state and society until after the middle of the nineteenth century. Saddled with oppressive obligations, they had few rights and fewer freedoms. Equal opportunity was nonexistent unless it was not-to-have. Forbidden to move in space or station in life, if they did so it was in defiance of authority. Half a century after the Restoration of 1868, they had yet to emerge from the basic constraints, discrimination, and socio-economic stratification of the feudal order. There was no agricultural ladder in Meiji Japan in myth or reality.

As for factors of production in the two countries, clearly they are incomparable. Most farmers in Japan have never known the luxury of adequate, even minimal resources. Land, the most critical of them, has been the scarcest, and most of it not very fertile. The story goes of a visitor meeting "an old man in a mountain village piling stones one upon another to make a dike. He asked the man what he was doing. The old man replied that the dike would check mud flown down from the mountain by each rainfall and produce there a site for a paddy field."[6] This is perfectly plausible in Japan. Had the incident occurred in the United States, the old man would have found himself in a mental institution. That country has had a surfeit of every kind of resource required in agriculture in relation to the population engaged in farming. At no period in U.S. history did the number of farms exceed 6.8 million on a land area exceeding two billion acres.

3

In both countries World War II constitutes a major divide. The old political philosophy and system was scrapped in Japan and every vestige of feudalism with it. By order and under the surveillance of the Occupation Authorities a most revolutionary land reform was instituted.[7] It was so revolutionary that no American government would, or ever did, admit anything approaching it as desirable domestically, even when the number of tenants and croppers in the U.S. was large and their economic condition unsatisfactory.

In 1935, for instance, 45 percent of the farm land in the U.S.—the proportion was very much higher in several states—was being operated under lease.[8] It was not much less than in Japan at any period.

By 1964 tenant-operated farms in the United States were down to 17.1 percent of the total. But the improvement had come about mainly by a reduction in the number of farms and displacement of labor by machines, not by reform. Since the abolition of slavery American agriculture has been remarkably free from legislative interference and reform pertaining to land tenures. Moreover, although in the postwar years many more operators came to own all or part of their farms, they were faced with increasing inroads into their freedom to make decisions about production and the marketing of their produce. Washington began to decide the acreage, in the aggregate and on each and every farm, that could be planted to some of the most important crops, such as wheat, the feed grains, rice, cotton, tobacco, and peanuts. Some of the programs, as in wheat and the feed grains, were voluntary. Others were subject to mandatory controls and marketing quotas.

Government also fixed the price and regulated the sale of several farm commodities. For milk, eighty-two federal milk marketing orders were in effect in 1964. They governed the marketing area, price, and delivery of fifty-four billion pounds of milk of the value of $2.3 billion. It was produced by 172,000 dairy farms, and supplied two-thirds of the nonfarm population in the country. Similar marketing order programs covered fruits, vegetables, and nuts in twenty-five states.[9]

Besides, the normal commercial structure came to be organized in such a way that for several farm products a farmer *had* to get "vertically integrated" or coordinated with big private firms in the marketing business. If not, like Joe Brown's wife, he would not be able to sell at all— not even to the local store or to neighbors in the country.

The arrangements varied from verbal agreements for processing or marketing to ownership and operation of the farm by business. But they all infringed upon the production and marketing decisions of the operator. Often they did more than that. In broiler production the small independent producers were eliminated almost entirely. Of the broilers in 1960, 90 percent were produced on 28,000 farms. Even on these, field men employed by the contractor did most of the managing of the farm. In some cases, the producer was relegated to the role of a pieceworker, especially if the contractor controlled the buildings and equipment.[10]

After the war, although in Japan, too, nearly 70 percent of farm production came under some system of price subsidy or regulation, the farmer found himself generally in a situation of unprecedented freedom and favor. The American farmer, however, was constrained and restricted as never before. In important spheres such as marketing and technology of production, the latter was in effect left with little or no real choice. No commercial farmer in the United States could have refused, as did the big and small farmers of Mukaizima village in Kyoto Prefecture, to invest in bigger and more efficient machines without imperiling his prospects and future.

4

Nevertheless, and taking into account their respective histories as a whole, America has been a model of "modernity" and free enterprise to most countries in the world, including Japan. Comparatively a new nation, still in search of an authentic indigenous tradition, it is presumed to be free from its trammels.

The Orientals by contrast are an ancient people, burdened with a several-layered load of legacies, good and bad, which neither democracy nor economic reforms could completely exorcize. And so, by the 1960's, although Japan had largely established her credentials to "modernity" in the somewhat puzzled eyes of others, especially the Western world, a number of her own writers and intellectuals were not wholly convinced. They still saw "feudalism under every rice-stalk" and insisted that their farmers were incorrigibly traditional.[12] They attributed this generally to the hangover from history and to the Buddhist faith that preaches virtues of contentment and sacrifice rather than aggressive acquisitiveness that supposedly led to economic betterment in the West. A university professor of economics recalls how his mother had instructed him in the philosophy of "being happy always with whatever you have."[13] He would be scolded if he expressed dissatisfaction or ambition for anything more and beyond the pale of their legitimate due and expectations.

A Japanese Jesuit, educated in California, says over a Western-type breakfast:

"Our farmers are traditional."

"But why?"

"Well." There is a pause as he chews his toast. "For example, they will leave their fields to go to the temple. They will not care what happens to the crop."

"So! How often?"

"Oh, twice in a year. Also," he hastens to add, "they will hold a religious ceremony at the time of sowing rice. They think it will give them a good harvest!"[14]

This outrageous display of irrationality seals the matter in his eyes—as well as in those of a distinguished foreign scholar. According to Arnold J. Toynbee:

> Shinto as a cult of fertility is still an integral part of Japanese rice-cultivation. In Japan, growing rice is not just an economic operation; it is also a religious rite which has to be practised for its own sake, whether or not rice happens to be the most remunerative crop to raise. . . .[15]

Speaking of Hokkaido, where "Rice is not at all the obvious crop. . . ," and where in the fall of 1956, Toynbee visited a dairy and a rice farm:

> Sure enough, the dairy-farmer was the greatest radical. . . . The rice-farmer had built himself a fine house in an ultra-traditional Japanese style with a holy shelf for the Shinto gods and a miniature chapel for the Buddhist bodhisattvas and a row of enlarged photographs of revered ancestors. The dairy-farmer had built himself an American two-storeyed house with a barrel roof in corrugated iron, and he and his family sat on American-like chairs and ate their meals at an American-like table. He had taken the impious plunge of making cheese and butter instead of cultivating a paddy-field. . . .

"That revolutionary dairy-farmer's grandchildren," the author predicts, "will be as modern as their contemporaries in Wisconsin and Minnesota." By implication the rice farmer could not look forward to the same honor.

CHAPTER XXVI

Sickle and the Combine

1

In several important respects, therefore, farmers of the two countries and their social organization, resources, and opportunities in agriculture have been strikingly dissimilar—as a sickle is to a combine harvester. In both we encountered instances of not inconsiderable deviations from classical concepts and from the many stereotyped images and assumptions concerning common traits, beliefs, and behavior of the farm people.

In the United States for example, we found the farm population (and the nation) not to be wholly secular, free from superstition, or *sans* tradition. Many concepts underlying public policy and economic organization are shot through with, and stem from, religious doctrine about the creation of man in general and the status of Americans in particular in the eyes of God. The Farm Bureau goes to the extent of stating:

> The principles of our competitive enterprise system *derive* from, and are consistent with, our *religious values* and the highest goals that mankind seeks.[1] (Italics mine.)

Despite the country's supreme dedication to science and technology, occasions far less critical to the material prospect of the cultivator than the sowing of his main or only crop are preceded by prayer and request for divine favor and blessing. And in whatever manner the church chooses to interfere in the ordering of the life of an individual and community—be it in the sphere of education or in purely economic action such as organizing a trade union —it is generally respected and obeyed.[2]

Nor are American farmers entirely free from the shackles of tradition. Aside from the veneer of the regional and national culture, to which conformity is strong, the tendency to adhere to custom and disposition derived from the country of origin is clearly apparent. Father-son partnership arrangements on the farm, attitudes toward education, efficiency, and material wealth, the kind of work if any that women may do on the farm, and propensity to cooperate, often continue to be determined by what was customary in the "home" country, or in a particular part of it, at the time the family's forbears emigrated to the New World.

Some historians have suggested that in the early period aptitudes, skills, and farming practices differed significantly between neighbors of different cultural and national groups.[3] In more recent times, Robert was not a lone eccentric in refusing to have running water in the house. Since 1857, in his and a neighboring county in Wisconsin, there has been a concentration of farmers who like Robert are of Polish descent. A sample survey of this group revealed, among other things, that:

> Modern plumbing is perhaps the greatest need in farm homes. Lack of money however does not appear to be the sole reason for failure to have a modern plumbing and sanitation system. Neither does a lack of information about modern construction seem to be an important factor. Several new and remodeled homes were observed which involved a considerable outlay of money and which incorporated modern features. However, no provision what-

soever had been made for a bathroom or for a pressure water system.[4]

About Wisconsin as a whole, the same survey pointed out:

> Wisconsin, more than most states, is the result of direct European settlement. When one looks at a nationality map of Wisconsin, one sees the state covered with nationality "islands." . . . Each of the immigrants from the thirty-odd nationalities which came to Wisconsin brought with them a set of ideals and values which are projected into their religious lives and in the way they responded to educational needs and opportunities, to employment and industrial opportunities, and to agriculture. . . . In many cases it can be demonstrated that the peculiar pursuits or specialities in Wisconsin are related to previous activity in the homeland.[5]

The observation could be broadly true of several other states as well.

It was in attitude to work, however, that we found conclusive evidence of variance and deviation from the much publicized creed and philosophy of the nation—of "dirty hands." The differences were regional rather than ethnic or sectarian. But the Protestant ethic on the subject failed ostensibly to permeate and overcome the temptation of *not*-working unless circumstances permitted no choice. And in the absence of choice, the ethic was not confined to Protestants. It is difficult, therefore, to find typical "dirt farmers" wherever labor has been and still is available to do the "dirty" work. Prejudice against certain types of farm work runs strong and is shared by farmers and agriculture labor alike.

More important in view of its impact on the total farm economy, farmers in the U.S. have not proved to be as mobile as is generally believed, or as one would expect, considering history, the magnificent roadways and the

countless vehicles on them, the multiple channels of com-
munication, and the sheer scope, facility, and lure of movement in a commercial and expanding economy of a magnitude the world has never before seen. Some twenty-five
million people left agriculture between 1940 and 1965. But
whatever the rate of outflow of the American farm population, it has not been sufficient to offset the inflow of new
capital and improved practices into agriculture. Hence its
constant state of excessive productive capacity.[6] Hence,
also, the disproportionately large number of low-income
and, in effect, surplus farm operators outside the main
stream of commercial production, with whom the Commodity Credit Corporation has no means of dealing.

2

In Japan, on the other hand, it is true that an over-
whelming majority of the farmers do *not* live like
Americans.

They live in typical Japanese-style houses with
unpainted exteriors and sliding paper panels for interior
walls.[7] They remove their footwear at the door and sit and
sleep on floors covered with thick straw mats. They eat at
low lacquered tables with chopsticks from little bowls filled
with boiled rice and drink endless cups of light green tea or
saké. They bow low from the waist several times when
greeting friends and strangers and do not mind stoop, squat,
or *any* kind of farm work. Moreover, they often cultivate
rice when in the opinion of scientists and economists they
should be milking cows—as in Hokkaido; or raising cocoons
—as in Gumma Prefecture.

In several such respects the Japanese farmer lives,
looks, and acts typically "traditional." Only the man's
outdoor dress is invariably Western. Yet somehow, he does
not give the impression of being any less "radical," "revolutionary," or "modern" than his contemporary anywhere
in the U.S. Moreover, and contrary to what one would
expect in a "traditional" peasant society, he appears to be
not only remarkably secular but a-religious in his everyday

conduct. Flowers at the feet of the deity I found often to be dead. But never those in a vase.

Even the much-criticized rice farmer is extremely pragmatic and commercial in outlook despite the divine associations of rice and the somewhat ostentatious Buddhist and Shinto shrines in almost every home. He has the facts and figures of his farm operation at his finger tips and has carefully recorded them in a notebook. He also has a perfectly plausible justification for whatever he does. It is no more irrational than the several preferences and prejudices encountered among farmers in the U.S. In neither country did we find people's preferences to be governed wholly by an orthodox profit-maximizing rationality.

As for peasants performing religious rites at the time of sowing rice, or like Kyuzo Doi sowing it on the day traditionally called lucky, they believe no more in magic than Carl, the dairy farmer in Wisconsin, who has a cross and an icon of Jesus and Mary in his milkhouse. Their faith in divine intervention does not approach that of Hurlbut, who would not irrigate the crops if his turn to take water fell on the Sabbath. More typical of the Japanese approach is that of Max in the state of Washington. He, too, is Christian. But he risks his salvation rather than let a weed alone for a day, even on Sunday.

And if plain statistics are any indication, it is the "traditional" rice farmer in Japan who has *always* produced more bushels per acre than his American counterpart. The "radical" dairy farmer in Hokkaido does not normally obtain as much milk per cow as the best in Wisconsin or Minnesota.

3

Historically, in three significant respects the peasant society of Japan did not conform to conventional wisdom, theory, and precepts of behavior.

First, it increased farm production more than three times in the period between 1878 and 1962, *with labor remaining virtually constant*. After World War II agriculture in Japan engaged an even larger population than before the war, due to a heavy influx of evacuees, displaced emigrants, and urban unemployed. People in farming increased by about 20 percent over the prewar level. The number of peasant households went up from 5.5 million in 1940 to 6.1 million in 1950. The number of persons in peasant families increased from 31.03 million in 1940, to 37.8 million in 1950. The farming population in 1959 was 14.5 million as against 14.79 million in 1872. Land and capital inputs, on the other hand, increased much more slowly than production, especially in the prewar era.[8]

Second, during the Tokugawa period, whereas production capacity of agriculture as well as of the rest of the economy was rising, the total population appears to have remained constant. In an important part it was due to voluntary control. This was contrary to the classic Malthusian response.[9]

Finally, despite the manifold constraints and strictures through all but the most recent postwar era, the rural population in Japan has been highly mobile. Even in the Tokugawa times, it appears to have been ahead of economic opportunity—whatever and wherever—to an extent that traditional peasant societies are not reputed to be.

To cite one instance: at the turn of the seventeenth century, the silk weaving industry was a near monopoly of urban artisans in the Nishijin district of Kyoto. Though organized in powerful guilds, by the early eighteenth century the Nishijin weavers were complaining of rural competition. A century and a half later, only 10 percent (by value) of the silk cloth coming into Edo was made in Kyoto. The rest was *inakamono*—"country stuff."

The government did its best to protect the *town* workers. It prohibited silk weaving in rural areas. It also forbade merchants to purchase silk cloth in the country. The order was repeated in 1773, 1779, 1795, 1816, and 1885. Yet the peasant working in his spare time had the entrenched professional city weavers beaten. In 1859 the Kyoto *Bugyō* says:

The output of cloth in the provinces has recently been on the increase, throwing industry into
confusion. The Kyoto weaving masters and a great
many others connected with their trade have lost
their living and face the cruelest hardships as a result.
But for the time being there seems no way of helping
them.[10]

As noted earlier, from about 1700 agricultural labor
was continually in short supply because it was moving out
into other areas and sectors of the economy. Again, the
government took drastic measures such as to stop ". . . immigration to Edo and even to return recent immigrants to
their villages; to prohibit the migration of labor from one
lord's jurisdiction to another; to prevent labor in the village
from following occupations other than farming; to stimulate
the birth rate, to fix wages, and much else."[11] But to no avail.

And when after the Meiji Restoration the modern
factory type of industry developed, it did not lack for
labor, which came mainly from the farm population. Furthermore, these workers were of good quality. According to
Smith: "Few countries have embarked on industry with a
superior labor force at hand." It was because, "Migration
in Japan was a selective social movement. . . ." For over a
century the villages had "been exporting much of their best
human material. . . ."[12]

In more recent times population employed in agriculture declined from 16.41 million in 1955 to 13.03 million in
1961, at an average annual rate of 3 percent. Between
1960–65 there was a further decrease of three million farm
workers. The outflow consisted mostly of males between
the ages of eighteen and fifty-nine.[13] Not for the first time
in her history, therefore, Japan appeared to have reached the
point of declining productivity in the national average yield
of rice per unit of land owing to a shortage of hands on her
farms. A new technology to replace labor had yet to be
established.[14] But *technology* was clearly trailing the depart-
ing labor force, and not vice versa, as in the U.S.

4

None of the above examples of deviance help, however, to bring the farmers or conditions of farming in the two countries in the period under review, any closer to each other. This raises some interesting questions.

Why, for instance, this similarity of effort on the part of farmers under such diverse circumstances?

If Americans have produced well and increasingly because of near-ideal conditions of freedom and equality, availability of technology, inputs, and resources of oceanic dimensions, a suitable religion and ethic of work, appropriate incentives, and the sheer scope backed by an intuitive or acquired desire and drive for making profit, why did farmers in Japan also produce just as well, if not better, and often beyond the limits of reasonable feasibility? They have done so most of the time in the absence of most of the factors and endowments that American farmers have had. Why did they both produce equally well in situations of such tremendous contrast: of plenty and poverty?

Why should the Tokugawa, or even the Meiji, peasant have sweated so to produce the most that he could—a surplus above subsistence, and always that one *koku* extra of rice? Not only was he under a constant and considerable squeeze, but whatever the returns and rewards, they were at differential rates for different strata of society till after World War II—the bulk of the producers receiving the least. Why this extensive identity and uniformity of purpose —more or less an equal spread of effort at such a high level of efficiency—in what was till recently a grossly inegalitarian and inequitable situation?[15]

As for the postwar period, of the 73 percent of gross agricultural produce marketed in Japan in 1961, two-thirds was sold by farmers operating less than 1.5 hectares of land each.[16] Almost 90 percent of the households were cultivating less than a hectare and a half.[17] But their fences were not down, nor their rice field levees in disrepair. Many were poor. But they were not driftwood, apart and of a distinct culture—of poverty. On the other hand, in the case of full-time operators, not only did capital and labor intensity become higher as the size of farms decreased, but land productivity (net agricultural product per *tan* under cultivation) also increased.[18]

Disparity in land productivity between different size groups, however, is not significant. It is negligible within a hamlet and between regions if climatic and soil factors are discounted.[19] In 1963 it would have been rare to find four rice farmers within a rice region in Japan as different in the quality and efficiency of production as Robert, John, Ray and Carl—the four dairy farmers in Wisconsin.[20] Yet, the scope for variation would have been far greater in rice as grown in Japan at this period than in dairying in the U.S.

The *average* spread of efficiency in cultural operations in Japan is so remarkable that it leaves little or no scope for improvement in the framework of prevalent practices and know-how. According to experiments conducted in 1963, using the standard "ordinary" management and cultivation procedures, the *experiments* yielded *less* rice (98 percent) than the average obtained by farmers—4.77 tons per hectare as against 4.85 tons per hectare, which was the *national* average yield for the year.[21] It could be so only because a majority of very small peasants like Susumu were producing half a ton more rice per hectare than the average for the prefecture.

Conversely, why have such a few farmers—and a diminishing number—in the U.S. cared to grasp the by far greater opportunities at their disposal both to maximize their output and to make good commercially? Why by 1960 were the bottom 78 percent of all farms producing less than the top 3 percent? Why in 1965 did the *majority* (70 percent) produce enough to earn less than 20 percent of the total receipts from the sale of farm products, as against 14.8 percent who took 63.8 percent of the market proceeds? Why did only a million farms account for over 80 percent of the total farm production?

Why this spectacle of unequal effort and achievement

of such magnitude in the midst of such immense and equal opportunities in a protected market with guaranteed prices in all the important farm commodities?[22]

Beneath the overall similarity in the national aggregates of the two countries, of a consistently rising production curve in agriculture, why this very significant difference in the pattern, extent, and quality of response, effort, and achievement at the level of individual farmers, in *inverse* ratio virtually to the range of resources, incentives, and opportunity?

CHAPTER XXVII

The Rains Failed

1

In another country, however, the lag in farmers' response and in agricultural output was alleged to be due to precisely and in *exact* proportion to the shortfall in physical resources and economic incentives.

In 1967 India faced a major disaster and threat of widespread famine. Since the year had been preceded by two consecutive years of the worst drought in four decades, the dimension of the shortfall in production was not typical. But the trend was. In ten years since 1956 farm commodities worth $3,672.6 million had been imported from the U.S. alone, under Title I, PL–480. Of these the largest item was wheat—39,687.2 thousand metric tons valued at $2,415.8 million. Even in 1964–65, when internal production was eighty-nine million tons—the highest ever in India's history —net import of food grains was 7.45 million tons.[1]

Moreover, there was evidence of a decelerating or, at best, stagnant rate of growth. New area under food crops was increasing at a slower pace than in the early 1950's. Improvement in yields per acre was not sufficient to offset the decline in output from acreage expansion. Total increase in production from additional land and its productivity was barely matching the annual growth of population. It was inadequate to feed the extra mouths and to satisfy the demand for more food arising from larger money incomes.

Such was the situation after a decade and a half of careful planning by the government of India for developing agriculture in general and attaining self-sufficiency in the production of food grains in particular by 1965-66. Beginning April 1, 1951, three Five Year Plans had been completed. The first two fulfilled and in fact exceeded the targets set for food grains.[2] The Third Plan (1961–62 through 1965–66), however, ran into heavy weather right from the start. In the first three years output of cereals was virtually stagnant at around eighty million tons. It shot up by nine million tons in 1964–65, but only to collapse by about seventeen million tons in the following and final year of the Plan that had been scheduled to achieve self-sufficiency. The rains failed extensively over large areas of the country in 1965. Production of food grains fell to seventy-two million tons as against the initial target of a hundred million, and a mid-term revised plan for ninety-two million tons. Net imports mounted to over ten million tons. A worse year was to follow.

2

Yet, except for the rains, the Planning Commission in New Delhi had provided for every conventional factor that at the time was considered important for increasing output of agriculture more rapidly in the Third Plan period. It was proposed to double the rate of growth and raise production of food grains by 30 percent in five years over the estimated produce in the final year of the Second Plan.[3] Most of the increase was to have accrued from higher yields per unit of land.

A sum of $2700 million was allocated accordingly for projects and programs designed to enable farmers to fulfill national goals. It was 92 percent more than the financial outlay for agriculture in the preceding plan. Irrigation from all sources was to have been extended to an additional twenty-five million acres, and the area under improved seeds increased from fifty-five million acres in 1960–61, to 203 million acres in 1965–66. In the same period consumption of nitrogenous fertilizers was to have risen from an estimated 230,000 tons (N) to one million tons, and of phosphates (P_2O_5) from 70,000 tons to 400,000 tons. Similarly, plant protection measures were to be extended from sixteen million to fifty million acres, while soil conservation and improved dry farming practices were to cover an additional eleven million and twenty-two million acres respectively.

The Plan had an ambitious program for expansion of the cooperative sector in spheres of agricultural credit, marketing, processing, and farming operations. There were 212,000 primary agricultural credit and multipurpose societies with seventeen million members in 1961. The Third Plan called for an extension of cooperative institutions to cover 60 percent of the agricultural population in five years. Short- and medium-term loans advanced through cooperative societies were to increase from $432 million to $1128 million. Long-term credit was slated to grow from $81 million to $319 million by 1965–66.

Identification with and participation of the people in the official plans on a massive scale were to be ensured by speedier enforcement of tenurial reforms, legislation for which had been enacted earlier, and strengthening of local governments at the village, block, and district levels. These were entrusted with considerable responsibility and powers for planning and implementing development schemes within their jurisdiction. Care was taken of agricultural extension and education. A comprehensive program of community development had been instituted earlier to cover the entire rural population spread over some 564,258 villages by October 1963, which it did.

A more concentrated effort to induce the cultivator to adopt a package of improved practices was initiated in 1960. It assumed that if farmers could be motivated to apply better more of the available yield-increasing technology and the associated production inputs, impact on output would be considerable. Called the Intensive Agricultural District Program (IADP), it was first introduced in seven select districts

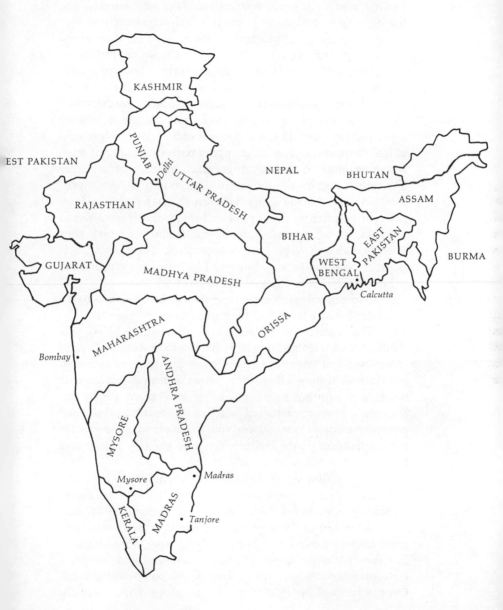

India

having good soils, assured irrigation, favorable climate, and the necessary institutional facilities and infrastructure.

A "package of practices" was evolved for each of the major crops and region. It included better seeds, fertilizers, pesticides, and soil and water management. The "package" was to be reviewed annually and improved with the assistance of the agricultural research stations. Furthermore, *every* cultivator in the area was to be interviewed to prepare a production plan. It made recommendations for his individual farm, specifying the cropping pattern, variety of seed, seed-rate, time of sowing, types and quantity of fertilizer application and its timing, pesticides, and so on. An inventory was to be made every year on the basis of this farm plan for calculating the inputs and credit the farmer would need. Government undertook to make the necessary supplies available through local cooperatives. The existing network of cooperative warehousing facilities was improved to provide an efficient channel for marketing.

Additional staff was appointed in the designated "package" districts, including a number of foreign consultants. The number of Village Level Workers (VLWs) was doubled, and training programs for the extension staff were intensified and improved. Also, each district was provided with a soil testing laboratory, an agricultural implements workshop, printing press and other equipment for an information center, assorted market laboratory and seed processing equipment, power spray equipment, and tractor for cultivation with trailer for transporting seeds and fertilizers.

In the first seven districts, IADP covered some 700,-000 farmers operating 5.4 million acres. It was expected to increase production of food crops such as rice, wheat, millets, and pulses in the area by 60 percent in five years. The program was extended subsequently to nine more districts. But the "package" approach, farm planning, and the principle of intensive and select area development caught on. On the basis of specific crops it was adopted more widely under another name—Intensive Agricultural Areas (IAA) Program. Introduced in 1964–65, IAA was scheduled to cover 114 districts and nearly a quarter of the cultivated area in three years. And it was not limited to food grains, but included the development of cash crops, such as cotton and groundnut, and of dairy products, poultry, and livestock. Millions of elaborate farm and crop plans incorporating the "package" were prepared and written out by the extension staff. Since most of the peasants were illiterate, however, the plans were tucked away usually into the thatch of the hut or inside a clay pot for safe keeping.

3

Planners in the Indian government were aware that "In any plan, which is not purely academic, it is important to be reasonably sure that the tasks are physically and organizationally feasible of attainment.[4] Nevertheless, for a variety of reasons, most of the Third Plan targets in the agricultural sector were attained only partially.[5] To their nonfulfillment primarily was attributed the poor performance of agriculture in some of the most exhaustive appraisals made by economists and consultants of international repute.

It was admitted that in three of five years of the Third Plan—1962–64 and 1965–66—seasonal factors had been, in the net, adverse for India as a whole. The critical role of the weather in determining the volume of production in a given year also was admitted. It was stated, for instance, that increase in the production of food grains from 76.7 million tons in 1959–60 to 82 million tons in 1960–61 was unreal, since there had been no rise in that year in the consumption of chemical fertilizers. No significant crop increase, therefore, should or could have taken place but for fortuitous, better-than-normal weather conditions.

When between 1962–64, growth was nearly stagnant and below the trend, however, it was claimed that if *only* price incentives had been more appropriate, and various inputs such as fertilizers, water, plant protection materials, etc., been available as planned, output would have been very much more notwithstanding the adverse climatic conditions. T. W. Schultz stated the underlying basis for this reasoning more bluntly as follows:

> It has been convenient to conceal the mistakes in economic policy that account for the failures in modernizing agriculture by blaming the poor performance of the agricultural sector in poor countries on the adversity of Nature. . . . A sequence of bad monsoons or droughts, a spell of bad weather—thus Nature is to blame. . . .
>
> In my judgment the real culprit causing the poor performance of agriculture in the less developed countries *is the lack of economic opportunities in agriculture, opportunities that are rewarding to farmers*. It is this lack of viable opportunities that is the crux of the matter.[6] (Italics mine.)

How many of the sixty million farmers would avail themselves of the economic opportunities (and inputs), in what manner, how efficiently, on how much acreage, was not even considered to be a problem because "farmers are not perverse in their economic behavior." Perversity, on the contrary, lay "in national economic plans that fail to provide economic incentives to farmers."[7]

The problem, therefore, is one of governmental wisdom, will, and policy. It is for the government to find resources for the requisite inputs—to produce with and to purchase. And it is for the government to encourage farmers to use the necessary inputs by proffering proper price incentives and the necessary credit for investment. By way of further inducement, it is for the government and its scientists to discover a "revolutionary" technology that would offer spectacular returns on each additional input and that would be persuasively profitable for the "traditional" farmers to adopt.

To the extent that during the three Five Year Plans, all or some of these factors—inputs, incentives, gainful technology—had been lacking or were inadequate, politicians, planners, administrators, and scientists were held to be the delinquents, responsible for the poor showing of Indian agriculture. Not farmers.

CHAPTER XXVIII

Instant Technology

1

By the mid-1960's therefore, except for the farmer, everyone concerned with development of agriculture in India was stricken with remorse.

While framing the Fourth Plan, the Planning Commission confessed contritely: "Where performance has been woefully short of expectations is in the agricultural sector; and it is this fact that has been largely responsible for limiting the increase in consumption standards of the common people. . . ." It further resolved, that "In setting the targets for the Fourth Plan, the scope that exists for corrective measures in implementation has to be taken fully into account."[1] There was accordingly, a major shift in policy with the accent on neon-lit incentives and a "new technology" that would do the job of expanding agricultural production rapidly in a very short time.

Prices of food grains had risen 51 percent in three years between 1962 and 1965. In 1952–53, when the First Five-Year Plan was initiated, price of wheat and rice was more than five times the prewar level. In 1957 cereals were costing 54 percent more than in 1955. In January 1967 their prices were 150 percent higher than in 1955–56.[2] Nevertheless, the government reaffirmed its anxiety, responsibility, and commitment to maintain fair, favorable, and stable price levels, to eliminate undue fluctuations and risk so that farmers would make the necessary investment to increase their output.[3] Earlier an Agricultural Prices Commission was appointed to advise on proper floor prices for various crops. A National Food Corporation was set up to purchase in surplus years to reinforce the floor price guarantees and build up stocks. It would sell in deficit years to equalize food supplies year by year. Thereby, it would protect consumer interests as well and contribute to price stability in the economy as a whole.

For the Fourth Plan period the government also assured the supplies of all critical inputs at a reasonable, and if need be, subsidized cost. It promised to import them on priority basis if there should be a shortfall in domestic production. Industrial policy was oriented toward the needs of agriculture and toward giving greater scope to private initiative in the production, pricing, and distribution of manufactured goods used by farmers. Several state governments resolved to abolish the land revenue. As the chief minister of Madras, Mr. Bhaktavatslam, stated in the State Assembly on November 2, 1966, it was to give farmers relief "as an incentive to step up production." Land revenue is about the only direct tax paid by farmers in India and amounts to 2 percent of the value of agricultural production.[4]

Meanwhile, scientists were working on a "new technology." Its key feature was varietal improvement of seeds that would be high-yielding and responsive to large inputs of chemical fertilizers. The assumption was that only by yielding *dramatically* more than the traditional strains were genetically capable of, would the new seeds make it worthwhile for Indian farmers to adopt modern scientific methods of farming without which it would be futile to expect a striking increase in productivity.

Fortunately, such "miracle" seeds were in sight and actually available by 1966–67, for rice, wheat, maize, *jowar* (sorghum), and *bajra* (millet). These crops accounted for about 85 percent of the normal output of food grains and 70 percent of the acreage. Parent stocks of some were imported, as of rice from Taiwan (via Manila), and of dwarf wheat from Mexico.[5] For maize, *jowar,* and *bajra,* hybrids were developed within the country under a coordinated program with the Rockefeller Foundation.

Absolute yields per acre were higher for the new varieties at given levels of fertilizer application. Maximum yields possible by increasing inputs of fertilizer were found to be considerably greater in every case. Even at less than optimal application of nutrients according to one estimate, it was expected that the dwarf varieties of wheat, for example, would yield 40 to 60 percent more than the native breeds; rice, 80 to 100 percent more; maize, 40 to 50 percent better; *jowar,* possibly 100 percent or more; and *bajra,* 60 to 80 percent higher.[6] The difference between the old and new genetic base was so fantastic that any development strategy based on the yield-potential of the new seeds was believed to hold a promise bordering on certainty of revolutionizing India's agriculture.

However, aside from very much larger quantities of fertilizers, the new varieties required much more of every other factor of production—water, plant protection materials, equipment, credit, and so on. The government could not possibly have provided them all immediately for all the acres under these crops and to all the farmers cultivating them.[7]

As in the earlier IADP and IAA programs, therefore, it was decided to ration scarce inputs and resources to ensure that they were used intensively to maximize output at greatest profit and least risk. Called the High-Yielding Varieties (H.Y.V.) Program, the "new strategy" also was designed to stagger the spread of new seeds and the technology associated with them—on a select and restricted regional basis—in the most favorable soils and climes having assured irrigation.

The designated regions under the H.Y.V. Program were to add up to a total of 32.5 million acres by 1970–71. It would cover 11 percent of the area under the crops concerned in 140 districts.[8] It was assigned to yield an *additional*

25.5 million metric tons of food grains in five years. This, with a more modest increase of ten million tons in the remaining areas using traditional seeds and techniques, was expected to make the country self-sufficient in food by 1970–71.[9]

2

To the extent, therefore, that technology and government could grow more food in a country having a geographical area of 806.3 million acres, of which 330 million were being cropped by more than sixty million farm households to obtain among the world's lowest yields, prospects for growth at an annual rate of over 6 percent compound had been assured for Indian agriculture by 1966.[10]

Analyzing the reasons for inadequate progress in the preceding decade and a half, C. Subramaniam, the then minister of Food and Agriculture in the federal government, stated:

> It is because so far, our effort had been to intensify in the same old traditional way. But simply more intensification of irrigation gives only marginal increase. Or traditional seeds and manures—they do not give a dramatic increase in yields. Our effort so far has been to intensify the traditional methods. But after centuries of cultivation our forefathers had already reached the optimum in the use of traditional methods. So any increase is only marginal. That is why our farmers have not been interested.[11]

Question: "The new High-Yielding Varieties Program is calculated entirely on the basis of regions, acres, and yardsticks of physical inputs. Have you any data or analysis of the *farmers* who would be expected to implement the program? Do you even know, for instance, how many farmers there are on these millions of acres set aside for the 'new technology?'"

Answer: "No. We do not know. But on an area of say thirty-two million acres, if you take the average holding to be roughly five acres, there would be about six million farmers. But it is not a question merely of farmers' response, but also of fertilizers, seeds, credit, plant protection materials, etc."

Quest.: "But assuming that supplies of these various inputs will be available and adequate, what is your assessment of farmers' attitudes to the "new technology" and goals for production that you have set for them to achieve in the next five years?"

Ans.: "Our assumption is that response will be quite adequate. Incentive pricing system has brought about a new awakening among farmers. Also, we are using our past experience for locating proper areas. Within them the target will be to cover all farmers.

"Now, what we do for the farmers to take up the program—they would require certain preparation. Otherwise, they will fail. Now what we do first is that at the state level we have a conference of officials to identify the problems. Then at a higher level we hold four regional conferences. And then at the national level we have an all-India conference where all problems are discussed and action is decided. Then the reverse process starts. To reach the farmer, to orient him, and to implement the program—it goes back to the state. The state initiates the program. Then at the block level all farmers are assembled for two days to impart information to them. Only when it percolates to the farmer will the program succeed—to that extent."

Quest.: "Your plan, however, is to attain certain levels of production within a set period on the basis of acreage and physical coefficients. You are assuming, therefore, that *all* the six million farmers cultivating those particular 32.5 million acres will adopt the "new technology" fully and almost instantaneously—that they will apply the various inputs in the right mix, measure, and manner. Otherwise, they will not produce the additional twenty-five million tons of food grains as scheduled. What makes you believe that they *will* do it; if not all, at least a sufficient majority of them?"

Ans.: "Cooperation of six million farmers will be necessary. That is true. At this point, it would be impossible to say who will come in, or how many will drop out. It will be known only each year as the program proceeds—at the block and village level; not here in New Delhi. The farmers will be identified because they will have to be given credit. They will come for the seed and fertilizers. We have to deal with the individual then. But we shall get at them by the method of hit and miss, trial and error. If a gap develops, to the extent there is a shortfall in a selected area, we shall have to supplement it. It will be a continuous process.

"But in the first two years at least, I do not foresee any problem. In fact, I shall have to restrict the acreage because of shortage of inputs. You see, the farmer who accepts the program is assured higher credit, and more fertilizers, pesticides, etc., on a priority basis and in preference to others sticking to traditional varieties. Naturally, he will have a higher incentive."

Quest.: "You are depending on that incentive?"

Ans.: "Yes. We are depending on it. Also, in the first year, farmers may say it is too difficult. But if one person in a village takes up the program and succeeds, others will take it up as well. How do you introduce a new variety? By demonstration that it is better—gives higher yields. Then it spreads immediately in the area.

"We expect the response because of the attractive economic returns the new technology offers. Economic incentives are the most potent force in bringing about a transformation from traditional to modern techniques. Take the example of the United States. Development (in agriculture) there started really only since the last war when prices increased."

3

But is that so? In the postwar period, agricultural production in the U.S. has *not* risen under the stimulus of high prices and profits, but "in the face of falling product prices and falling incomes to factors of production. . . ."[12]

To give a brief resume. Level of prices received by American farmers fell 43 percent between 1919 and 1921. They fell another 56 percent between 1929 and 1932. They rose 185 percent between 1940 and 1948. But they fell again by 22 percent between 1951 and 1955. Twelve years later, prices were still falling and the cost of production was rising. On March 14, 1967, the harassed secretary of Agriculture asked: "Why have farm prices dropped each month for the last six months until today they are 9 percent below where they were 20 years ago? Can we overcome the cost-price squeeze?"[13]

Rate of growth in agricultural production, on the other hand, was continuous at 1.1 percent per annum between 1920 and 1940. During and after the big spurt in prices it improved by 0.9 percent to 2 percent a year between 1940 and 1955. As for farm output per capita, "Far from showing the expected sharp rise . . . since 1940, it shows a remarkable stability from 1942 through 1957."[14] Moreover, growth continued at the annual rate of 2 percent *after* 1955, despite a falling price trend and the various programs of control and acreage diversion imposed by the government. An FAO review of 1965 comments as follows:

> It is remarkable . . . that in the United States production rose somewhat faster during the last ten years, when efforts were being made to slow it down, than the previous decade, during the latter part of which (from the Korean War) the aim was a rapid increase. The national indices of farm production show an increase of only 13 percent between 1942–44 and 1952–54, compared with 18 percent from 1952–54 to 1962–64.[15]

Furthermore, although unusually favorable weather in the early 1960's was a factor, a noticeable increase in yields per acre in U.S. agriculture came about only *after* and as a result of acreage restrictions and not in response to increase in prices. Earlier growth was due predominantly to expansion of area. In the absence of land diversion programs since 1955, overall farm output could conceivably have been at a higher rate than 2 percent a year. But then it is admitted that the "acre yields would likely have been lower."[16]

As Harvey said in Utah in the fall of 1963, "We did not used to use any fertilizer here, till ten years ago. Only when they put the restrictions on, we started using it. When returns are small, we've got to produce more to make ends meet."[17]

A second important assumption of India's Food minister—pertaining to the processes and procedures of adoption and spread of new technology—is also open to question.

Japan, as we saw, has never had a momentous revolution in the technology or organization of its agriculture. Her farming continues to be essentially "traditional." Marginal returns on small improvements in the method and practice of traditional techniques did not, however, deter the mass of Japanese peasants from adopting them to increase their output. It has been the method of improving farm production in Japan since Tokugawa times.

On the other hand, there is little evidence of an invariable, instant, and universal adoption of a new technique simply because it offered a "dramatic increase" in yields and "attractive economic returns." Farms in the U.S. afford innumerable examples of such techniques either not being adopted, or more commonly, not being exploited fully to maximize production.

Why, for instance, did commercial farmers like Harvey forego the substantially larger volume of produce (and income) that they could have obtained by using chemical fertilizers even when there were no acreage restrictions? In the early 1950's prices were better, and the margin of profit was greater than a decade later. Fertilizers were available, so also the equipment, and the know-how.[18]

Hybrid corn provides another good example. According to T. W. Schultz who believes that *"The rate of acceptance depends predominantly on the profitability of the new input.* . . . hybrid corn was such a discovery, and as a consequence, farmers in the heart of the Corn Belt—where hybrid corn proved to be most rewarding—adopted the hybrid seed rapidly in spite of the very low corn prices that prevailed during the early and middle 1930's."[19]

In the first place, however, why should they *not* have adopted it? There is nothing unusual about farmers trying to increase the volume of their production when prices are low in order to maintain even the same income. That is exactly what they have been doing since the last war.

More significant and relevant than the mere adoption of the seed is the fact that after more than thirty years of growing hybrids, not only was there still a striking variation in yields, but in the eight Corn Belt and Lake states the average output per acre was well below the level of what was considered to be technically and economically feasible.[20]

Yields on farmers' fields had always been very much lower than the potential long before hybrids were developed. But to trace the performance of the "wonder seed" in three of the main corn states—Indiana, Illinois, and Iowa:

In 1940, when hybrid corn was being grown on 90 percent of the corn acreage in these three states, average yields were thirty-seven bushels an acre in Indiana, forty-three in Illinois, and fifty-two in Iowa.[21] This is against an average yield of thirty-three bushels an acre in 1913–15 (in Iowa), long before the introduction of hybrids, and a ten-year average yield of 66 bushels on the best tenth of 5245 farmers' samples back about 1905. The average for the whole group was 55.4 bushels an acre.[22] In 1962 corn yields in Indiana were eighty-two bushels, in Illinois eighty-three, and in Iowa, seventy-six bushels an acre. But these could have been bettered substantially—by twenty to twenty-four bushels an acre—at a very low cost and simply by using more fertilizer.[23]

4

The Food minister of India overlooked some significant facts nearer home. As for instance, returns on improved methods proffered prior to the High Yielding Varieties Program were ostensibly not too "marginal" to ensure a universal *non*-adoption of new practices or inputs by all farmers in the country.[24]

The notable feature of agricultural development in India during the first three Five Year Plans was *not* the absence of growth and increase in output per acre, but the very striking variations in the rate and pattern of increase. These variations occurred within the same framework of constraints and incentives (or disincentives) whether of prices, profits, institutions, and public policies. But they were considerable between farmers in the same or neighboring villages, between districts within a state, and between the states themselves.

According to one study of the Planning Commission, as against a compound annual increase of 3.57 percent in the total crop output between 1951–54 and 1958–61, the rates of growth in the states ranged from 0.21 percent in West Bengal and 1.04 percent in Orissa, to 6.54 percent in Gujerat and 5.17 percent in the Punjab.[25]

At the district level, of 184 districts for which estimates had been made, whereas thirty-three districts achieved an annual increase of 7.5 percent or more, seventy-four districts gained less than 2.5 percent. The remaining districts were ranged between.[26]

Even the seven original IADP districts, all of which had favorable natural resources and assured irrigation and whose farmers were subjected to an intensive educational program in better farming practices, showed a significant variation in growth experience. And *within* each "package district" as well, there were farms producing more than double the average for the district, and three, four, and even more times the yield of other cultivators. There was a very wide range between the low and high decile or quartile groups, indicative of the large differences among farmers in the kinds and combination of resources used, rates of application of various inputs, and the quality of effort and husbandry.[27]

Furthermore, it could be that "after centuries of cultivation our forefathers had already reached the optimum in the use of traditional methods." But it did not mean that all or even most farmers used the traditional methods efficiently to obtain optimum yields. The "Four Faces" of Wisconsin would be a common phenomenon in almost every hamlet in India.

The district of Tanjore in the state of Madras, for example, has been cultivating rice for centuries. It has had the benefit of the IADP program since 1960, and is now an H.Y.V. district. The soil is rich. Climate and rainfall are good. Most of the land is irrigated and is double-cropped to rice. It is practically the only crop cultivated in the district.[28]

Sundaresa Ayyar is a substantial landowner and president of the *panchayat* board in a village in Tanjore.[29] A short man of slight build, he is light-skinned with fine regular features. He has long hair which he wears in a knot at the back of his head.

"We have divided the land. We are three brothers. I have twenty-five irrigated acres in rice. . . . No. I will not be entering the paddy field. I only supervise. I manage my brothers' lands as well."[30]

Ayyar has two tenants and three wage laborers on a monthly basis. He hires casual daily wage labor at the time of sowing, transplanting, and harvesting.

"No," he admits frankly, "I can't say I am getting the maximum yield. I get around 2000 pounds of rough rice per acre now. I can easily double it. But this is a communist area. There is always labor trouble. They do not work efficiently. Operations get delayed. They are not done on time. Also, drainage is bad. We are desilting only the main channels. But the field channels are not desilted. Under the Act, it has to be done by the cultivator. In case of tenants it should be enforced in some manner. In many cases, landowners also are not doing it. Even so, there is great scope to improve yields," he repeats. "There are farmers here getting 4000 pounds an acre."[31]

Ayyar is still using a wooden plow.

In another village, Vettaguda, in the same district there is a group of half a dozen small owner-cultivators, each owning one to two acres of irrigated land. They are getting yields of about 1800 pounds of rough rice per acre.

"Do you think you could raise more than 1800 pounds?"

"Oh yes," is the unhesitating reply.

"How?"

"Well, if we plowed better, weeded a couple of times more often, transplanted on time, irrigated just right, and fertilized the soil better and on time. What we do now usually is to throw in some fertilizer when we see the crop looking yellowish. But that is not how it should be done."

"How much more do you think you could get if you did everything right?"

"A thousand pounds an acre, even more."

"Then why don't you?"

"It's funny you know," Vishwalingam, the man in a pink shirt, says with a smile and shrug of the shoulders. The others nod in agreement. "It's funny. But every year we decide we are going to do it. We *want* to do it. And then we don't."

"But why?"

"Oh! We say we'll do it tomorrow. And it gets delayed. Or it is not done at all. Sometimes we leave the village at the time of transplanting. Or we have to go to court, or attend a marriage, or some social function comes in. And so, for one reason or another, the various operations are not done as and when they should be . . ."

In Aryacheri, twenty-five-year-old Nagamuthu and his wife Veeramal are purely agricultural laborers. They do not own any land. However, they work on part wage and part crop share basis for only one landlord. His name is Kodandpani. He has three acres of irrigated land under rice and three-tenths of a dry acre besides. Kodandpani *never* works on the farm—only supervises. Nor does he do anything else.

217

Nagamuthu is vague about the exact production figures. "But this year, the yields were depressed," according
to him, "because Kodandpani went away at the time of transplanting and returned only at the time of harvest. So no
weeding was done."

If Nagamuthu were to own the land, he would not
want more than 1.3 acres. "It would be sufficient. But I think
I could raise another 1000 pounds more rice per acre."

"How would you do it?"

"Well. I would apply more farmyard manure. I would
plow better. At present it is plowed three times. I would plow
two more times. That would increase yields." He does not do
it now because "the *mirasdar* does not ask me to.[32] I do what
he tells me. He did not ask me to weed this year, so I didn't.
That is why no weeding was done while he was away."

It is the month of November. Small ponds that dot
the landscape are full of water. They have pink—occasionally
white—lotuses in bloom. Coconut palms—banana gardens
—mud walls—thatched roofs—hay ricks—cattle the size of
calves—goats and stray dogs basking in the middle of the
streets—creaking bullock carts—a bright red letter box
nailed to the trunk of a *tamarind* tree. . . .

Everywhere, in the irrigated tracts in Tanjore, the
kuruvai crop has just been harvested. Dry stubbles stand
stiffly in the fields. The harvested grain is spread out on the
road to dry—on the sides and in the middle of it. Crows
peck at it and vehicles drive over it. The *samba* crop is in the
fields—green and rippling in the wind. *Thaladi* is being
transplanted in flooded fields. Paddy fields on all sides extend
as far as the eye can see.[33]

Men—short, thin, dark bodies, stripped except for a
brief loin cloth—kneel or squat as they pull out the young
rice seedlings. They tie them into bundles with a seedling,
which is later planted, and throw them into heaps to be
transported to the main field.

Women do the transplanting, bending over in ankle-
deep water. They are supposed to plant in regular rows. But

they are scattered, working all over the field. They snatch four, five, six seedlings at a time, whatever comes into their grasp, and push the roots into the soil with the thumb in one quick action.

"But look," I protest, "only three seedlings will suffice to each hill. And why don't you treat them more gently? You should first make a hole and ease the roots in with your forefinger, and then cover them with the soil. You may hurt the roots the way you are doing it. They will yield less rice. And those seedlings you have tied the bundles with—they are bruised. Don't plant them. Why don't you use straw to tie the bundles?"

"What does it matter?" is the brief reply. "We are working for wage. We do it like this. This is how it is done."

CHAPTER XXIX

Wheat and the Tares

1

Why did Ayyar, Vishwalingam, Kodandpani, and Nagamuthu not do everything that they knew they should (and could) to increase their yields by as much as one to two thousand pounds per acre? It would be difficult to imagine a Japanese cultivator—Susumu, Takeo, Kyuzo, Yamayasu—letting such an opportunity go by. On the average, they were producing more than three times as much as the Indian farmers. Yet, they would have sweated for even one extra *koku* of rice, that is for less than 250 pounds.

The price of rice had hit an undreamt of high by now in Tanjore. Farmers were exceedingly happy. However, Ayyar alone was foregoing an income from fifty thousand pounds of paddy from just his portion of the land. His family, three times as much. Ayyar never steps into a field and blames the low output on his tenants and wage workers. But Vishwalingam works on land that he owns. Similarly, Kodandpani and Nagamuthu would share the profit from higher yields. Except for the women transplanting rice, all the four farmers would have gained directly and immediately from increased production.

Furthermore, if they were to adopt a high-yielding variety of rice, it would require more of precisely the quality and timeliness in the performance of various cultural operations that they were neglecting presently. Mere substitution of one kind of seed for another would not suffice. The new rice yields well only under optimal conditions of care and environment. The seed bed must be prepared with extreme care. Transplanting must be done on time. Fertilization must be heavy, exact, and correctly applied. Irrigation has to be controlled, and drainage good. There will be many more weeds, and pests and diseases, that must be checked and eradicated effectively.

The first high-yielding strain of rice to be introduced and widely accepted in Tanjore was called ADT-27. A cross between Indian and Japanese types, it tillered profusely and responded to heavy application of fertilizers without lodging. When cultivated under farm conditions in 1965, on three thousand acres, it yielded 3820 pounds of paddy to an acre —more than half again as much as the district average. But, whereas the top decile of growers obtained 5140 pounds, the lowest decile had only 2480 pounds. Output of individual farmers ranged from 1600 to 5500 pounds to an acre. As with the earlier varieties, a wide variation in yields, and presumably therefore, in effort, and in the quantity and combination of physical inputs, persisted among even the first few hundred adopters.[1]

Nevertheless, initial response to the high-yielding varieties of seeds was spectacular throughout the country. In 1967–68, the first normal crop year after the drought, some sixteen million acres were sown to new strains of rice, wheat, maize, *jowar*, and *bajra*. A record crop of 95.6 million tons of food grains was harvested. Farmers, traders, and the government ran out of storage space, and the grains lay in heaps out in the open.

The High Yielding Varieties Program and the strategy underlying it were an obvious success. According to T. W. Schultz, agriculture was entering upon "a secular production boom." Its "modernization" was underway. Were it to succeed, the increase in production could be expected to outstrip the birth rate and convert the food grains deficit of recent decades into a constant surplus.[2]

The modernization process could be expected to create another, more massive surplus also, of small peasants like Vishwalingam. Their output would no longer be critical to aggregate production. The yield potential of the new grain varieties is so high, that only the top tenth of the cultivators would need to cultivate them. Rapid enough growth could take place without the rest. They would become irrelevant. In any case, their lands would soon be taken over by the more aggressive and competent commercial farmers (and nonfarmers). These would have a strong incentive and the means to invest to increase the size of their holdings and operation. It would be profitable now for them to do so, provided the government did not "return to a cheap urban food policy."[3]

Long before the surplus in food grains was in sight, it was apparent that the small farmer was in trouble; under a financial squeeze. The cost of all factors including land was rising, and he was not participating in the production revolution significantly. What is more, the trend was being generally accepted, as natural, inevitable, and even desirable. *The small farmer was not expected to survive and stay in agriculture.* He must move out into urban industries and the service sectors of the economy. The very economists who had argued that the production behavior of traditional peasants comes close to perfection in exhausting the available economic opportunities, whose acceptance of new techniques is contingent upon and proportional to their profitability, affirmed now that the situation had altered. Although a fabulously profitable technology was available, the vast majority would *not* adopt it. They would not have the requisite entrepreneurial skills for the more complicated changes in techniques and management of a modern scientific-commercial agriculture.[4]

Furthermore, small cultivators would be confronted with the problem of resource proportionality or scale, that would not be easy to resolve, except by enlarging the size of the operation.

A modern tractor or threshing machine or tube-well is typically too large relative to the acreage of a small farm to combine into an efficient operation. . . . In sum, modern units of agricultural technology are often too large, relative to the scale of operation of a small farmer, to be efficiently incorporated into his operation.[5]

The long-awaited millennium in Indian agriculture had finally arrived. But it was not for the multitudes. Like Bob Miller in Mississippi, and for the same reasons, they too would be *the tares in a field of wheat*, fit only for burning.[6]

2

Even prior to the varietal revolution, around 95 percent of the farm households in India owned less than 20 acres of land each; 75 percent possessed less than 5 acres. Less than 13 percent had more than 10 acres each. Only 1 percent held 50 acres and more.[7]

Depending on the horsepower of tractors, threshers, and other such "modern units of agricultural technology," it would mean that 99, 95, or a minimum of at least 75 percent of the farmers would not be able to modernize their production techniques. They would lack the acreage or the managerial talent. In most cases, both. In any case, the number of man hours required to produce considerably larger quantities of food and fibre would be reduced drastically; and as new technology increases the marginal productivity of capital relative to labor, capital will substitute for labor. Moreover, as production functions and assets become concentrated and specialized, millions would be forced into obsolescence and out of agriculture, as in the United States.

As a first step in the "modernization" process, even if only the less-than-five-acre farms are eliminated, some thirty-three million families, aside from the fifteen million or so, that do not own any land, would be on the road in India. The question is, *where* would they go? Storage space could be built fairly quickly for surplus grain. And if the glut becomes too large, it can be destroyed. But a nation cannot put most of itself on the dole, even if money and food are available for distribution. And for at least half a century— possibly much longer—neither the city slums, nor the industrial sector of the Indian economy, whatever its rate of expansion, would have the space or capacity to absorb an influx of so many displaced and virtually, unemployable people. Even if the entire urban-industrial complex of the U.S. were transported to Indian soil, it would fail to cope with the problem.

The urban centers would be in difficulty with the natural increase in their own population. Assuming that there is no change (from 1961) in the birth rate and in the sectoral distribution of workers, industry would have to provide additional employment for 22.1 million hands by 1975. The corresponding figure for agriculture would be 56.4 million. Farm workers would have increased from 135.3 million to 191.7 million in fifteen years.[8] If their proportion to the total labor force were to decline by even 5 percent in this period, 35.8 million new jobs would be needed in the urban sector, while agriculture would still have to absorb another 42.7 million workers.[9] These are some of the givens that cannot be altered.

Short of putting the lid on progress, however, *is* there a choice? Is there a policy approach whereby agriculture can be modernized without creating the twin surpluses of farm commodities and farmers? There will be a third problem, also intrinsic to growth, of converting the additional produce into real income for the benefit and welfare of the people who need it most.

In India increase in agricultural production is not required only to eliminate imports, and to stock the grocery stores, so that housewives can purchase all they need. It is required as imperatively for improving the purchasing power of the vast majority of the people who live in the rural areas. They constitute 82 percent of the population, and the bulk of the consumers. And their poverty is as staggering as their numbers.[10] Agriculture is the main, and often, the sole source of their sustenance, even if it be at a half meal a day. For several decades to come, they will have no option, unless it be for no meal at all. *A sustained increase in commodity production, and in the income level of all sections of the farm people within agriculture, without forcing them out ahead of offsetting nonfarm job opportunities*, will have to be treated, therefore, as a single problem of *economic*, and not of welfare, planning, and development.

It would be pure folly and poor economics to focus attention on *production first* in the framework of a price efficiency model, on the simplistic assumption that equitable distribution of the national product is always easier if there is a product to distribute.[11] To expand output by making it possible for the "adequate-size commercial-size family farm unit to earn enough to attract the capital and the know-how to do the job," and at the same time, reduce tens of millions into refugees without a refuge, would be simple.[12] In the Indian situation, however, the resulting disequilibria would not be in the nature of residual problems of growth, mere lags in adjustment that could be consigned to the police, sociologists, psychologists, and welfare agencies, as in the U.S. They could overwhelm and destroy the total fabric of society, economy, and the state.

3

This does not mean that Indian agriculture should not modernize, or await "economic development in general, which would relieve the pressure of population from land."[13] It can be done prior to, or simultaneously with overall development, and without creating a surplus of manpower, *if all farmers are required to share in all factors of production including land equally, to contribute to growth in the same proportion*. That, and that alone, would take care of the problem of income distribution as well.

But then, technology, tools, markets, rural institutions and services will have to be designed accordingly, *to subserve the resulting scale and level of skills, and primarily to*

increase output per unit of land. For two of the most important yield increasing components of modern technology,
seeds and chemicals, scale is not even relevant. The smallest
farm can use fertilizers and pesticides as efficiently as a large
operation, or more so. Irrigation too is neutral to size. And
just as farmers do not own large projects that distribute
water to millions of acres, so each need not possess his own
tubewell.

The *only* production factor to which the scale of operation is crucial, and which farmers are generally averse to
owning or operating jointly, is farm machinery. It is not
essential, however, that machines be large, unless the goal
is to save man-hours and substitute capital for labor. If the
average size of operational units is fixed and inflexible, equipment can be designed, improved, and made increasingly efficient to operate within the limits of the given acreage.
Neither *large* machines nor *large* farms are indispensable to
"modernity" or efficiency in agriculture. As, when, and if
the farmers become fewer and the farms can be bigger, the
machines could be changed. That would be no problem. But
in the current demographic and economic situation of India,
the sequence must not be reversed. Machines must not be
permitted to determine the economic scale of efficiency
and thereby liquidate the small cultivator or prevent him
from participating in the varietal and chemical revolution
underway.[14]

The problem of quality and managerial skills also is
tied in intimately with machines and scale. Nagamuthu
would have no difficulty in using an improved plow or a
small power tiller. He could learn to drive a tractor. But he
would not be able to manage the economies of a farm that
could use a fifty-horsepower tractor. When I pressed him
further to explain why he would not like to own more than
1.3 acres, his reply was that he could not cultivate any more
land with family labor. If he had more, he would have to
hire help. But that would involve financial and managerial
responsibilities that he did not think he could handle. Aside
from that, Nagamuthu is conversant with every cultural

operation that the new seed requires. He has been using irrigation, fertilizers, and pesticides. None of the new practices would be beyond his educational level—that he could not grasp without going to school.[15] Except for substituting one seed for another, and that would be no problem (it has been done many times before), he would have to be induced mainly to do more of exactly the same operations better, with greater precision.

4

That "modern units of agricultural technology" can be exceedingly small and yet produce the most that any seed and soil are capable of yielding, is clearly demonstrated in Japan. On 0.16 ha of poor soil in Gumma Prefecture, Susumu raised more rice per hectare than Russell Carrino did on a farm over a hundred times as large, in the salubrious climate and fertile soil of California. That he used more than fifty times the number of hours to produce a unit of rice than did Carrino, is totally irrelevant under Indian conditions where the peasant could put in much more rather than less labor.[16] But on a per acre average, Susumu applied more fertilizer and pesticides than the American farmer did.[17] And, he used irrigation and quality seed.

It is equally clear that minute farms with very modest capital and operating expenses can be viable commercial units. For instance, farm households operating less than 0.3 ha each in Japan, marketed 38.4 percent of their produce. Farms in the range of 0.5 and 1.0 ha each, sold as much as 63.3 percent of their output. They produced for the market. Of all farms 51 percent had sales exceeding 100,000 yen in 1961; most of them were between 0.5 and 1.5 ha each.[18] Fujita, Takeo, Kyuzo, earned a million-yen income from farms infinitely smaller than the grounds of a university professor's country house in the United States.

Furthermore, despite modernization, Japan still had roughly twice as many farms as does America, and on a total land surface smaller than California. *And, there were no surplus farmers; no class of landless agricultural laborers;*

and virtually no tares in the field among those in farming.
If the future scale and pattern of commercial farming
in India is to approximate that of Japan, however, it would
require a radical shift from the dominantly physiocratic approach underlying the High-Yielding Varieties Program of
1966.[19] *The national goal then would have to be, not to
modernize a decreasing number of farms in a few favored
regions to increase production endlessly, but to modernize
the total farm labor and upgrade its operative efficiency.*

Whereas less than six million farms of adequate size
could produce all that the Indians could consume and more,
the number of agricultural workers will have exceeded 170
million by 1970. It would be impossible to equate the two.
Production plans, therefore, would have to be formulated
primarily in terms of farmers, not acres. And if all farmers
share land and other factors of production more or less
equally, everyone's produce, and not that of just a few,
would be centrally important to the economy. It would mean
*that unless they all improved and modernized their farm
practices, similarly and simultaneously, aggregate production
would not increase at the requisite rate*—initially at about
three times the best rate ever achieved in the U.S. This, moreover, will have to be achieved essentially within the framework of existing resources and institutions, beset by the
myriads of constraints normally inherent and routine in any
underdeveloped country—that is, in spite of perhaps indifferent research, indifferently conveyed, inefficient and often
corrupt administration, shortage and maldistribution of
credit, supplies, and services, imperfect markets and communications, and above all, the low level of literacy and skills
of the majority of the cultivators. It would be wholly un-
realistic to expect a radical improvement in these factors and
in the necessary institutional adjustments, to synchronize
with the availability of new varieties in certain grains.

But then it would be legitimate to ask: if and under
the circumstances, would it be possible to transform sixty
million or more "traditional" peasants into "modern" commercial farmers? Can it be done?

*And yet, in India it must be done in order to mod-
ernize agriculture. There is no choice. The question is not if,
but how?*

Again, however, the answer will have to be sought not
in the marginal productivity of another ounce of nitrogen in
the production of rice, nor in farm factor and product prices,
though these will always be pertinent, but in a clear compre-
hension of the production behavior of the cultivator. To
return to the original query then, with which this study
began: *Why do farmers, any farmers anywhere, work and
produce as they do?*

5

The world is larger. But the mere fact that agriculture
could be such an outstanding success in Japan *and* the United
States clearly establishes that it is possible for farmers to
work and produce equally well under almost diametrically
different resource and environmental conditions—cultural,
political, economic. Within American agriculture moreover,
there is incontrovertible evidence of significant variations in
the production behavior of individuals and communities having access to *similar and plentiful* resources, incentives, and
opportunities, often within the same region and type of
farming.

If, however, farmers can act so similarly in such different and geographically distant situations, and differently
within exactly the same opportunity environment in the same
country, it would be logical to assume that the values, beliefs, and attitudes that condition and in effect determine the
quality and extent of their economic effort and efficiency are
not inborn, universal, or immutable. It makes matters exceedingly complex, especially in family-type farming, because millions of virtually autonomous individuals, who are
not wholly or equally subordinate to a larger organization
and technology, are the primary producing and decision-
making units. No modern steel mill, for instance, could operate the equivalent of the substandard dairy plant that
Robert owns, with similar substandard efficiency, and stay

in business.[19a] If the farmers' goals and motives are dissimilar, therefore, inevitably, their individual preferences and performance on the farm will also vary. *Given the choice of a dozen routes, they will not, and cannot be expected to take only one and the same route.* If they do, it will be a coincidence.

The key to the production decisions of a cultivator, in that case, must lie in the number and variety of routes open to him, and not in special traits or attributes, such as reason and greed, presumed to be inherent in the nature of all men, or in some standard measure and mix of resource and opportunity variables. Effectiveness of a profit incentive, generally believed to be the most universal and infallible device for regulating economic behavior, will also differ, with levels of living and aspiration, with competing incentives that may be social, cultural, religious, and with the nature of an individual's involvement in the market and its structure. A cultivator vertically integrated with a large marketing firm or agri-business, for instance, will react in a very different fashion from one who sells at the local retail store or at the weekly village *hat.*[20] All three will have a different approach and attitude to production and profit from the peasant who does not grow for the market. *They could be equally greedy and rational, but there is no key efficiency price, or rate of return on investment and labor, to which the four farmers will respond similarly.*[21]

It would follow then, that there cannot be a single and uniform formula for agricultural development for all nations, for all times. Furthermore, within a region and country as well, there could be a bewildering range of differences in behavior and response among farm communities, subgroups, and individuals on neighboring farms, requiring as many distinct policy approaches to attain the same end result.

It would be manifestly impossible for public policy to cater to a multiple variety of highly dispersed differences. Generally, as in the U.S., the differences are ignored; policy is directed at only a small segment of the farm population.

But they cannot be ignored in a country like India, where it is imperative to achieve a pattern of production described earlier, of some sixty million cultivators producing predictably, in a similar manner and measure to fulfill preset targets according to a plan. If their attitudinal and behavioral differences, and the reasons underlying them, are significant, they could introduce an element of uncertainty so large as to make nonsense of all planning. Even institutions of identical structure and organization will function differently—or not function. Unless the differences are first removed, therefore, the most perfect plan will not work, or work very imperfectly. And the differences will not disappear if simply one more route is added to the dozen and made somewhat more attractive than the rest. Some will take it, but not all, or even the majority, necessarily. On the contrary *the only feasible solution would lie in cutting off the unwanted eleven of the twelve choices.*

6

It would involve a radical change in the value premises and assumptions regarding causal principles and the behavior norms of farmers that underlie most current theory and approach to large-scale directed change in developing agriculture. But if the total farm labor of India is to be modernized and its operational efficiency upgraded simultaneously with the modernization of agriculture, it could be done only if national policy is formulated on the principle *that the rate of adoption and diffusion of new techniques, and of the requisite changes in farmers' values, attitudes, and practices will be in inverse ratio to the range of available alternatives.*

Within the framework of a given technology the level of operative efficiency also will be determined in the final analysis, not by the olympian heights of the potential, of production and profit, but by the *floor* of economic and technical feasibility and social expectation below which it is impossible to farm. And the scale and spread of efficiency among cultivators will depend upon whether this floor is the same for all, or different for various strata and sections. If there is a significant differential in levels, there will be a corresponding differential in response and effort, even to similar and equal opportunities.

The above hypotheses would hold valid equally for peasants and farmers, traditional and modern, developed and backward rural societies. In Wisconsin, John is late by a month in cutting his first crop of hay, just as in Tanjore, Vishwalingam is late in transplanting the rice. Harold Whitman, in Mississippi, does no work and operates the farm virtually from his living room, exactly like Sundaresa Ayyar. On the other hand, whereas a modern commercial operator like Harvey in Utah, farming a thousand acres, of which two-thirds is irrigated, did not use any chemical fertilizers till acreage restrictions were imposed in the 1950's, by the close of the eighteenth century expenditure on purchased fertilizers had become the largest item in the meager budget of the typical Japanese peasant.

Again, in the 1960's, beneath the impressive national aggregates of agricultural production and productivity in the United States and Japan, there is the remarkable difference in the structure of response and achievement at the level of individual farmers, in "inverse ratio virtually to the range of resources, incentives, and opportunity."[22] It is astonishingly uneven, and at the base very much poorer in America, where average investment per farm worker at the time exceeded $35,000, as against less than $74 in Japan. And it is so, not because the farmers of the two countries are of different breeds, but because, in addition to the fabulous factors of production and opportunity, Americans have also enjoyed the freedom to select from a wide range of choices. The efficiency floor, moreover, still varies greatly in the U.S. for different socio-economic and ethnic groups and regions. And it is vastly lower than the national average *for the majority*, like Robert and Bob Miller.

In Japan, on the contrary, farmers have had few resources and, till very recently, even fewer choices within agriculture. For nearly three centuries, they have had to grow all they could, as efficiently as possible, or quit. The survival floor has been extremely high for everyone, and it has always *been higher for the majority*, like Susumu. Hence, the spectacle of Susumu producing more rice per hectare than the average for the prefecture. Historically, according to the weight and distributive pattern of the factors and forces that determined the choices and levels of operational efficiency, the structure of individual and community values, effort, and excellence in farming has varied in the two countries.

The still backward economy of India offers many more choices than does either the United States or Japan, of routes, goals, norms, techniques. And for the great majority it offers a survival floor that is practically a bottomless pit. There is no level of inefficiency so low, at which a cultivator cannot operate with perfect economic rationality. It accounts for the abysmal state of productivity nationally. In 1962 India produced half, or less, rice per hectare, than Japan did in 1882.[23] It is also responsible for the striking variations in farmers' responses and behavior, as reflected in the rate and pattern of increase in agricultural output in the first decade and a half of planned effort. As noted earlier, the variations "were considerable between farmers in the same or neighboring villages; between districts within a state; and between the states themselves."[24]

Under the circumstances, specific measures to modernize and elevate the efficiency of Indian farmers and farming will have to be worked out in the particular context of each goal and problem. They lie outside the scope of this study. However, and even though it cannot be repeated, the history of Meiji Japan could be instructive in several respects. The entire subsistence sector of the farm population, for example, was commercialized at a stroke, so to say, by the conversion of the agricultural tax from kind to cash and from share to fixed, along with the appropriation of monopoly control by the government over the production and sale of saké, tobacco, and salt. Even the smallest peasant was compelled, thereafter, to produce a portion of his product for sale in a free market. Again, the differential pricing and procurement policy of 1941 reduced the percentage of non-cultivating farmers dramatically, by making it unprofitable to be a landlord. Similarly, sheer economies of scale and efficiency had reduced the size of operational holdings to a uniform average of one hectare, a century prior to the land reform of the postwar period.

In India, too, fiscal measures relating to prices, taxes, credit, wages, tenurial arrangements, procurement and marketing regulations for farm inputs and commodities, institutions, norms, and ideologies could be used, separately and together, to induce the necessary changes in the structure and techniques of farming. And the sixty million or more peasants also could be modernized, provided and to the extent *any constellation of factors—technical, economic, social, political—makes the national goal and purpose attainable, and concurrently, narrows choice to make any but the desired production behavior impossible for all cultivators.*

Seed varieties will come and go. But it should not be feasible for Ayyar to own land and not enter his fields and not work himself; for Vishwalingam to go away to any wedding but his own when he should be transplanting the rice or applying fertilizer; and for Nagamuthu not to weed the paddy. In effect, and for whatever the reason, it should be impossible for anyone to farm and not produce at least as much as he knows he can, and how. And then, perhaps, he will try also to produce a little more—*that one extra koku of rice.*

Notes

CHAPTER I

1. Their countries of origin are Poland, Ireland, Norway, and Germany.

2. During this period, whereas about one-third of the milk in America came from 8 percent of the 1.8 million dairy farms; 40 percent of the farms produced only 13 percent of it. *Source:* United States Census of Agriculture, 1959.

Other references for the chapter:

John R. Moore and Robert L. Clodius, *Market Structure and Competition in the Dairy Industry,* Research Bulletin 233 (Madison: University of Wisconsin, March 1962).

Alfred L. Namejunas, *Growth of a Dairy State: A Profile of Wisconsin Agriculture,* Agricultural Extension Service, Circular 429 (Madison: University of Wisconsin, August 1952).

Robert J. Rades and Glen C. Pulver, *Large Milking Operations in Wisconsin,* Agricultural Experiment Station, Bulletin 556 (Madison: University of Wisconsin, June 1962).

Peter Dorner, *Farming Changes in Wisconsin 1940–1960,* Agricultural Experiment Station, Bulletin 561 (Marison: University of Wisconsin, January 1963).

Wisconsin Rural Resources: Marathon County, Crop Reporting Service Bulletin, Agricultural Extension Service (Madison: University of Wisconsin, November 1956).

Wisconsin Rural Resources: Waupaca County, Crop Reporting Service Bulletin, Agricultural Extension Service (Madison: University of Wisconsin, February 1957).

Notes

Wisconsin Rural Resources: Manitowoc County, Crop Reporting Service Bulletin, Agricultural Extension Service (Madison: University of Wisconsin, October 1956).

Wisconsin Rural Resources: Portage County, Crop Reporting Service Bulletin, Agricultural Extension Service (Madison: University of Wisconsin, January 1958).

Preliminary Overall Economic Development Plan: Redevelopment Area, Portage County. Prepared by the Rural Area Development Committee, Wisconsin.

Walter L. Slocum, *Agricultural Sociology: A Study of Sociological Aspects of American Farm Life* (New York: Harper and Brothers Publishers, 1961).

Eric E. Lampard, *The Rise of the Dairy Industry in Wisconsin; A Study in Agricultural Change 1820–1920* (Madison: The State Historical Society of Wisconsin, 1963).

Willard W. Cochrane, *Farm Prices: Myth and Reality* (Minneapolis: University of Minnesota Press, 1958).

CHAPTER II

1. Farm population dropped from 31 million in 1920 to 12.4 million in 1965.

Unless specified otherwise, sources for the statistical data in the chapter are as follows:

Farm Income Situation, FIS–203, Economic Research Service (Washington, D.C.: USDA, July 1966).

Office of Information, *Fact Book of U.S. Agriculture* (Washington, D.C.: USDA, January 1965).

Legislative Reference Service of the Library of Congress, *Farm Programs and Dynamic Forces in Agriculture*, 89th Cong. 1st Sess. (Washington, D.C.: GPO, 1965).

Economic Research Service, *Economic Tables* (mimeo; Washington, D.C.: USDA, January 1967).

Handbook of Agricultural Charts, 1965, Agriculture Handbook No. 300 (Washington, D.C.: USDA, 1965).

The People Left Behind, A Report by the President's National Advisory Commission on Rural Poverty (Washington, D.C., September 1967).

2. According to the 1959 census, this group having sales of $40,000 or more constituted 3 percent of all farms and produced more than the bottom 78 percent. Also, 3.7 percent of all

farms, each of 1000 or more acres had acquired 49.2 percent of the total farm land, although nearly 80 percent of farm operators owned their farms in whole or part. Of the total productive assets (land, buildings, machinery, livestock, feed crops inventory, and working capital) in agriculture in 1959, one-fifth of the farms, marketing 72 percent of all of the agricultural produce, controlled three-fourths or more of the assets. Returns on this large capital investment accounted for a major portion of their income.

3. This concentration in production functions does not represent merely a postwar trend or a new feature of American agriculture. Even in 1939 one-third of the 6.1 million farms produced less than $400 worth of commodities, which they sold, traded, or consumed. It amounted to 5.4 percent of the total value of agricultural products. Output of the other two-thirds averaged less than $1000. On the other hand, only 2.5 percent of the farms produced over $6000 worth of produce each, or 25.7 percent of the total. Of these, 58,000 farms, that is, less than one farm in every hundred, had an output valued at $10,000 or more. Source: 1940 census data. See also Joseph Ackerman and Marshall Harris (eds.), *Family Farm Policy* (Chicago: University of Chicago Press, 1947), pp. 58–62.

4. *White House Press Release* (Washington, D.C.: USDA, February 4, 1965), (mimeo).

5. Wayne D. Rasmussen, *Readings in the History of American Agriculture* (Urbana: University of Illinois Press, 1960), pp. 67–68.

6. The average horsepower of farm tractors produced in 1965 was more than double the 1940 average. Most of them were of the higher-priced diesel type.

7. Total assets in American agriculture in 1966, in current dollars, were valued at $255 billion. These estimates were preliminary at the time of writing. The number of persons engaged in farming (includes operators, unpaid family workers, and hired hands) was 5.6 million, out of a total population of 193.7 million in 1965.

8. On the above and other points see: Willard W. Cochrane, *The City Man's Guide to the Farm Problem* (Minneapolis: University of Minnesota Press, 1965); Dale E. Hathaway, *Government and Agriculture: Public Policy in a Democratic Society* (New York: The Macmillan Company, 1963); Dale E.

Hathaway, *Problems of Progress in the Agricultural Economy* (Chicago: Scott, Foresman and Company, 1964); Edward Higbee, *Farms and Farmers in an Urban Age* (New York: The Twentieth Century Fund, 1963).

CHAPTER III

1. William Bradford, *History of Plymouth Plantation* (Boston: Little, Brown, and Company, 1856), pp. 100, 105. Also see Wayne D. Rasmussen, *Readings in the History of American Agriculture* (Urbana: University of Illinois Press, 1960), p. 24.

2. Harold Underwood Faulkner, *American Economic History* (New York: Harper and Brothers, 1954), p. 60.

3. Lewis C. Gray, *History of Agriculture in the Southern United States to 1860*, Carnegie Institution of Washington, 1933.

4. "Ninety-Eight Years Ago in Bloomington," *Journal of the Illinois State Historical Society*, XXVIII (April, 1935-January, 1936), p. 209, cited by Allan G. Bogue in "Farming in the Prairie Peninsula, 1830–1890," *The Journal of Economic History*, Vol. XXIII (March 1963), p. 3.

5. Morris Birbeck, *Letters from Illinois* (1818), p. 18.

6. Illinois State Agricultural Society, *Transactions*, III, 1857–58 (Springfield: Bailhache & Baker, Printers, 1859), p. 431.

7. Fred A. Shannon, *The Farmer's Last Frontier: Agriculture, 1860-1897, The Economic History of the United States*, Vol. v (New York: Farrar & Rinehart Inc., 1945), p. 170.

8. See Marvin W. Towne and Wayne D. Rasmussen, "Farm Gross Product and Gross Investment in the Nineteenth Century," in *Trends in the American Economy* (Princeton: Princeton University Press, 1960), pp. 258–60.

9. Shannon, *op. cit.*, Vol. v, p. 171.

10. Feed grains are the most strategic group of commodities in U.S. agriculture, and corn is the most important of them—72 percent of the total feed grains production. Feed grains occupied 40 percent of the harvested cropland, and "accounted for 62 percent of the farmers' cash receipts from marketings in 1960." *Farm Policy In The Years Ahead: A Report of the National Agricultural Advisory Commission* (Washington, D.C.: USDA, November 1964), pp. 18, 19.

11. In 1963 fertilizer was applied on 87 percent of the

corn in the Corn Belt and Lake states at an average of 145 pounds an acre. Corn yields could have been raised at comparable unit costs, by increased use of fertilizer in other producing states as well. Other crops, such as wheat and cotton, would have responded to higher levels of fertilization. Legislative Reference Service of the Library of Congress, *Farm Programs and Dynamic Forces in Agriculture*, 89th Cong. 1st Sess. (Washington, D.C.: GPO, 1965), pp. 5, 6.

12. Although the average cost of all nitrogen applied in the Corn Belt at this period was 11 cents a pound, many farmers were getting it applied at a much lower cost in the form of anhydrous ammonia. In most cases the additional corn obtained by heavier rates of fertilization could have been produced at a fertilizer cost of 40 to 70 cents a bushel. *Ibid.*, pp. 3, 5.

13. Agricultural exports in 1965 totaled 6.1 billion dollars.

14. The daily diet per person in the U.S. averages 3000 calories, as against an estimated requirement of 2600. Some $15,000 million worth of American agricultural products were shipped abroad in 12 years under Public Law 480. Enacted in 1954, the law authorized the sale of surplus stocks of farm products to foreign countries for foreign currency.

15. Dale E. Hathaway, *Government and Agriculture: Public Policy in a Democratic Society* (New York: The Macmillan Company, 1963), p. 92.

16. In the absence of price support and acreage diversion programs, it is estimated that net farm income that averaged $12.5 billion in these years, would have dropped to about $6 billion per annum. *Farm Programs and Dynamic Forces in Agriculture*, p. 11.

17. It has been calculated for 1961 that for all farm operators to have obtained a 5 percent return on the market value of their productive assets, to have paid a minimum of $1.25 per hour for all hired labor, and to have received an average of $2.32 per hour for their own and their family's labor, a 28 percent increase in gross farm income would have been necessary. Farms selling more than $5000 worth of produce annually, would have required an increase of 9 percent in gross income to have provided the same returns on investment.

18. Parity ratio measures the ratio of prices received by farmers to prices paid by them for production and living costs.

In 1964 the parity ratio was 76 percent of the 1910–14 average. Preliminary estimates for April 1967 put it lower—at 72 percent.

19. Out of the total per capita income of the farm population of $1664 in 1965, $552 were earned from nonfarm sources.

20. Hathaway, *Problems of Progress in the Agricultural Economy*, p. 35.

21. The crisis of surplus stocks, especially in wheat, was mitigated about 1965 because of an overall world shortage in food grains and a severe drought in India. Wheat acreage allotment was increased in May and again in August of 1966, as the stocks were depleted. Acreage restrictions also had had their effect. The cotton crop in 1966 was the smallest since 1950. Wheat acreage, however, had to be cut back again in 1967 by 13 percent, as world prices slumped.

22. Overall food consumption by the average consumer has changed little since 1910. Measured in pounds of food consumed per capita it has become less. In 1910 it was 1594 pounds per year. In 1954 it was 1531 pounds. In the early 1960's, an American spent less than 19 percent of his income on food; an Englishman, 29 percent; and a Russian, 40 percent.

23. Leonard C. Lewin, *A Treasury of American Political Humor* (New York: A Delacorte Press Book, The Dial Press, 1964), p. 323.

Other references:

George Rogers Taylor, "American Economic Growth Before 1840: An Exploratory Essay," *The Journal of Economic History*, Vol. xxiv (December, 1964).

Harold U. Faulkner, *The Decline of Laissez Faire, 1897–1917, The Economic History of the United States*, Vol. vii (New York: Holt, Rinehart and Winston, 1951).

F. W. Parker, *Fertilizers and Economic Development* (mimeo; F.A.O., 1962).

James O. Bray and Patricia Watkins, "Technical Change in Corn Production in the United States, 1870–1960," Reprinted from *Journal of Farm Economics*, No. 1–65 (Stanford: Stanford University, November, 1964).

Fact Book of U.S. Agriculture (Washington, D.C.: USDA, January 1965).

A Look at Minnesota Agriculture, 1954–1959, University

of Minnesota, Agricultural Extension Service, USDA, Special Report 8, September 1962.

ERS, *Farm Income Situation* (Washington, D.C.: USDA, November 1964).

Ibid., July, 1966.

Agricultural Handbook, 1965 (Washington, D.C.: USDA, October 1965).

Willard W. Cochrane, *The City Man's Guide to the Farm Problem* (Minneapolis: University of Minnesota Press, 1965).

Willard W. Cochrane, *Farm Prices: Myth and Reality* (Minneapolis: University of Minnesota Press, 1958).

Ezra Taft Benson, *Farmers at the Cross Roads* (New York: The Devin-Adair Company, 1956).

The People Left Behind.

CHAPTER IV

1. Despite the decline in farm prices and income the number of tractors on farms increased 41 percent from 1950–60, corn pickers and picker-shellers increased 71 percent, pickup balers and field forage harvesters tripled, as did most of the other items of equipment in various proportions.

2. From 1956 to 1963 the price of farm machinery advanced 24 percent, of motor vehicles 22 percent, as did every other item purchased by farmers. Only the price of fertilizers averaged the same. The index of prices received by farmers for all farm products rose at half the rate of the parity index (prices paid by farmers) in this period.

3. "Analyses of the Economic Research Service indicate the large farms with over $40,000 sales per farm would face greater financial difficulties than smaller ones if price supports were discontinued. This is because of the high ratio of cash expenses to cash receipts. Large farms with more purchased supplies and hired labor per $100 sales have a higher breakeven point than smaller farms. Had price supports been absent the past 3 years, expenses probably would have exceeded cash receipts for the group of farms having sales of over $40,000." Legislative Reference Service of the Library of Congress and Transmitted to the Committee on Agriculture and Forestry United States Senate, *Farm Programs and Dynamic Forces in Agriculture—A Review and Appraisal of Farm Price Support*

Notes

*Programs and the Dynamic Functioning of Agriculture in
Recent Years* (Washington, D.C.: GPO, 1965), pp. 13, 14.

4. Return to the farmer as manager, laborer, and tech-
nician is called incentive income—a concept developed by J. R.
Bellerby to describe the return simply to human effort and
enterprise. Not only were the returns to farmers, according to
Bellerby, shockingly low compared with the country's nonfarm
workers, but during the interwar period, when farm technological advance in the U.S. was the most rapid in the world, the
incentive income ratio for American farmers was near the bottom of the list. Australia, New Zealand, France, United Kingdom, Denmark, Sweden, and Canada all had higher incentive
income ratios. Only countries like Egypt, Mexico, and Thailand
were below the U.S. figure. Immediately following World War
II, the income incentive ratio in America rose to 50 percent of
the nonfarm incentive incomes. But during the 1950's, the ratio
fell back to the level of the depressed 1930's, in spite of the
dazzling new and more productive techniques and machinery.
Willard W. Cochrane, *Farm Prices: Myth and Reality* (Minneapolis: University of Minnesota Press, 1958), pp. 103–4.

5. According to Willard Cochrane, "The average farmer
is on a treadmill with respect to technological advance." For
fuller explanation of the theory see this authors *Farm Prices:
Myth and Reality* and *The City Man's Guide to the Farm
Problem.*

6. In the state of Pennsylvania.

7. His total assets are worth $37,090, and he has a
gross annual income of just under $10,000. Living expenses are
$1675 per annum.

8. He himself has had eight grades of schooling.

9. His total assets are worth $31,658. His debts amount
to $18,646. His gross cash income would be $9000 to $10,000
per annum. Living expenses for the preceding year were $1525.
He has no off-farm income.

10. Wheat acreages are small in this region. But it is
the only cash crop, since all other grains go into feed for livestock. Wheat, therefore, is known locally as the "tax crop." The
program offered a high level—$2 a bushel—of price support
with mandatory output controls, *or* low level of price support—
$1.25 per bushel approximately, for those who stayed within

242

their acreage allotment, and no price support for those exceeding their acreage allotment. In a nationwide referendum of all wheat growers held in May 1963, despite intense government propaganda, farmers rejected the proffered program of mandatory control by a decisive majority. Small growers of 15 acres and less voted for the first time in a wheat referendum and heavily against it, contrary to Washington's anticipation, hope, and expectation.

11. Government considered outdoor recreation a promising new use of agricultural land. In these years several plans were being promoted to provide vacation farms, fishing waters, hunting areas, and camping and picnic sites on private farms and ranches as a means for the farmer to earn extra income and for families with extra income to expend their surplus money and some of the nationally mounting hours of leisure.

12. In Wabash Valley, important for cash grain and livestock farming. Farmers here have a reputation for reluctance to move out. Sometimes they will not go across the county border even. Sons usually settle on or close to the father's farm. Illinois ranks fourth among the states. Only New York, California, and Pennsylvania have larger populations.

13. Average size of farms in the county is 174.4 acres (1959 census).

14. Another reason could be hesitation to borrow sufficiently. Philip said he had been afraid to take more loans for fear he would not be able to repay them. His total debts are $9900. His gross farm income in 1962 was $6706, and his net income $2926. He has no off-farm income.

15. The percent of farms in each tenure group in the state reporting use of fertilizer was 68 for owners, 81 for tenants, and 86 for part-time owners (1959 census). In 1959 the percentage of acreage in the state *not* fertilized for corn was 35; soybeans, 90; hay and cropland pasture, 92.

16. As opposed to 59 percent for the whole state. In some of the counties tenancy goes up to 80 percent. On the basis of land operated, tenants are the dominant tenure group in Illinois, and they market the most products in total worth per farm and per acre. They also cultivate the most valuable land. Next in line are the part-owners. Full owners account for only one acre in four. Sources:

Notes

F. J. Reiss, *Some Tenure Facts About Illinois Farmers* (Urbana: University of Illinois, Dept. of Agricultural Economics, November 13, 1961).

F. J. Reiss, *Tenure Distribution of Farmland by Economic Areas In Illinois* (Urbana: University of Illinois, Dept. of Agr. Economics, June 1, 1962).

F. J. Reiss, *A Graphic Summary of Land Tenure in Illinois* (Urbana: University of Illinois, Dept. of Agr. Economics, June 1962).

17. Direct individual to individual lease in Illinois is usually oral, and the terms are based mainly on local custom and tradition. Duration is normally for a year at a time, and the tenant is informed in September if his lease is not being renewed. At times he may be given only 90 days' notice. The moving day for tenants is on the first of March. A landlord need not give any reason for terminating the lease. In the U.S. as a whole, most farm leases are oral, for one year, with provision usually for a thirty-day notification if the lease is to be terminated.

18. Generally, the landlord does not encourage a tenant to keep livestock (unless he also has a share in it), for fear that the tenant may feed the animals on the landowner's portion of the grain, and also crop the land less intensively. Tenancy in the state is most strongly associated with field crop farming. Livestock share tenants are a significant exception.

Reiss, *A Graphic Summary of Land Tenure in Illinois,* p. 40.

19. Tenant housing is normally provided by the landlord.

20. The three earlier farms were all in the neighboring, equally rich-soil county of Champaign.

21. Banks handling estates in these counties for absentee landowners generally have a long waiting list of tenant applicants. It is entirely a sellers' market. Unless he is related to the renter, normally the tenant who eventually gets the farm has a "pull" in the right quarter. Or, he "purchases" the lease at a price—say $500. Sometimes he may offer better terms by agreeing to give to the landlord a larger share in the produce. But then he incurs the displeasure of other tenants in the locality.

22. In the relatively poorer soil areas of the southern counties, the rent is normally one-third or two-fifths share in

the produce. Crop-share and crop-share-cash leases are the most numerous in Illinois. Of 48,630 tenant operated farms in 1959, only 6 percent had cash leases.

Reiss, *Some Tenure Facts About Illinois Farmers*.

23. Average size of farms in the county is 206 acres (1959 census).

24. The return from all labor on farms in the U.S. averaged about $1.05 an hour compared with $2.46 in the factory in 1963. In the hog-beef-fattening farms in the Corn Belt, return per hour to operator and family labor was $.54, on a gross farm income of $31,024, and total capital investment of $98,920 on 153 cropped acres. Sources:

Willard W. Cochrane, *The City Man's Guide to the Farm Problem* (Minneapolis: University of Minnesota Press, 1965), p. 19.

Fact Book of U.S. Agriculture, p. 87.

25. Total average capital investment in this region of central Illinois, for an adequate family-size farm at this period, would require more than $130,000. Some family farms in the state had investments of more than $230,000. In any case, very little land was available for sale, and rarely a whole operating unit.

Fact Book of U.S. Agriculture, p. 88.

26. Farmers Home Administration (FHA) is a federal government agency set up especially to provide credit to small farmers who are unable to secure loans from banks and other commercial establishments. Ralph is now an FHA client and has borrowed $19,450 since 1960.

27. Unless there is a written lease, a great deal depends on the personal relationship a tenant is able to strike with his landlord. The latter vary greatly in their attitudes and treatment of tenants.

28. He has no off-farm income. Gross earnings in 1962 came to $14,020. Family living expenses were $3,356.

CHAPTER V

1. Land here is selling at around $250 an acre.

2. In the state as a whole, however, 19 percent of all farm operators are tenants; 23 percent are part-owners; and 58 percent full owners, according to the 1959 census.

3. Average size of the farm in the county in 1959 was 371.2 acres. In 1950 it was 302.2 acres. Acreage of both wheat and sugar beet is controlled.

See also Lee Taylor and Glenn Nelson (eds.), *Minnesota's People and Farms 1950–1960* (Agricultural Experiment Station, Minneapolis: University of Minnesota, Misc. Report 45, March 1961), p. 25.

4. His gross farm income in the past year was $58,103, and expenses $55,184, including living ($7,500). He completed high school but did not go to college.

5. His total current assets are worth $223,623, of which land is valued at $157,000.

6. By the end of 1963 the total farm debt in the U.S. stood at $35 billion. By January 1, 1966, it had mounted to $41.5 billion. Of this, farm mortgage debt came to 21.1 billion dollars. Source:

Economic Research Service, *Economic Tables* (mimeo; Washington, D.C.: USDA, January 1967).

7. He has about $14,000 invested in machinery.

8. He and most farmers in Utah are of the Mormon faith. A unique element in early Mormon society was the institution of polygamy. Most of them were 2-wife families. Polygamy was ended compulsorily in 1890 by an act of Congress.

9. Average size of farm in this county is 237.7 acres (1959 census).

10. The then secretary of Agriculture, Orville L. Freeman.

11. He did not go to college, but has attended short courses in agriculture at the State University.

12. Columbia Basin Project is located in the south-central region of the state of Washington. It encompasses 2,500,000 acres, more than a million acres of which is suitable for irrigation. Key structure of the project is the Grand Coulee Dam on the Columbia River, 60 miles north of Ephrata. The irrigation system is operated by the Bureau of Reclamation.

13. This is a major wheat producing county in the state and nation, and it is also the first in dry peas and lentils. Dry wheat culture here is of a very extensive type and highly mechanized. Verl claims that 75 percent of his time is spent in the workshop on maintenance and repair of equipment. The

average farm in the county is of about 750 acres—usually partly owned and partly leased.

14. The average yield of wheat per acre in Columbia Basin was 67 bushels in 1962. Average for the state as a whole was 39.4 bushels in the same year. Sources:
Washington Crop and Livestock Reporting Service, *Washington Agricultural Statistics—Annual Crop Report 1962* (Washington, D.C.: USDA, 1962), p. 13.
(Statement showing) The Acreage, Yield, Price per Unit, Percent of Total Acreage and Percent of Total Value of 39 Crops Grown in the Columbia Basin Project in 1962 (February 1963), p. 1.

15. In the official publication of the Washington Association of Wheat Growers, *Wheat Life*, vol. 8, no. 7 (Ritzville, Washington, August 30, 1963).

16. In a survey conducted in the Columbia project area, when farmers were asked to name the aspect of farming which they liked least, "the most frequently disliked was being tied down so continuously to irrigating during the crop season. . . . The need for and ability to put in long hours of hard work over a sustained period of time is something very much in the forefront of the thinking of the farmers in the Columbia Basin." The same survey also revealed, that "the economic return to be expected from farming in the Columbia Basin . . . is apparently not what is valued most highly. . . . When questioned about what they liked most about farming, they hardly mentioned income."
Murray A. Straus and Barnard D. Parrish, *The Columbia Basin Settler: A Study of Social and Economic Resources in New Land Settlement* (Washington Agricultural Experiment Stations, Institute of Agricultural Sciences, State College of Washington, Bulletin 566, May 1956), pp. 13, 15.

17. There is a saying here, and it is largely true, that "the first generation is a lost cause in irrigation." Historically, one of the greatest problem in the settlement of newly irrigated lands in the U.S. has been the lack of a sufficient number of well-qualified settlers. In the Columbia Basin also, actual development of land in farms has lagged behind the available irrigation facilities. In 1948, when water first became available to 5760 acres, the actual irrigated area was 119 acres, or 2.1 percent.

Even a decade later, 57.1 percent of the irrigable land was actually irrigated. In 1962, whereas the irrigable acreage was 452,756 acres, 339,496 acres actually took the water. Originally designed to water more than a million acres, the project had by this time been cut down to irrigate only 600,000 acres, because the rest of the land had been withdrawn from the scheme by private owners and government agencies. Sources: Straus and Parrish, *The Columbia Basin Settler: A Study of Social and Economic Resources in New Land Settlement*, p. 3; Columbia Basin Project, *Farming Opportunities* (Ephrata, Washington: U.S. Dept. of the Interior, Bureau of Reclamation, October 2, 1962); E. R. Franklin, W. U. Fuhriman, and B. D. Parish, *Economic Problems and Progress of Columbia Basin Project Settlers* (Washington Agricultural Experiment Stations, Institute of Agr. Sciences, State College of Washington—Bulletin 597, January 1959); Columbia Basin, *Crop Production Report 1962* (Bureau of Reclamation, Washington, October 1956).

18. Few Japanese farmers here would be found cultivating dry wheat. Mostly, they would be in the irrigated tracts in row crops. Also, few tenants among them will have a crop-share lease. They prefer to pay a fixed cash rent and take the risk. White American tenants generally prefer the safer crop-share basis.

19. Mormons were irrigating their crops in Utah as early as 1847, because as Daniere said, they had to in order to survive. At the time, they were a persecuted sect and so elected to settle in a desert that no one else wanted. Even now the largest single denomination to which settlers in the Columbia Basin belong is the Mormon Church of Jesus Christ of Latter-Day-Saints. One of them is a son of Harvey. Sources: Straus and Parrish, *The Columbia Basin Settler: A Study of Social and Economic Resources in New Land Settlement*, p. 10. Bureau of Reclamation, *Reclamation* (Washington, D.C.: U.S. Dept. of the Interior, 1962), p. 4.

20. This is done frequently to dodge the ceiling on acreage of irrigated farms in the Columbia Basin. In 1963 the limit was 160 acres in one ownership and 320 irrigated acres if husband and wife owned it jointly. In earlier years it used to be less.

21. Rate of absentee ownership and tenancy is high here. More than 60 percent of the irrigated farm units are

Notes

rented. In 1940, prior to irrigation, the average wheat farm in this region was 3000 acres; some farms had as many as 8000 acres. Many cattle and wheat ranches not interested in irrigation sold out to the government. Sources:

Franklin, Fuhriman and Parish, *op. cit.*, pp. 9, 10.

Carl C. Taylor, *Rural Life in the United States* (New York: Alfred A. Knopf, 1949), p. 390.

22. Rainfall in the basin averages 6 to 10 inches a year. It falls mainly in winter and early spring.

CHAPTER VI

1. "American" here, and in the previous chapter, connotes north European stock. The pattern of women's participation appears to be dictated by the ethnic tradition of the family rather than by the labor requirements of the farm.

2. As in several vegetable and fruit crops. In 1963 there were about 400,000 domestic migrant farm workers in the country. They belonged mostly to minority groups—two-fifth were Negro and one-fourth Spanish-American. They tended to follow well-defined paths developed over a period of years. The longest of these was the midcontinent stream. In Texas nearly 100,000 U.S. migrants left their home areas each summer for employment farther north or west. In some cases their departure created a local labor shortage which was filled by foreign workers. The East Coast pattern involved 30,000 to 40,000 workers moving up the coast from Florida and other southern states. Michigan alone, in the far north, engaged 44.6 thousand migrants in 1963—the second largest in numbers in the country. Along the West Coast, there was a substantial shifting of workers for fruit and vegetable activities. U.S. Dept. of Labor, Bureau of Employment Security, *Hired Farmworkers in the United States* (Washington, D.C.: December 1964), p. 26.

3. Of all farms in the U.S., 52 percent used no hired workers in 1959, while 1 percent of the total number of farms paid 30 percent of all wage expenditures. The latter had sales of $100,000 or more per farm per annum. *Hired Farmworkers in the United States*, p. 6.

4. Of the 3.6 million persons who worked on farms for a wage during 1963, 2 million (55 percent) were living in the South, although the region had only 43 percent of the farms and

46 percent of the total farm population of 14 years of age and over.

Gladys K. Bowles and Walter E. Sellers, Jr., *The Hired Farm Working Force of 1963 with Supplementary Data for 1962* (Washington, D.C.: USDA, Economic Research Service, May 1965), p. 8.

5. Mechanization has proceeded more slowly in the cotton belt (includes 690 counties stretching from Texas to North Carolina) than in other commercial farming operations. Even so, the number of cropper units decreased from 776,000 in 1929 to 273,000 in 1954, and to 121,000 in 1959. In 9 Southern states, nearly 20 percent of the farms disappeared in 5 years, between 1959 and 1964.

Walter L. Slocum (ed.), *Agricultural Sociology: A Study of Sociological Aspects of American Farm Life* (New York: Harper and Brothers Publishers, 1961), pp. 139, 140.

Hearings Before the National Advisory Commission on Rural Poverty (Washington, D.C., February 15, 16, 17, 1967), p. 44.

6. Between 1950 and 1960, whereas farm operators and unpaid family workers in the county decreased by 74 percent, hired farm hands increased 30 percent. A survey made of 40 cotton plantations in the Delta area of Mississippi showed 439 tractor drivers in 1957—an average of 11 per plantation, or one for each 37 acres of cotton. More than three-fifths (62 percent) of the tractor drivers came from resident wage families, while the rest came from cropper families. See:

W. A. White, *Overall Economic Development Program,* Comprehensive Report, Yazoo County, Mississippi (Yazoo City, Miss.: 1962), p. 15;

Nelson LeRay, Jr., and Grady B. Crowe, *Labor and Technology on Selected Cotton Plantations in the DeltaArea of Mississippi, 1953–1957* (Mississippi Agricultural Experiment Station, Bulletin 575, State College, Mississippi, April 1959), p. 23.

7. On 50/50 share basis.

8. Of a total of 5370 farm housing units in the county, 2285 were constructed in 1929 or earlier, and 4081 did not have public sewer, septic tank, or cesspool sewage disposal in the early 1960's. *Overall Economic Development Program,* pp. 62, 64.

9. He also raises beef cattle. Of the 5300 acres, he owns 2700 acres and rents the rest. Cotton is the major crop in the state and county, followed by soybeans. The majority of farms in this area are large units. All the farm investment and production statistics are as stated by the farmer in interview with the author. See:

Mississippi Employment Security Commission, Mississippi State Employment Service, Farm Placement Dept., *Mississippi Farm Labor 1962—Annual Agricultural Report* (Jackson, Mississippi, 1962), p. 6;

Overall Economic Development Program, p. 10.

10. And with government price support. Commodity Credit Corporation expenditure for 1964–65 commodity programs equaled 26 percent of the cotton produced. Had price supports been discontinued and prices fallen to world levels in the preceding 3 years it is estimated that on specialized cotton farms having sales of over $40,000, production expenses would have exceeded the net cash receipts by more than $10,000 per farm.

Legislative Reference Service of the Library of Congress, *Farm Programs and Dynamic Forces in Agriculture: A Review and Appraisal of Farm Price Support Programs and the Dynamic Functioning of Agriculture in Recent Years* (Washington, D.C.: GPO, February 4, 1965), pp. 14, 15.

11. "The large plantation operator has three potential sources of farm labor for seasonal jobs: Individuals living on the plantation, day-haul workers, and migratory workers. Primary dependence is on resident and day-haul labor. Little migratory labor is employed." Operators hesitated apparently to depend upon season off-farm labor for cotton chopping and picking.

LeRay, Jr., and Crowe, *Labor and Technology on Selected Cotton Plantations in the Delta Area of Mississippi, 1953–1957,* p. 4.

12. While the number of horses and mules in the county declined from 8213 in 1950, there were still 2664 farm animals in 1959. It was not uncommon in this region, even in 1963, to see a man working with a team of horses.

Overall Economic Development Program, p. 51.

13. Even if they have 200 acres besides.

14. In Washington County in the same state, farther to the west on the east bank of the Mississippi.

15. His outstanding debts are $5756, and total assets, $20,972.

16. Gross farm income is around $6000.

17. The county seat.

18. Nor can a brown-shelled egg be marketed, due to popular superstition and prejudice about color and quality.

19. In 1959, 43 percent of the cotton and 30 percent of soybeans in the country were harvested on farms with sales of $40,000 or more. *Farm Programs and Dynamic Forces in Agriculture,* p. 10.

20. Commodity price-support programs at this period, benefitted primarily only about 1,500,000 farmers, or fewer than half of *all* farm families, since they produced over 92 percent of the total farm products marketed. During 1966 total payments to a single farm ranged up to $2.8 million, and 9 farms each received more than $1 million. *Farm Programs and Dynamic Forces in Agriculture,* p. 9. *The People Left Behind,* pp. 142–46.

21. Merchant pays cash down. The Association sells on behalf of the client and pays only after the cotton has been sold. Price of both cotton and soybeans is supported by the government. In 1963–64 cotton subsidies alone were costing the U.S. taxpayer $500 million a year. First, the government fixed the price of domestic cotton at 32½ cents a pound, which was 8½ cents above the prevailing world market price. Then it paid 8½ cents subsidy to exporters so they could sell U.S. cotton at the world price. Later, in August 1964, farmers' support price and export subsidy was reduced by 2½ cents, but the U.S. textile manufacturers were given a new subsidy of 6½ cents a pound, so they could buy U.S. cotton at the cheaper world price. *Time* magazine described cotton as "the only U.S. crop that is subsidized from stem to steam whistle." *Time,* March 5, 1965.

CHAPTER VII

1. In 1961, whereas about 90 percent of the cotton in California was harvested by machine, the proportion was 57 percent in the Mississippi River Delta region, 50 percent in the southwestern states, and 24 percent in the southeastern states.

Cotton harvest in the U.S. employed more seasonal hired labor than any other single crop—about 700,000 in 1961. California was the second largest producer of cotton in the country. Besides cotton the state supplied about one-third of the nation's production of fresh market vegetables and melons, one-third of the principal processing vegetables, 41 percent of the tree fruits, nuts, and grapes, 36 percent of strawberries, and 11 percent of the potatoes. Sources:

Report and Recommendations, *Third Annual Conference on Families Who Follow the Crops*, March 1, 2, 1962, Governor's Advisory Committee on Children and Youth, Subcommittee on the Migrant Child (Sacramento, California, June 1962), pp.4, 5.

Effect on Seasonal Hired Labor, *Cotton Harvest Mechanization*, BES No. 209 (Washington, D.C.: U.S. Dept. of Labor, Bureau of Employment Security, June 1962), pp. 1, 2.

Report of the Senate Fact Finding Committee on Labor and Welfare, *California's Farm Labor Problems, Part I* (published by the Senate of the State of California, 1961), pp. 21, 44.

2. In California in October 1959, less than 35 percent of the workers on farms were family members. In the U.S. the national percentage was 71. Conversely, whereas California agriculture depended on wage workers for nearly two-thirds of its labor, the agriculture of the U.S. employed labor for only 29 percent, or less than one-third of the work. *California's Farm Labor Problems*, p. 50.

3. In 1960. At the lowest they were 68.6 percent of the total hired farm labor force. *Ibid.*, p. 74.

4. *Ibid.*, p. 78.

5. The number of their placements (under the nominal supervision of Farm Placement Service of the California Department of Employment) increased from 374,294 in this category in 1955, to 541,160 in 1960. *Ibid.*, p. 79.

6. Lloyd H. Fisher, *The Harvest Labor Market in California* (Cambridge, Mass.: Harvard University Press, 1953), p. 7. For more details on legal and welfare rights of agricultural workers, see *The People Left Behind*, pp. 22, 85, 86.

7. *Time*, April 15, 1966, p. 55.

8. Fisher, *op cit.*, p. 4.

9. *Oakland* (California) *Daily Transcript*, July 15, 1869; quoted by Fisher, *op. cit.*, p. 21.

10. Paul S. Taylor, quoted in *Calfiornia's Farm Labor Problems,* p. 13.

11. *Sunset Magazine,* Vol. 41, November 1918, p. 30; quoted by Fisher, *op. cit.,* p. 22.

12. *California's Farm Labor Problems,* pp. 13, 15, 19–21.

13. Total number of farms in California in 1959 was 99,232 embracing 36,853,851 acres. Of the estimated total gross income of $2,862,511,403 from the sale of farm products in the state in 1959, more than 75 percent went to 14.5 percent of the farmers, each of whom marketed products worth $40,000 and more. Income of the farmer in California was 3 times larger than that of the average farmer in the United States. All the figures are based on 1959 census. Also see:

Julian A. McPhee, chairman, Cooperating Agencies, Dept. of Employment, Dept. of Agriculture and Dept. of Industrial Relations, State of California, *Report and Recommendations of the Agricultural Labor Commission* (Sacramento, California, January 31, 1963), pp. 47, 49.

California's Farm Labor Problems, p. 47.

14. In 1959. The *total* number of average monthly work force, excluding farmers and unpaid family workers, was 300,-300. At peak season it was as high as 411,500. Of this, temporary domestic hired farm labor was 132,300 at an average, and 205,600 per month at peak. Sources:

California's Farm Labor Problems, p. 74 (Table 45).

Report and Recommendations of the Agricultural Labor Commission, p. 56.

15. Varden Fuller, professor of agricultural economics at the University of California; quoted in *California's Farm Labor Problems,* p. 14.

16. Compared with 10,000 Japanese in 1900. Only the main categories of bulk immigrants who remained wage laborers for all times are listed. "Laborers of European origin, notably among them Italians, Spaniards, Portuguese, Russians, German-Russians, and Armenians, also have been important at one period or another in California agricultural history, and in one locality or another. Generally, these European (and Near Eastern) immigrants have served as farm laborers for only a few years, until able to acquire farms of their own." Nearly all the Chinese, Filipinos, and Mexicans, however, lived and died as wage laborers. Only a quarter of the Japanese rose above that

status, and of these, one-third were farm managers and foremen rather than owners or tenants. The structure did not provide much scope for upward mobility for these workers. See Fisher, *op. cit.*, pp. 4, 5; *California's Farm Labor Problems*, p. 15.

17. It is estimated that by July 1, 1961, 50,000 permanent immigrants from Mexico had been added to the U.S. farm labor force—22,000 of them in California. Mexico is one of the few exceptions to the nationality quota system. Some 217,000 workers from foreign countries were admitted to the U.S. under contract to do farm work in 1962. This included 195,000 Mexicans; 13,000 British West Indians; nearly 9,000 Canadians; and a few hundred Japanese and Filipinos. See *Seasonal Labor in California Agriculture* (Division of Agricultural Sciences, University of California, 1963), p. 21; Bureau of Employment Security, *Farm Labor Market Developments*—Review and Outlook (Washington, D.C.: U.S. Dept. of Labor, January 1963), p. 5.

18. Also, cost of hired labor since 1949 has shown less relative increase in California than any other input factor with the exception of net rent to nonfarm landlords and of seed. The relative share of gross income accruing to hired labor in the decade 1949-58, fell 7.2 percent, while that going to farm operators increased 3.1 percent. Sources: *California's Farm Labor Problems*, pp. 40, 51; *Hired Farm Workers in the United States*, BES No. R–200 (Washington, D.C.: U.S. Dept. of Labor, Bureau of Employment Security, December 1964–65), pp. 27, 33.

19. Remarks by Charles E. Warren, a fruit grower. *Transaction of the Commonwealth Club of California*, Vol. XIII, No. 3 (San Francisco, May 1918), p. 114; quoted in *California's Farm Labor Problems*, p. 14.

20. *California's Farm Labor Problems*, p. 16.

21. In 1959 Fred Herringer, farmer and second vice-president of the California Farm Bureau Federation, expressed the contemporary farmers' attitude as follows: ". . . we have a very ineffective labor supply today to meet these new peak demands in agricultural production and harvesting. Therefore, we continue to support the principle of supplementing domestic labor to meet these demands until it is demonstrated that domestic labor with new management techniques will respond to the needs of agriculture." *California's Farm Labor Problems*, p. 113.

22. In San Joaquin County. Stockton is the state's second largest day-haul center.

23. In interview with the author. Subsequently, restrictions were placed on immigrants. Since 1951 braceros were contracted under procedures authorized by P.L. 78. This was allowed to expire on Dec. 31, 1964. In 1964 more than 100,000 braceros had worked in California. Thereafter, foreign (including Mexican) labor was permitted to enter the U.S. under the general immigration law only if the government was satisfied that no domestic workers were available and if farmers promised to pay a uniform minimum wage to all—$1.40 an hour in California in 1965.

CHAPTER VIII

1. The ten crops in California employing highest number of braceros in 1960 were, in descending order of utilization, tomatoes, lettuce, strawberries, sugar beets, lemons, melons, asparagus, miscellaneous vegetables, grapes, and cotton. *California's Farm Labor Problems*, p. 105.

2. "The average Mexican National is a small man, five foot five, six or seven inches tall, weighing approximately a hundred and thirty pounds. . . . No individual could be more unskilled than the average bracero imported from Mexico, but with the interest and desire to work, most of them quickly learn to perform the tasks required with very adequate skill." *Ibid.*, p. 113.

3. "The physical tasks of much farm work require stooping, digging, cutting, pulling, walking, climbing, reaching, lifting, and carrying. Such arduous tasks must often be performed in an environment which may be disagreeable because of dust, heat, cold, or rain and mud. There may be other discomforts such as from scratches, blisters, cuts, and insect bites." Row crops generally require hand thinning, hoeing, weeding, and general cultivation. *Ibid.*, pp. 51, 52.

4. It was difficult to find a farmer in any income category who hired labor and who thought differently. Yet, "Foreign labor is more expensive and ten times the trouble, because of Federal and State agencies that police the farmer, but the difference is that foreign labor is more efficient and dependable on the harvest and stoop phases of labor." The main appeal of the bracero appeared to lie in his dependability—that he could be counted upon. *Ibid.*, p. 113.

Notes

5. In New Mexico cotton is the most valuable crop and represents about 45 percent of the total value of all major crops (1961). In this particular county of Dona Ana, in the Southeast District, all cotton is irrigated. Statistical Reporting Service, Field Operations Division, *New Mexico Agricultural Statistics,* Vol. I, New Mexico Dept. of Agriculture (University Park: New Mexico State University, September 1962), pp. 6, 77.

6. Hired labor on farms in New Mexico is from three major sources: (1) domestic-locals, (2) domestic nonlocals, i.e. migrants, and (3) Mexican nationals (braceros). George R. Dawson, *Preliminary Investigation and Farm Labor Conditions in New Mexico,* Research Report 41, Agricultural Experiment Station (University Park: New Mexico State University), p. 19.

7. His total acreage is 51 acres. He has had 8 years in school, but he read and kept up with the trade journals. The farm had belonged to his father.

8. Domestic migrant workers were not well thought of by the farmers here. They were not considered dependable. Braceros had increased in importance as a source of seasonal agricultural labor since 1954, although they had declined in absolute numbers. Dawson, *op. cit.,* pp. 30, 67.

9. Mostly native Mexican-Spanish. There is very little Negro labor on farms here.

10. Actually, even before the war (1937) only about 50 percent of the cotton in New Mexico was picked by local labor. Sigurd Johansen, *Migratory-Casual Workers in New Mexico,* Press Bulletin 870, Dept. of Agricultural Economics, New Mexico Agricultural Experiment Station (State College, March 21, 1939), pp. 7–8.

11. Yet several thousand workers from the poorer and less developed regions of north-central New Mexico migrated every year to Colorado, Utah, Idaho, and Arizona to work on farms and ranches—primarily in sugar beets, potatoes, and as sheepherders. Efforts to shift them to farm jobs within the state did not prove successful. The reason appeared to be traditional and personal choice rather than economic. Many of them could have had jobs in New Mexico at the same or higher wages than they received in out-of-state jobs. Dawson, *op. cit.,* pp. 23–25.

12. "There is strong reluctance on the part of workers, although unemployed, to return to agricultural jobs upon termination of their non-agricultural jobs, because agricultural work

is no longer appealing to them, for both economic and socio-logical reasons. A serious problem exists for these workers and the community. . . . Often when such men return to agricultural jobs, they do not perform satisfactory work." They had a taste of nonfarm work during the war and also since 1950, due to phenomenal increase in employment in military and defense installations at White Sands Missile Range in New Mexico. Buses traveled the length of Dona Ana County each day transporting workers to and from the site of White Sands. Dawson, *op. cit.*, pp. 26–28.

13. In the same state of New Mexico in Dona Ana County.

14. Wages had registered the largest percentage increase of all farm production costs in this period. Labor costs in New Mexico ranged from 30 to 70 percent of the total cost of production of farm commodities about 1960. Dawson, *op. cit.*, pp. 14, 66.

15. He made $12,000 on onions in one year, he said, and then lost $40,000 in another year.

16. According to a survey of 232 farms in the main cotton producing counties where Mexican nationals were employed, "it appeared that farmers were in many instances paying local workers a higher cash wage than they were paying Mexican nationals." Dawson, *op. cit.*, pp. 43–44.

17. He expected a net annual income of $8000. They lived comfortably but not extravagantly. He went to high school for 2 years. They have 2 children, a girl and a boy.

CHAPTER IX

1. Approximately 1000 counties in the U.S. and all the counties in Mississippi had been declared as low-income counties. In 1959 more than half the commercial farms in Alcorn County had sales of farm commodities worth less than $2500 a year. Andrew W. Baird, Lucy W. Cole, and Harold F. Kaufman, *Development of Human Resources in Alcorn County, Mississippi*, Agricultural Experiment Station (State College, Mississippi, Sept. 1961), pp. 2, 6, 22, 37.

2. *Ibid.*, p. 49. Also see Lucy W. Cole, *What Is Happening to Rural Neighborhoods*, Agricultural Experiment Station (State College, Mississippi, July 1958).

3. Mary B. Whitmarsh and Harold F. Kaufman, *The Church and the School in Community Development*, Proceedings of the Tenth Annual Institute for Town and County Church Leaders, Sociology & Rural Life Series 5 (State College, Mississippi, February 1958), p. 44.

4. According to the 1960 census the rural population of Alcorn County comprised 13,829 persons in 3687 households. *Development of Human Resources in Alcorn County, Mississippi*, p. 4.

5. Edwin E. White, *Religious Attitudes and Ideals in the Cumberland Plateau*, p. 15 (mimeo.).

6. In 1966, 12,000 such young and nonprofessional missionaries were serving their church in the field in all parts of the world.

CHAPTER X

1. Ward is the smallest unit of the Mormon church.

2. The Book of Mormon contains the sacred and secular history of the people who were ancestors of some of the American Indians in the period from about 600 B.C. to 421 A.D. The Book takes its title from a man whose name was Mormon and witnesses that Jesus the Christ visited the inhabitants of the Western Hemisphere after His ascension. It was first published in America in 1830 and has had a place beside the Bible in the Church of Latter-Day Saints.

3. In the early 1830's the Mormons published the "Word of Wisdom" revelation which counseled, among other things, abstention from tobacco, intoxicants, and such "hot drinks" as tea and coffee. Complete abstinence is the hallmark of a "good" Mormon. At the Utah State University, signs everywhere request: "Please do not smoke." Mormons are an interesting sect because they closely resemble the early Puritans in the United States.

4. I did not see in any other state such shabby, dilapidated, and unpainted fences, barns, and farm buildings on even prosperous farms, as in Utah. When I mentioned it to farmers, they were usually surprised. They had not even noticed it. New houses of modern design also are not common in the rural areas here. It may have some connection with the emphasis on frugality and the importance attached to staying out of debt in the Mormon Church.

5. Unlike certain other religious sects, as for example, the Amish and the Hutterites. Utah has more of its young people in school and college than probably any other state in the U.S. About 72 percent of the state's population is of Mormon faith. The percentage would be very much higher in the rural communities. It comes closer to being dominated by a single church than any other state. The Church of Jesus Christ of Latter-Day-Saints, with headquarters in Salt Lake City, numbered some two and a half million members by the end of 1966.

6. Economist and economic historian. In an interview with the author.

7. A basic revelation in the *Doctrine and Covenants* of the church asserts that all things are spiritual and that no policy is temporal. Of the 112 revelations announced by the Prophet Joseph Smith, 88 dealt partly or entirely with matters that were economic in nature.

8. Leonard J. Arrington, *Religion and Economics in Mormon History,* reprinted from *Brigham Young University Studies,* Vol. III (Spring and Summer 1961), p. 15.

9. Including faith healing. This is fairly widespread among several denominations and sections of the population in the country.

10. In an interview with the author in Salt Lake City in August 1963. At the time, Benson was one of the Council of Twelve Apostles in the Mormon Church. He was secretary of Agricultrue for eight years beginning 1953.

11. Therel R. Black and Jerrilyn Black, *Community Problems and Group Participation,* Bulletin 411 (Utah State University, Agricultural Experiment Station, March 1959).

12. 95 percent of the rural extension workers in Utah State would be church leaders as well.

13. Phillip F. Aylesworth, *Keeping Abreast of Change in the Rural Community,* Bulletin No. 215 (Washington, D.C.: USDA, Federal Extension Service, October 1959), p. 11.

14. *Ibid.,* p. 11.

15. *Community Problems and Group Participation,* p. 17.

16. Raymond Payne and Harold F. Kaufman, *Organizational Activities of Rural People in Mississippi,* Circular 189 (Mississippi State College, Agricultural Experiment Station, November 1953).

17. Till the Supreme Court banned recitation of the

Lord's Prayer and Bible reading as part of regular *public* school devotional exercises on June 17, 1963, 38 states permitted religious exercises, particularly Bible reading. Among them 13 states required Bible reading by law. In 12 other states Bible reading was specifically permitted by law or as a result of judicial decision. A third group of 13 states permitted Bible reading "under the general terms of law or by reason of silence." Only 11 states did *not* permit Bible reading. The majority of the public schools in the country thus practiced Bible reading. *New York Times,* June 18, 1963, p. 27.

18. Reported in *The Commercial Appeal,* Memphis, April 4, 1963. Again on April 15, 1967, another 24-year-old high-school science teacher, Gary L. Scott, was dismissed for teaching the theory of evolution in Jacksboro, Tennessee. Later he was reinstated. On May 16 the Tennessee Legislature finally succeeded in voting to repeal the so-called "monkey-law."

19. In an interview with the author in April 1963.

20. The state of Illinois did *not* permit Bible reading in public schools even prior to the Supreme Court ban of 1963.

21. In an interview with the author in September 1963.

22. The school here is administered by a board of 7 members elected by the district. Its curriculum is set locally and even textbooks may vary from one (school) district to another within the same state.

CHAPTER XI

1. And other similar pronouncements. Average level of education for farm people was 8.8 years of schooling in 1960.

2. Commercial farms are defined in the Census of 1959 as having annual sale of farm products worth $2500 or more.

3. 1775 to 1783.

4. C. and M. Beard, *Rise of American Civilization,* I, p. 294, quoted by Harold Underwood Faulkner in *American Economic History,* Eighth Edition (New York: Harper and Brothers Publishers, 1954), p. 130.

5. Homestead Act of 1862. For a detailed description of the farm-tenure system in the United States, see Harris and Ackerman (eds.), *op. cit.,* Chapter II, pp. 39-61;

Faulkner, *op. cit.,* pp. 197, 328, 353.

6. Technically defined as a region with more than 2, and less than 6 people per square mile.

7. Faulkner, *op. cit.*, p. 375.

8. It was known as such because the act provided 30,000 acres of public land to be given to each state for each senator and representative in Congress. Funds from the sale of these lands went toward financing the agricultural colleges. *Ibid.*, pp. 336, 375.

9. The U.S. Department of Agriculture was instituted in 1889.

10. Everett E. Edwards, *Jefferson and Agriculture*, Agricultural History Series No. 7 (Washington, D.C.: USDA, 1943), p. 23.

11. Despite commodity price support often justified as "for the small farmer." According to John A. Schnittker, under-secretary of Agriculture: ". . . it is now clearly understood and widely accepted that most small farmers in the U.S. cannot attain good incomes and living standards from farming alone." Summary of remarks by Under-Secretary of Agriculture John A. Schnittker, to the American Farm Economics Association, (mimeo; University of Maryland: USDA, August 22, 1966). The term "fences were down" is used metaphorically here. Generally, farms in America do not have fences any more.

12. In 1963, 3.6 million persons did farm work for cash wage at some time during the year. Of these 1.7 million were classified as casual workers, who worked for less than 25 days; 1.2 million were seasonal (25–149 days); 0.3 million were regular (150–249 days); and 0.4 million year-round (250 days and over). As against the sharp decline in the number of farm operators and unpaid family workers in the postwar decades, the average number of hired hands in agriculture in 1959–63, was 4 percent higher than the average for 1945–49. Economic Research Service, Agricultural Economic Report No. 76, *The Hired Farm Working Force of 1963* (Washington, D.C.: USDA, May 1965), pp. 3, 6.

13. He would fall in the category of 44.3 percent of all farmers who sold less than $2500 worth of farm produce in a year (1963). Robert's gross income was more than $2500, but under $5000 per annum.

14. Hydrologically defined as the Yellow Creek Watershed Area. It is characterized by a large number of relatively small farms. Yellow Creek is a tributary of the Tennessee River. Yellow Creek Watershed Authority was created by the Missis-

sippi state legislature in 1958 to coordinate local, state, and federal efforts toward development of the economy of the area.

15. A great deal of work on farms in this region was still being done with horse-drawn equipment. Some tractors could be seen, but also a number of teams with mostly old men operating, helped by their wives—all white. There are few or no Negroes in the hill districts in the South.

16. Many such small, shoddy, dilapidated houses can be seen all over the countryside.

17. "Let me admit we don't work with this group of farmers," was the frank reply of a senior executive of Yellow Creek Watershed Authority in Iuka, the county seat. "Even if ten years ago, when he was still farming, the county agent had gone to Miller on his own initiative and suggested ways and means of improvement, he would have got a blank stare and no cooperation or response. It would have been a complete waste of his time." Extension workers here knew nothing about them either except from "surveys." I had to visit the offices of four agencies, all concerned with agriculture, to locate unsuccessfully, half a dozen low-income families in a county where more than two-thirds of the farmers are in the low income group—with incomes of less than $2000 per annum. See also *Hearings Before the National Advisory Commission on Rural Poverty*, pp. 132–33.

18. The county falls within the juridisdiction of the Tennessee Valley Authority, which has played a notable role in the economic and agricultural development of the entire region. The basic tradition and philosophy of its programs designed to improve living conditions has been involvement of the local people.

CHAPTER XII

1. "Paddy" means irrigated rice field, as against "upland" field that is normally not irrigated. In this prefecture 65 percent of the land is not suitable for cultivation at all. Of what remains, 65 percent is in upland crops. Of this area again, over 95 percent consists of volcanic ash soil of low fertility.

Of the upland acreage, 37 percent is planted to mulberry trees, cocoon being the main farm product in the prefecture. At one time this area was famous for sericulture, but it has been declining. On a per hectare basis, raising cocoons is probably more profitable than rice, though price is liable to fluctuate, and cultivation is very labor intensive. Only 18.5 percent of the land is in upland rice (figures of 1960). Ministry of Agriculture and Forestry, Japanese Government, *Volcanic Ash Soils in Japan* (Tokyo: Sakurai-Kosaido Printing Co. Ltd., June 1964), pp. 14, 23.

2. Been adopted into another family. The practice is common in Japan both as a means of increasing the size of family labor and to provide a male heir if a couple should not have a son.

3. The soil here is not really suited for rice cultivation, especially upland rice of which yields are very low. "Yet every farmer considers it essential to raise some rice probably because he feels ashamed to purchase it. The attitude cannot be explained in economic terms," according to an official in the prefectural government in interview with the author.

CHAPTER XIII

1. In 1961, there were 404,211 transactions of agricultural land sold to and by farmers, involving only 63,000 hectares. Sale, ownership, price, and rent of farm land are closely regulated by law. Sources: Tomomi Ashikaga, *Agriculture in Japan* (Japan FAO Association, 1963), pp. 103, Table 38, 100–102; The Ministry of Agriculture and Forestry, The Government of Japan, *Annual Report on the State of Agriculture, 1962*, p. 114; *Theory and Practice of Growing Rice* (Tokyo: Fuji Publishing Co. Ltd., 1965), p. 7.

2. Seiichi Tobata, *An Introduction to Agriculture in Japan*, Agriculture, Forestry, and Fisheries Productivity Conference (Tokyo, 1958), p. 20.

3. Holdings in this region are somewhat larger than the national average. In 1962 Iwate Prefecture had 128,255 farms on a cultivated acreage of 173,000 hectares. Of this 87,900 hectares were planted to paddy on 106,737 farms.

Statement (mimeo) giving total cultivated land area of Tohoku Region from the *Statistical Yearbook of the Ministry of Agriculture and Forestry*, 1962, p. 2.

4. Although since 1948 the law prescribes equal division of property among all children, actually a farm is rarely divided.

Land continues to be inherited by the oldest or one of the sons. The usual practice is for the other children to renounce their rights for a consideration, either by the legal process or simply by default.

R. P. Dore, *Land Reform in Japan* (London-New York: Oxford University Press, 1959), pp. 264–65.

5. The country is divided roughly into two zones: (1) the snowy, cold zone, which includes Hokkaido, Tohoku, Hokuriku, and Tosan districts; and (2) the warm zone, which includes all districts southwest of Kanto. As regards rice, most of the former are single-crop areas, while the warm districts can have 2 and at places 3 crops a year on the same land.

Katsumi Amatatsu, *Growing Rice in Japan*, Agriculture, Forestry and Fisheries Productivity Conference, Agricultural Development Series 11 (Tokyo: December 1959), p. 37.

6. Average for Iwate Prefecture in 1962 was 432 kilograms per 10 ares (4.080 *tan* = 1 acre, 1 *tan* = 9.915 ares or 0.245 acre). Average yield for Tohoku District as a whole was 427 kg. per 10 ares (1955–61). The national average for the same period was 378 kilograms. In 1963, however, Tohoku average stood at 443 kg. of brown rice per tan. It was the highest for any district in the whole country. Excluding Hokkaido, average yields in Tohoku used to be the lowest in Japan till after World War II, as shown in the table on p. 266.

Takekazu Ogura, *Agricultural Development in Modern Japan* (Japan FAO Association, 1963), p. 451, Table 24–1;

Statistical Yearbook of the Ministry of Agriculture and Forestry, 1962.

7. Price protection is given to rice, wheat, barley, and naked barley.

8. For some years the government had been making an earnest effort to encourage and persuade farmers to form agricultural cooperatives in order to enlarge the operational unit of farms. It would enable them to utilize bigger and more efficient machinery more economically, make labor more productive, and also help meet the situation created by the increasing shortage of labor in the rural areas. Till the early 1960's, however, the effort had not been very successful. Thus, by 1961, there were in all about 2500 farming cooperatives, of which 90 percent were partial—in some specified field only. Of them 70 percent were in livestock and poultry breeding. Even their average scale

National and District Levels of Paddy Rice Yield
per 10 Ares, by Period, 1883–1961 (in Kilograms)

Period District	National	Hok-kaido	Tohoku	Kinki	Northern Kyushu
Early Meiji Period	204	169	181	245	205
(1883–92)	(100%)*	(83%)	(89%)	(120%)	(100%)
Late Meiji Period	226	182	195	272	238
(1893–07)	(111)	(89)	(96)	(133)	(118)
Early Taisho-Showa	279	198	262	330	299
(1908–30)	(137)	(97)	(128)	(162)	(147)
Late Taisho-Showa	299	188	285	339	328
(1931–40)	(147)	(92)	(140)	(166)	(161)
War Period	282	204	218	314	294
(1941–45)	(138)	(100)	(107)	(154)	(144)
Postwar Years	316	267	327	331	332
(1946–54)	(155)	(131)	(160)	(162)	(363)
Present Period	378	344	427	371	267
(1955–61)	(185)	(169)	(209)	(182)	(180)

* Percentages, both national and district, were calculated on the basis of the national average of the rice yield per 10 ares in the Early Meiji Period.

moreover, was less than 5 hectares in area, and less than 10 cows, and less than 100 pigs per unit. They could scarcely be described as large, or even medium-scale operations.

Ashikaga, op. cit., p. 91;

Economic Planning Agency Japanese Government, Economic Survey of Japan (1961–1962) (Tokyo: The Japan Times, Ltd.), p. 137.

CHAPTER XIV

1. See Theory and Practice of Growing Rice, op. cit., p. 17, Table 1—11.

2. Tobata, op. cit., p. 20.

3. The figures exclude Hokkaido which is more sparsely populated than the rest of the country because of its soil and climate. See Ashikaga, op. cit., p. 80, Table 27.

Notes

4. *Ibid.*, p. 78, Table 26.

5. Both quotations are from *A Strategy for New Agriculture* (Japan FAO Association, 1962), pp. 9, 10.

6. Hogs and poultry are fed mainly on imported commercial feed concentrates. See Ashikaga, *op. cit.*, p. 53, Table 14.

7. *Annual Report on The State of Agriculture, 1962,* p. 78.

8. Whereas the swine population increased by 52.7 percent over the corresponding month a year earlier, hog raising farmers increased only 10.3 percent. In February 1962 the total number of hog farmers was 1,025,260, and of hogs, 4,032,740. *Annual Report on The State of Agriculture, 1962,* p. 80.

9. By 1880 thirty-four foreign experts on agriculture had been engaged by the Japanese government. Thereafter, the tide turned in favor of native and more rustic talent. Of plants also, in 1876 Shinjuku Experimental Station—established in 1872 for this purpose—was growing 313 strains of foreign wheats and 398 varieties of foreign trees and grasses in order to test them. Johannes Hirschmeier, *The Origins of Entrepreneurship in Meiji Japan* (Cambridge, Mass.: Harvard University Press, 1964), p. 128.

R. P. Dore, *Agricultural Improvement in Japan: 1870–1900*, Economic Development and Cultural Change, Vol. 9, No. 1, Pt. 2, p. 72.

10. See Ogura, *op. cit.*, p. 568, Table 29-1.

11. *A Strategy for New Agriculture*, pp. 14, 15.

CHAPTER XV

1. See *Japanese Import Requirement: Projections of Agricultural Supply and Demand for 1965, 1970 and 1975,* Institute of Agricultural Economic Research, Dept. of Agricultural Economics (University of Tokyo, March 1964), p. 61, Table 30.

2. Phosphate content is generally very low in volcanic ash soil, and it is poor in dispersible colloidal clay content. Ministry of Agriculture and Forestry, Japanese Government, *Volcanic Ash Soils in Japan* (Tokyo: Sakurai-Kosaido Printing Co. Ltd., June 1964), pp. 73, 165.

3. Soil dressing of paddy fields with new, usually clayey soils is widely practiced in Japan as a means of radically improv-

Notes

ing its productivity. Weathered product of basalt, andesite, chlorite schist and shale, and also river or lake-bottom muds are used as materials for the admixture. Sources: Ogura, *op. cit.*, p. 379; *Theory and Practice of Growing Rice,* pp. 16, 19, 203, 486, 495; *Volcanic Ash Soils in Japan,* p. 188.

4. While Kyushu begins at 31 degrees N, Hokkaido ends at about 45 degrees N latitude. Altitudes range from 30 m to about 3000 m. The annual mean temperature lies between approximately 5 degrees C to 17 degrees C.

5. It is impossible to grow rice in the winter months anywhere in Japan as the annual range (between the highest and lowest) of temperature of most districts is over 20 degrees C. Most of the rice in Japan is grown in districts where the average temperature is from 10 to 15 degrees C.

6. In Purchas, *Pilgrimes,* p. 240, quoted in *They Came to Japan: An Anthology of European Reports on Japan, 1543–1640,* by Michael Cooper, S.J. (Berkeley & Los Angeles: University of California Press, 1965), p. 7.

7. Growth rate of the total Japanese economy in the years 1955–60 was over 10 percent per annum. For the decade, it averaged more than 9 percent a year. It was the highest in the world (outside the Communist bloc). The ratio of savings was 36 percent in 1960 and 40 percent in 1961, as against 25 percent in the years 1950–55. *Japanese Import Requirement,* p. 25.

8. It comes to an investment of about 26,545 yen per person actively engaged in agriculture. Total number of farm households in December 1961 was 5,923,000. It gives an average investment of a little over 58,000 yen per household. *Annual Report on the State of Agriculture 1962,* pp. 4, 96, 101; *Japan Economic Year Book, 1965, The Oriental Economist,* p. 94, Table 4.

9. Income from nonfarm sources constituted 48.5 percent of the total earnings of a farm family in 1961. The per capita farming income of those engaged in agriculture was only about 30 percent of the income of the nonagriculture population. *Annual Report on The State of Agriculture 1962,* p. 14; *Japanese Import Requirement,* p. 54.

10. The figures exclude Hokkaido. Nearly 74 percent of this credit came from cooperatives. Average rate of interest charged by cooperatives is around 10 percent per annum. In

Notes

1961 farm loans constituted a mere 4.8 percent of the total loans made by all the finance institutions in the country. Ashikaga, pp. 11–12, 93, Table 35; 92–98.

11. In 1961 investment in farm implements was 38.1 percent, as against 26.3 percent in land, 17.8 percent in buildings, 5.2 percent in plant, and 12.4 percent in livestock. Expenditure on machinery per acre in 1955 was estimated to be three times as high as in 1934–36. Ashikaga, *op. cit.*, p. 67, Table 21; p. 68.

12. According to the 1960 Agricultural Census. Of the paddy fields, 36.4 percent were cultivated by power. The number of farms using tractors in 1950 was 31,356. *Japanese Import Requirement*, p. 58.

13. In 1960 the total number of power cultivators and tractors was 517,000. Some farms would be owning more than one of the smaller machines. By December 1961, however, the number of power tillers had increased to 1,020,000, and the number of households using them had gone up to 54 percent of the total. Sources: *Japanese Import Requirement*, p. 58, Table 29; *Annual Report on the State of Agriculture 1962*, p. 90; Ashikaga, *op. cit.*, p. 73.

14. Also in 1960, there were 843,000 husking machines, 262,000 power sprayers, 143,000 power dusters, and 362,000 power cutters. *Japanese Import Requirement*, p. 58, Table 29.

15. See Ashikaga, *op. cit.*, p. 69, Table 23.

16. In 1963–64, whereas North America (including Canada) used 44 kilograms of fertilizer per hectare of arable land, Japan used 298 kilograms. The average for Western Europe was 120 kilograms per hectare for the same year. Per acre consumption of nitrogen in the U.S. in 1961 was 13 pounds as against 111 pounds in Japan. See John W. Mellor, *The Economics of Agricultural Development* (Ithaca, New York: Cornell University Press, 1966), p. 301; Food and Agriculture Organization of the United Nations, *The State of Food and Agriculture 1965: Review of the Second Postwar Decade* (Rome, Italy, 1965), p. 93, Table VI–1.

Investment in pesticides came to $4.40 per acre in Japan, as against $1.40 per acre in the U.S. See *The State of Food and Agriculture*, Agriculture Division USAID (New Delhi, March 1968), p. 13.

17. Labor Requirements per 100 Kilograms for Agricultural Production in the U.S.A. and Japan

		Rice	Wheat	White Potato	Milk
U.S.	1910	5.8 hrs.	4.1 hrs.	2.8 hrs.	8.4 hrs.
	1950	1.3	1.0	1.0	5.3
Japan	1954–56	49.0	54.0	7.0	17.1

Theory and Practice of Growing Rice, p. 15, Table 1–10.

CHAPTER XVI

1. Overall agricultural production in Japan in the postwar period has been increasing at a considerably faster pace than the growth of population. Level of production in 1960 was 39 percent higher than the 1950–52 level. Its annual growth rate averaged 3.8 percent. Between 1955–60 the rate of increase was 4 percent every year. Sources: Bruce F. Johnston, *Agricultural Development and Economic Transformation: A Comparative Study of the Japanese Experience*. Reprinted from Food Research Institute Studies, Vol. III, No. 3 (Stanford: Stanford University, November, 1962), p. 252; *The State of Food and Agriculture 1965*, pp. 20, 59; Ogura, *op. cit.*, pp. 91, 93; Ashikaga, *op. cit.*, pp. 6–7.

2. In 1963, value of American exports of rice came to $176.6 million (f.o.b.). Of this, however, 49 percent ($86 million worth) was under special programs, mostly under Title I of Public Law 480. Cash sales for dollars amounted to $83 million, and these received government subsidy to bridge the gap between U.S. domestic and world prices—an average of $50 per ton in 1962–63. Acreage under rice is controlled and limited by the U.S. government. Food and Agriculture Organization of the United Nations, *FAO Rice Report 1964* (Rome, Italy, 1964), pp. 10, 11.

3. In 1963 U.S. exports of rice were the third largest in the world (1,197,000 metric tons of milled rice). The other two countries with higher exports were Burma (1,664,000 tons) and Thailand (1,442,000 tons). Sources: *The State of Food and Agriculture 1965*, p. 45; *FAO Rice Report 1964*, pp. 10, 11, 18, 20; *FAO Rice Report 1965*, pp. 12, 15.

Notes

4. Mississippi and Missouri also grow rice, but on a smaller scale.

5. American farmers spend $24 million every year to control weeds in rice. Yet, losses due to weed competition are assessed at more than $60 million per annum. In 1959 only 31.8 percent of the rice farmers in Japan were using herbicides on about 20 percent of the cultivated area. See *Rice In the United States: Varieties and Production* (Washington, D.C.: USDA, 1966), p. 111; *Rural Economic Problems*, Vol. 1, No. 1, May 1964, The International Association for Agricultural Economics in Japan (Tokyo, Japan: Fuji Publishing Co. Ltd.), p. 8.

6. Of the important ones, The Rice Experimental Station at Crowley, Louisiana, was established in 1909. The Biggs Rice Field Station in California, and the Rice Experiment Station at Beaumont, Texas, were founded in 1912. The Rice Branch Experiment Station at Stuttgart, Arkansas, was established in 1926. *Rice in the United States*, p. 19.

7. Cost of production per metric ton of rice in Arkansas —the largest rice producing state in the U.S.—came to $112 in 1962. In Japan (1961) it was $114. Cost of production per acre in both these countries is equally high and is the highest in the world. Comparing costs between countries, however, is difficult and can be misleading. The above estimates were prepared by the Food and Agriculture Organization of the United Nations. Food and Agriculture Organization of the United Nations, *FAO Rice Report 1963* (Rome, Italy, 1963), pp. 30, 31, 32.

8. Average yield in hundred kilograms per hectare in Japan in 1962–63, was 52.8 as against 41.8 in the United States in the same year. *Production Year Book 1964*, Vol. 18 (Rome, Italy: FAO, 1965), p. 54.

9. In 1962–63, the area under paddy in Japan was 3,285,000 hectares as against 724,000 hectares in the United States. In wheat the position is reversed in terms of acreage and volume. In 1962–63, United States had 17,620,000 hectares under wheat, and produced a total crop of 29,765,000 metric tons. Japan had only 642,000 hectares in wheat and produced 1,630,000 tons. Herein too, however, the Japanese yield per hectare was 2540 kilograms of wheat per hectare as against the American yield of 1690 kg. In 1961–62 climatically a more favorable year, the Japanese yields hit the high of 2740 kg. per hectare, while U.S. yields were 1610 kg. The climate of Japan is

not particularly favorable for wheat cultivation. It usually rains heavily at the time of harvest. Also, since all land under wheat in Japan is double-cropped, it requires early ripening. This has retarded the development of high-yielding strains. See *FAO Rice Report 1965*, p. 17, Table 7; Food and Agriculture Organization of the United Nations, *The World Rice Economy in Figures 1909–1963*, Commodity Reference Series No. 3 (Rome, Italy, 1965), pp. 27, 31; *FAO Rice Report 1964*, p. 34, Table A; p. 25, Table 9; *Japanese Import Requirement*, pp. 79, 85; *Production Year Book 1964, FAO*, p. 39.

10. In 1962–63 in Japan, 150,000 hectares was in upland unirrigated rice. Percentage of double-cropping in paddy fields (1958–60) was 32.6 percent. Of the total (6,120,000 hectares) cultivated land, 30 percent was double-cropped. *Japanese Import Requirement*, pp. 61, 79, 83, 85; *The World Rice Economy in Figures 1909–1963*, p. 31.

11. The population of Japan in 1960 was 93,900,000. The total land area is 142,700 square miles. Per capita calorie content of national average food supplies was estimated for 1963–64, at 2280 calories per day for Japan, and at 3120 for United States. Consumption of cereals in the U.S., however, was only 65.4 kilograms per head per year in 1963, as against 148.3 kg. in Japan. Sources: *Japanese Import Requirement*, p. 43; Lester R. Brown, *The Japanese Agricultural Economy*, Economic Research Service, Foreign, 7 (Washington, D.C.: USDA, June 1961), p. 2; *The State of Food and Agriculture 1965*, pp. 74–75, 232, 236.

12. According to Harrison Brown and his associates at California Institute of Technology. Harrison Brown, *The Next Hundred Years* (New York: Viking Press, 1957), quoted in Modern Land Policy, Papers of the Land Economics Institute (Urbana: University of Illinois Press, 1960), pp. 76–77.

13. Commercial crops like cotton that were important in Japan a century ago have practically disappeared now. Flax, sugarcane, and millets have declined. According to R. P. Dore, substitution of one crop for another in response to price is almost exclusively limited to upland agriculture. It would be rare for a paddy field to be converted to grow mulberry, for example, however much more profit the latter may promise. Sources: Dore, *Agricultural Improvement in Japan: 1870–1900*, pp. 89, 90; Dore, *Land Reform in Japan*, p. 8.

14. Hokkaido lies between 40 degrees N and 45 degrees

N. Average temperature is 15 degrees C or higher during the 5 months of May to September, and 17 degrees C or higher during June-August.

15. William S. Clark, in his report to Director Kuroda of the colonial government of Hokkaido, in 1877. Tadashi (Gan) Watanabe, *A Brief History of the Development of the Dairy Industry in Hokkaido, Japan* (Sapporo, Japan: Bunyeido Printing Co., Foreign Dept., July, 1964), p. 10.

16. These were imported under the advice of Horace Capron and critically commented upon as quoted by his deputy, Edwin Dun, originally from Ohio, in his "Reminiscences." Dun came to Hokkaido in 1875, and after a few years residence, "ascertained that at least 90 percent of the Island was unfit for cultivation of any kind, owing to the very mountainous terrain and the extensive area destroyed by volcanic ash for agricultural purposes." Watanabe, *op. cit.*, pp. 3, 6.

17. Ogura, *op. cit.*, p. 443.

18. Set up in upland field, protected nurseries have frames covered with oil paper or vinyl sheeting. Seeds are sown in late April and transplanting is done in late May. Flowering and maturing is accelerated thus by 10 days or more and the crop gives substantially higher yields. Moreover, whereas the typical lowland paddy nursery requires one-twenty-fifth as large an area as of the main field, the upland protected nursery needs only one-sixtieth of the area of the main field for the seed bed. See Ogura, *op. cit.*, p. 441; Johnston, *op. cit.*, p. 249.

19. In net product per agricultural worker by agricultural districts, Hokkaido ranked first in 1961, with 168,000 yen. Its increase in output per worker, equal to that of the national average rate of 12.8 percent over the previous year, was due wholly to increase in the production of rice. *Annual Report on The State of Agriculture 1962*, p. 33.

20. See Ogura, *op. cit.*, p. 466, Fig. 24-3.

CHAPTER XVII

1. During interviews with the author.

2. He tends to equate production maximization with profit maximization. " 'Labor' as defined in a modern economic sense does not exist in the farm community," according to economist Seeichi Tobata. Also, according to Clark and Haswell,

"The Japanese Ministry of Agriculture publish rice yields and labour inputs for the 46 prefectures (administrative regions) of Japan. There is no discernible statistical relation between these two. Labour inputs range from 1400 to 2500 man-hours (including female labour) /ha/year, all of them apparently above the economic limit. This result suggests the conclusion that above this limit additional labour inputs yield, in general, no return." Traditionally, saving on labor has never been the prime motive in the mechanization of farm implements in Japan as it has been in the United States. See Colin Clark and Margaret Haswell, *The Economics of Subsistence Agriculture* (London: Macmillan & Co. Ltd., 1964), p. 89. Tobata, *An Introduction to Agriculture of Japan*, p. 15.

3. Except in recent years when shortage of labor is compelling many farmers to use chemicals for weed control. The difference in 2 years between 1963 and 1965 in the number of weeds in the paddy fields was striking as a consequence.

4. For working intensity and energy consumption required by the different methods of transplanting, see *Theory and Practice of Growing Rice*, p. 396, Table 6–25.

5. Harvesting consumes 20 percent of the total labor input in rice cultivation. *Theory and Practice of Growing Rice*, pp. 425–26.

6. There were 150,000 air dryers in use in 1960. For natural drying the grain is spread thinly on a straw mat out in the sun. Both the threshers and hullers are hand-fed. *Theory and Practice of Growing Rice*, p. 440.

7. Experiments in the United States had given similar results. "Yields of direct-seeded and transplanted rice were compared in a study conducted by Adair and others (7) in the major United States rice areas during a 3-year period starting in 1937. . . . During the 3 years of these tests, the average yields of some of the varieties at some locations were significantly higher from direct seeding than from transplanting. None of the varieties at any of the stations produced significantly higher average yields when transplanted than when directly sown." Agricultural Research Service, USDA, *Rice In The United States: Varieties and Production*, Handbook No. 289 (Washington, D.C.: GPO, 1966), p. 91.

8. *Japanese Import Requirement*, p. 87, Table 34.

9. In interview with the author in the fall of 1963.

10. *Japanese Import Requirement,* p. 82.

11. Whereas, in an ordinary irrigated nursery the date of transplanting falls at a time when the average air temperature is 15–16 degrees C, by using the protected rice nursery the growing of seedlings and transplanting can be pushed earlier by a month or more. See Ashikaga, *op. cit.,* pp. 75–76; *Theory and Practice of Growing Rice,* p. 376; *Japanese Import Requirement,* p. 82.

12. In interview with the author.

CHAPTER XVIII

1. In interview with the author in the fall of 1965.

2. This was after the adoption in 1960 of the formula of production cost and income compensation as the basis for determining the procurement price of rice. It attempted to meet the production costs of a marginal producer as well as provide a reasonable wage for family labor. In the fiscal year of 1962, as a consequence, financial loss sustained by the government in supporting domestic rice and selling it cheap to the consumer amounted to 61,600 million yen—a sum greater than the total budget (55,700 yen) for the year for investment in the entire sector of agriculture. Prior to 1960, between 1946–51, the basis of fixing procurement price was price parity, and between 1952–59, income parity. Until about 1952, when agricultural production had been fully restored to the prewar level, price of rice was kept relatively low, the government relying mainly on compulsion to ensure deliveries. All rice had to be sold to the government. Till 1951 domestic rice and wheat were both cheaper than imported grains. After 1953, however, foreign wheat, and after 1954, Southeast Asian rice cost less than the home product.

For a comparison of the average rice price paid by the government and the black market prices between 1953 and 1961, see *Annual Report on the State of Agriculture 1962,* p. 56, Table III–7. Other sources: Ogura, *op. cit.,* pp. 208–9; Dore, *Land Reform in Japan,* pp. 229, 242; Ashikaga, *op. cit.,* p. 6.

3. In a SCAP memorandum addressed to the Japanese Government on December 9, 1945. It listed all "the pernicious ills which have long blighted the agrarian structure" of Japan, and further ordered the government to submit by March 15,

1946, proposals for land reform and a complete overhaul of the agricultural system. *Land Reform in Japan,* pp. 23, 135.

4. Dore finds little or no statistical correlation between postwar increases in yield of rice and the land reform. Nor did this author in interviews with former tenant-farmers. Many insisted that they had worked harder before the reform. "We had to," they said. Most felt that they had worked just as hard then as since. They attributed postwar increase in production mainly to new higher yielding strains of seed and better techniques of soil fertilization and plant protection than to any change in their attitude, motivation, or quality and quantity of effort and husbandry.

Land Reform in Japan, pp. 217, 254.

5.   THE TOKUGAWA SHOGUNS

1603–16	Ieyasu *(First)*
1616–23	Hidetada *(Second)*
1623–51	Iemitsu *(Third)*
1651–80	Ietsuna *(Fourth)*
1680–1709	Tsunayoshi *(Fifth)*
1709–13	Ienobu *(Sixth)*
1713–16	Ietsugu *(Seventh)*
1716–45	Yoshimune *(Eighth)*
1745–60	Ieshige *(Ninth)*
1760–86	Ieharu *(Tenth)*
1787–1837	Ienari *(Eleventh)*
1837–53	Ieyoshi *(Twelfth)*
1853–58	Iesada *(Thirteenth)*
1858–66	Iemochi *(Fourteenth)*
1866–67	Hitotsubashi Keiki *(Fifteenth)*

George Sansom, *A History of Japan 1615–1867* (Stanford, California: Stanford University Press, 1963), p. 2.

6. Below the daimyo there were other vassals of the shogun of lower rank. There were about 5000 *hatamoto* (Banner Knights), and another 15,000 *go-kenin* (House Men). They all had grants in varying measures of rice and constituted what might be called the rentier class. The office of the shogun was first created in 1192, when the emperor granted to Minamoto-no-Yoritomo, through the title of shogun, supreme authority over all military affairs and military houses. In the battles of 1600 and 1614–15, the Tokugawa shogun was able to gain powers of investiture over the other daimyo houses. It conferred on

him ultimate control over the administrative apparatus of the entire country. See G. B. Sansom, *Japan, A Short Cultural History* (New York: Appleton-Century-Crofts, 1962), p. 464; Robert E. Ward and Dankwart A. Rustow (Eds.), *Political Modernization in Japan and Turkey* (Princeton, New Jersey: Princeton University Press, 1964), p. 17.

7. Sansom, *A History of Japan 1615–1867*, p. 6.

8. Not only was the division of property unequal between sons—the greater share of it going only to the eldest—but the younger boys were not permitted to wear silk (only cotton) after the age of seven. They were forbidden also the pursuit of letters after the age of seventeen and any indulgence in fashionable and frivolous pastimes. Thomas C. Smith, *The Agrarian Origins of Modern Japan* (Stanford, California: Stanford University Press, 1959), p. 15 f.

9. William W. Lockwood, *The Economic Development of Japan: Growth and Structural Change 1868–1938* (Princeton, New Jersey: Princeton University Press, 1954), p. 78.

10. According to John Whitney Hall, in "The Nature of Traditional Society" in *Political Modernization in Japan and Turkey*, p. 27.

11. *Gonin-gumi* were groups of 5 householders jointly responsible for the administration of the village. They had to certify marriages, successions, testaments, and contracts for sale, purchase, and loans. They were appointed by the rulers and were, therefore, essentially agents of the government. Sansom, *A History of Japan 1615–1867*, pp. 101–2.

12. *Ibid.*, p. 99.

13. Smith, *The Agrarian Origins of Modern Japan*, p. 42.

14. *Ibid.*, pp. 25, 25b.

15. Edo, a fishing village in 1590, had grown into a crowded metropolis of more than half a million people by 1731—probably the largest in the world. By 1800 Edo had a million inhabitants; Osaka and Kyoto had populations of more than 400,000 each; while people in Nagoya, Kamazawa, and Nagasaki numbered between 50,000 and 60,000. Besides, there were roughly 40 castle towns with more than 10,000 people each. See Smith, *The Agrarian Origins of Modern Japan*, pp. 67–68.

16. According to Sydney Crawcour, even in the 1790's, it was not unusual for farmers to sell the bulk of the rice left

after tax. In any case, a large portion of the rice received in tax was eventually marketed. There were, however, wide regional variations. In the more commercialized areas the proportion of agricultural output marketed directly by farmers would be very much higher than in the more backward regions such as Kyushu, Shikoku, and Hokuriku. By 1860, according to Crawcour, "It seems safe to say that in Japanese agriculture as a whole over half and probably nearly two-thirds of output was marketed in one form or another."

William W. Lockwood, *The State and Economic Enterprise in Japan: Essays in the Political Economy of Growth* (Princeton, New Jersey: Princeton University Press, 1965), pp. 39–40, 57.

17. G. B. Sansom, *The Western World and Japan* (New York: Alfred A. Knopf, 1950), pp. 225, 226.

18. Sansom, *A History of Japan, 1615–1867*, p. 185.

19. Sansom, *The Western World and Japan*, p. 225.

CHAPTER XIX

1. Thomas C. Smith, "The Japanese Village in the Seventeenth Century," *Journal of Economic History*, Vol. XII, No. 1 (Winter 1952), p. 14.

2. Sansom, *Japan, A Short Cultural History*, p. 516.

3. Smith, *The Agrarian Origins of Modern Japan*, p. 83; also, pp. 127, 160.

According to Nakamura, "As a consequence of the food surplus policy, in most years the prices of agricultural products —particularly food products—were probably depressed relative to non-agricultural products." See James I. Nakamura, *Agricultural Production and The Economic Development of Japan, 1873–1922* (Princeton, New Jersey: Princeton University Press, 1966), p. 138 footnote 7.

4. By 1800, 20 percent of the population is believed to have been living in urban centers. Thomas C. Smith, *Landlords and Rural Capitalists in the Modernization of Japan* (Stanford, California: Stanford University, reprinted from the *Journal of Economic History*, June 1956), p. 169.

5. Sansom, *Japan, A Short Cultural History*, p. 516.

6. Transplanting would have to be completed in less than 10 days at this period. The village document is cited in Thomas C. Smith, *The Land Tax in the Tokugawa Period*, re-

printed from the *Journal of Asian Studies*, Vol. XVIII, No. 1 (November 1958), p. 10, (footnote 15). Also see Smith, *The Agrarian Origins of Modern Japan*, pp. 218 note 1, 83, 84, 110, 120, 124–127.

7. *Ibid.*, pp. 110, 111.

8. Quoted by Smith, *ibid.*, p. 126 footnote d.

9. Sansom, *Japan, A Short Cultural History*, p. 465.

10. Several scholars hold that the land tax under the Tokugawas was so heavy that agriculture generally yielded no surplus to the cultivator. Or at least, whatever the surplus, it was determined mainly by the land tax. See Smith, *The Agrarian Origins of Modern Japan*, p. 100 n; Smith, *The Land Tax in the Tokugawa Period*, p. 10.

11. Smith, *Landlords and Rural Capitalists in the Modernization of Japan*, pp. 178–79.

12. Higher than the estimated production in the interim years between surveys would naturally lower the tax rate. The benefit, however, went to improving peasants *only* in proportion to the increase in the productivity of their land. "For other holders it may have been very heavy. Hence the paradox of oppressive taxation and peasant poverty on the one hand and rising yields and the investment in land on the other may be an apparent contradiction only; it is probable that the two parts of the statement apply to different groups of peasants." See Smith, *The Agrarian Origins of Modern Japan*, pp. 100, 101, (footnote n). See also Smith, *The Land Tax in the Tokugawa Period*, pp. 10, 13.

13. Dr. Hugh Borton in *Peasant Uprisings in Japan*, quoted by Sansom, *The Western World and Japan*, p. 238.

14. Sansom, *A History of Japan, 1615–1867*, pp. 15, 99.

15. The amount of tax collected from agricultural land improved as a result from 1,320,000 *koku* of rice in 1736, to 1,800,000 *koku* by 1744. It was the most ever collected in the Tokugawa period. Sansom, *A History of Japan 1615–1867*, p. 166.

16. Thomas C. Smith, *Political Change and Industrial Development in Japan: Government Enterprise, 1868–1880* (Stanford, California: Stanford University Press, 1955), pp. 17, 18.

17. Smith, *The Japanese Village in the Seventeenth Century*, p. 14.

18. Smith, *The Agrarian Origins of Modern Japan*, p. 129.

19. *Ibid.*, p. 128.
20. Sansom, *Japan, A Short Cultural History*, p. 517.
21. Smith, *The Agrarian Origins of Modern Japan*, p. 161.

CHAPTER XX

1. According to Thomas C. Smith, the decades following the Restoration brought greater changes to Japan than the 1789 Revolution did to France.
Thomas C. Smith, "Japan's Aristocratic Revolution," *The Yale Review*, Vol. 50 (March 1961), p. 371.
2. A supplementary survey undertaken between 1885 and 1889 revealed that about 20 percent of the farmed area had escaped registration and was therefore omitted from the initial taxation list. Ogura, *op. cit.*, p. 183.
3. An additional one-third of the land tax was levied by local authorities. It raised the total tax to 4 percent of the value of land. *Ibid.*, p. 5.
4. This is why the rate of tax assessment was reduced in 1877, from 3 to 2½ percent.
Smith, *Political Change and Industrial Development in Japan: Government Enterprise, 1868–1880*, p. 79 footnote 22.
5. According to Smith, barring a small group of communists, "no pre-war party thought of the past, as such, as a barrier to progress." Smith, "Japan's Aristocratic Revolution," pp. 370, 371, 382.
6. Sansom, *The Western World and Japan*, p. 320.
7. *Ibid.*, p. 339.
8. Dore, *Land Reform in Japan*, p. 50.
9. Smith, *Political Change and Industrial Development in Japan: Government Enterprise, 1868–1880*, pp. 72–73.
10. Even in 1908, whereas the farmer paid 28 percent of his income in taxes, merchants and industrialists were required to pay only 14 percent. *The Economic Development of Japan: Growth and Structural Change 1868–1938*, p. 26.
11. P. Mayet, an agricultural expert employed by the Japanese government at the time, estimated that the land tax in 1878 was 2 to 7 times the rates charged in European countries at this period. *Agricultural Insurance* (London, 1893), p. 230 cited in *The Economic Development of Japan: Growth and Structural Change 1868–1938*, p. 98.

Notes

12. According to the original regulation, land was meant to be reevaluated every five years. Actually, it never was. In March 1884 another regulation was issued postponing reevaluation indefinitely. The original assessment therefore remained in force. As in Tokugawa times, therefore, one method of lowering the tax was by improving production. See Lockwood, *The State and Economic Enterprise in Japan: Essays in the Political Economy of Growth*, p. 252; Smith, *Political Change and Industrial Development in Japan: Government Enterprise, 1868–1880*, p. 79 footnote 21. Kazushi Ohkawa and Henry Rosovsky, "The Role of Agriculture in Modern Japanese Economic Development," reprint from *Economic Development and Cultural Change*, Vol. IX, No. 1, Part II (October 1960), p. 51.

13. Payment of the land-tax in rice was admitted until 1889. Thereafter, it had to be paid in cash. By 1887, however, money payment had become general. See Ogura, *op. cit.,* p. 184; *Rural Economic Problems*, Vol. 2, No. 1 (May 1965), The International Association for Agricultural Economics in Japan (Tokyo, Japan: Fuji Publishing Co. Ltd.), p. 3.

14. *Land Reform in Japan*, p. 17.

15. Even in 1943, rent on 66 percent of all tenanted farm land was paid in kind. On another 13 percent it was fixed in kind but paid in cash at current prices. *The Economic Development of Japan: Growth and Structural Change 1868–1938*, p. 26, (footnote 34).

16. Custom and social pressure of village opinion, however, usually protected the tenant from arbitrary dispossession. Even subtenancy or the private transfer of land between tenants, that is sale of tenancy rights, was often winked at. Lease agreements were mostly oral. *Land Reform in Japan*, p. 42.

17. Japanese population increased from 35 million in 1875 to 69 million in 1935. At the time of the Meiji Restoration there were about 225 persons per square mile. By 1935 the figure had increased to 469. Rate of population growth between 1878 and 1917 varied from 0.8 to 1.3 percent per year. From 1918 to 1942, it ranged between 1.2 to 1.5 percent per annum. The data, however, are not free of controversy: *The Economic Development of Japan: Growth and Structural Change 1868–1938*, pp. 153–54; *The Role of Agriculture in Modern Japanese Economic Development*, pp. 46, 56; *The Western World and Japan*, pp. 228–31; *Agricultural Production and the Economic Development of Japan, 1873–1922*, pp. 126, 140 ff.

18. Places of under 10,000 population accounted for 82 percent of the people in 1898. In 1930 agricultural labor in Japan was 50.3 percent of the total labor force despite the rapid pace of industrialization. This compared with 16.3 percent in Germany in 1933; 6.2 percent in England in 1938; and 18.8 percent in the U.S. in 1940. See *The Economic Development of Japan: Growth and Structural Change 1868–1938*, p. 18. Thomas C. Smith, *Old Values and New Techniques in the Modernization of Japan*, Stanford University (Paper read at the Annual Meeting of the American Historical Association in 1954), p. 363.

19. Interest, taxes, and rent amounted to 1259 million yen in 1930, according to the Cabinet Bureau of Statistics. Of this 336 million went in taxes, 173 million yen in rent to *absentee* landlords, and another 173 million in interest charges to persons outside agriculture. See *The Economic Development of Japan: Growth and Structural Change 1868–1938*, pp. 57, 100, 474.

20. In 1937 there were in all 187,813 power-operated machines owned by farmers in Japan. Another 59,047 were available from rental agencies. It came to 1 to every 22 families. About two-thirds of them were small kerosene or gasoline operated units averaging 2.9 hp. It represented a three-fold increase over the decade since 1927.

Number of Carts, Motor Vehicles, and Bicycles
Registered in Japan Proper, 1877–1937*

	1877	1897	1917	1937
Horsecarts	782	86,596	216,574	307,889
Oxcarts	1,786	16,430	35,362	111,146
Other goods-carts, human or animal drawn	158,240	1,225,923	1,936,406	1,519,334
Rickshas	136,761	200,690	113,274	15,376
Bicycles	—	—	1,073,444	7,878,463
Motor vehicles	—	—	3,856	128,735

*Data for 1877–1917 from Asahi Shimbun-sha, Nippon Keizai Tōkei Sōkan, Tokyo, 1930, p. 833; for 1937 from Imperial Cabinet, Bureau of Statistics, Nippon Teikoku Tōkei Nenkan, no. 58 (Tokyo, 1939), p. 214.
The Economic Development of Japan: Growth and Structural Change 1868–1938, pp. 107 Table 6, 195.

Notes

1. See Smith, "The Japanese Village in the Seventeenth Century," p. 13. Of the Japanese terms, *zōri* means an elegant type of straw sandal, *hoari* a very elegant type of coat, *wakizashi* a dagger worn at the side, and *shōji* sliding doors made of fine, translucent paper mounted on a light wooden frame and used as partitions between rooms.

2. Smith, *The Agrarian Origins of Modern Japan*, p. 92.

3. Yujiro Hayami and Saburo Yamada, *Technological Progress in Agriculture*, a paper written for the International Conference on Economic Growth—Case Study of Japan's Experience (Tokyo, Japan, September 5–10, 1966), p. 10.

4. Smith, *The Agrarian Origins of Modern Japan*, p. 88.

5. See E. Sydney Crawcour, "Tokugawa Heritage," in *The State and Economic Enterprise in Japan*, p. 41.

6. Townsend Harris, *The Complete Journal of Townsend Harris* (New York, 1930), p. 441, quoted by Crawcour in *The State and Economic Enterprise in Japan*, p. 26.

7. Sir Rutherford Alcock, *The Capital of the Tycoon* (London, 1863), II, 73, quoted by Crawcour in *The State and Economic Enterprise in Japan*, p. 26.

8. Sansom, *Western World and Japan*, p. 228.

1. According to Rosovsky, ". . . we should also take into account an important characteristic of Japanese economic life: the people work hard and continue to produce, no matter what happens. Despite the dislocations occasioned by inflation and deflation, aggregate output almost maintained itself. GDP, in 1934–36, prices, shows the following annual averages: 1879–80, 2.4 billion; 1881–85, 2.2 billion; 1886–89, 2.9 billion." Henry Rosovsky, "Japan's Transition to Economic Growth, 1868–1885," in *Industrialization in Two Systems: Essays in Honor of Alexander Gerschenkron* (New York-London: John Wiley & Sons, Inc., 1966), pp. 136, 139; see also *Economic Development of Japan: Growth and Structural Change 1868–1938*, p. 18.

2. *The Economic Development of Japan: Growth and Structural Change 1868–1938*, pp. 88, 476.

3. There was no serious setback to investment in agriculture even in the depression years. On the other hand, real income (i.e., income at constant prices) in the primary sector

(including agriculture, forestry, and fisheries) continued to increase between 1922 and 1932, from 2409 million yen to 2565 million yen. The improvement was much sharper in the post-depression era, till 1937.

According to Nakamura, growth rate of the total economy in Japan was at 3 to 5 percent a year in the interwar period after 1920, in sharp contrast to the economies of the Western nations that suffered a serious slowdown. See Ogura, *op. cit.* pp. 8, 38, 39; *Agricultural Production and the Economic Development of Japan, 1873–1922*, p. 21.

4. Labor productivity also more than doubled between the mid-1880's and mid-1930's. The increase was about 160 percent if calculated on the estimated increase in net real income produced in agriculture. *Agricultural Development and Economic Transformation: A Comparative Study of the Japanese Experience*, p. 228.

5. "The Role of Agriculture in Modern Japanese Economic Development," reprint from *Economic Development and Cultural Change*, pp. 44, 64–66.

6. Nakamura, in *The State and Economic Enterprise in Japan*, p. 274. For a more detailed exposition of Nakamura's thesis and arguments, see *Agricultural Production and the Economic Development of Japan, 1873–1922*.

7. Nakamura, in *The State and Economic Enterprise in Japan*, p. 290, also see p. 249.

8. *Ibid.*, p. 257.

9. Post-Restoration era known as *Gendai* (modern) is divided as follows: Meiji—1868–1912; Taishō—1912–1926; Shōwa—1926.

10. U.S. average yield of rice per hectare in 1934–38 was 24.7 quintals as against 36.3 quintals in Japan for the same period. In 1946 U.S. average was 23.1 as against 36.9 quintals in Japan, and in 1949 America produced 24.8 quintals per hectare against 40.2 in Japan. After 1938 Japanese production was depressed and greatly dislocated due to the war. According to Ohkawa's estimate, however, on the eve of World War II, net product per hectare of agricultural land in Japan was valued at $146. This was seven times that of U.S. Sources: "The Role of Agriculture in Modern Japanese Economic Development," reprint from *Economic Development and Cultural Change*, p. 65; *Agricultural Statistics 1962* (Washington, D.C.: USDA), p. 24; *The State and Economic Enterprise in Japan*, p. 331; Food

Notes

and Agriculture Organization of the United Nations, *Commodity Reports* (Rome, Italy, December 11, 1952), pp. 28–29, mimeo.

11. According to Nakamura, high level of savings became available in this period because of a radical redistribution of agricultural incomes after the land tax reform, and the basic fact that there was a substantial surplus above subsistence to spare. The transfer of income was from the Tokugawa ruling class, the daimyo and samurai with a high marginal propensity to consume, to peasants and landowners distilled in habits of frugality. The Meiji landlord—his was the biggest contribution to savings and investment—was according to G. Ranis, "a sharp contrast to Ricardo's wastrel type . . . there is no evidence of any sizeable diversion of the landlord's respectable surplus to high living speculation." The surplus consisted of the difference between the rent he received from tenants and the tax he paid to the state. See Nakamura, in *The State and Economic Enterprise in Japan*, pp. 260–61; Nakamura, "Meiji Land Reform, Redistribution of Income, and Saving from Agriculture," in *Economic Development and Cultural Change*, Vol. XIV, No. 4 (July 1966), pp. 428–39; G. Ranis, "The Financing of Japanese Economic Development," *Economic History Review*, XI, No. 3 (April 1959), p. 448.

12. There were three wars in this subperiod: Sino-Japanese (1894–95), Russo-Japanese (1904–05), and World War I. If the outlays of the Russo-Japanese War are included, military expenditures accounted for about a quarter of the total spending of Meiji governments between 1879 and 1912. Also, nearly 55 percent of the consolidated national and local expenditures for the entire Meiji period was spent on state services. "This," according to Harry T. Oshima, "is a phenomenon unparalleled in the financial annals of modern nations, especially for a period as long as half a century." See Harry T. Oshima, in *The State and Economic Enterprise in Japan*, pp. 367, 376. Ogura, *op. cit.*, p. 458.

13. *The Economic Development of Japan: Growth and Structural Change 1868–1938*, p. 99.

14. *The Agrarian Origins of Modern Japan*, p. 87.

15. The 3 countries are the U.S., Taiwan, and South Korea. India and others were still producing less rice per hectare in 1965 than Japan did in 1880. Lester R. Brown, *Increasing World Food Output: Problems and Prospects*, Foreign Agricul-

Notes

tural Economic Report No. 25 (Washington, D.C.: USDA, April, 1965), p. 77.

16. Ogura, *op. cit.*, p. 681.

17. Dore, *Agricultural Improvement in Japan: 1870–1900*, p. 75.

18. On the contrary, yearly revenue from land tax more than doubled between 1888–92 and 1908–12. And it continued to rise in the next decade. Its share in the total revenue declined later gradually because of an increase in income from other sources. See Ogura, *op. cit.*, pp. 22, 23, Table 1–10. *The State and Economic Enterprise in Japan*, pp. 357, 363.

19. Only after World War I did corporate enterprise assume a major share of the burden. Till 1940, however, large property incomes continued to receive a lenient and favored treatment if they were derived from nonagricultural sources. *The Economic Development of Japan: Growth and Structural Change 1868–1938*, p. 526.

20. The Matsukata Documents estimate that in 1884, rural indebtedness amounted to 230 million yen, and in 1885 to 330 million yen. Of this 4–5 percent came from national banks in respect of mortgaged land; 11–12 percent was loaned by private banks; the rest came mostly from money-lending companies (quasi-banks) and individual moneylenders at an extremely high interest rate. Rural pawn brokers were still in business in the early Meiji years, as in Tokugawa times. In 1890 Nigata Prefecture had 580 pawnshops and 25 private banks. Owners of private credit institutions were merchants and landlords, and they used credit primarily to acquire ownership of land. *Rural Economic Problems*, May 1965, pp. 25, 36, 38.

21. For the first 23 years of the Taishō-Shōwa period, weather conditions were much more equable than in the earlier Meiji years. Ogura, *op. cit.*, p. 459.

22. By the latter period of the Meiji era, many of the larger landowners had stopped cultivating their lands. See Ogura, *op. cit.*, p. 184, Table 9–1.

23. *The Economic Development of Japan: Growth and Structural Change 1868–1938*, p. 554.

24. In 1900 total subsidies amounted to less than 1 percent of the budget of the Ministry of Agriculture and Commerce. Until 1920 agriculture did not receive practically any subsidies. See *Agricultural Improvement in Japan: 1870–1900*,

Notes

p. 87; *The Role of Agriculture in Modern Japanese Economic Development,* reprint from *Economic Development and Cultural Change,* p. 62.

25. In 1910 a nation-wide rice inspection system was extended from the stage of marketing to production in order to standardize the quality of rice. This measure also benefited owner-cultivators and landlords—not tenants. Landowners could refuse to accept, as rent, rice rated as low grade by the inspection, and tenants would be penalized. Ogura, *op. cit.,* pp. 111, 165.

26. *Land Reform in Japan,* p. 65.

27. For a listing of disputes between tenants and landlords and membership figures of their respective unions in the years between 1917 and 1941, see Dore, *Land Reform in Japan,* p. 72, Table 2.

28. *Ibid.,* pp. 80, 81.

29. Some of the other notable legislative measures pertaining to agriculture taken in this period were: the Fertilizer Distribution Improvement Regulation (1930), the Major Fertilizer Industry Control Law (1936), the Livestock Insurance Law (1938), and the Central Bank for Industrial Cooperative Association Law (1923). Ogura, *op. cit.,* p. 113.

30. Supposing the rent was 1 *koku* of rice for every 2 *koku* produced per 10 ares, the rate of farm rent in 1941 would be 45 percent of the yield; in 1943, 38 percent; and in 1945, only 9 percent. Ogura, *op. cit.,* p. 59.

31. Although, between 1938 and 1946, there was a 5.3 percent increase in the *total* number of farm households. Also, while holdings under 0.5 hectare increased by 25.2 percent, those between 3 and 5 hectares decreased by 34.7 percent; and those above 5 hectares decreased by 27.1 percent in the same period. Ogura, *op. cit.,* p. 62, Table 3–8.

32. There was an upsurge of liberal and left-wing thinking in the intellectual circles at this time. The first Communist Party was formed in 1922. Its program—drafted by Bukharin—demanded the expropriation of landlords and transfer of land to the cultivators, though not as their private property. *Land Reform in Japan,* p. 74.

33. The first Japanese Constitution after the Restoration was promulgated in 1889. It created a House of Peers, like the British House of Lords, made up of nominated and elected mem-

bers of the nobility and a few privileged groups. The House of Representatives was to be elected by males over the age of 25, who paid an annual tax of 15 yen or more. This limited the initial electorate to 460,000, or slightly over 1 percent of the total population at the time. The first elections were held in 1890. Edwin O. Reischauer, *Japan: Past and Present* (Tokyo, Japan: Charles E. Tuttle Company), pp. 125–26.

CHAPTER XXIII

1. Cited by Harry T. Oshima, in *The State and Economic Enterprise in Japan*, p. 378.

2. Sources: Ogura, *op. cit.*, pp. 333, 336; *The Economic Development of Japan: Growth and Structural Change 1868–1938*, p. 511; *Land Reform in Japan*, p. 69.

3. *Land Reform in Japan*, p. 24.

4. It was essentially a continuation of the Tokugawa practice of diffusing techniques perfected by superior farmers.

5. Dore, *Agricultural Improvement in Japan: 1870–1900*, p. 77.

6. In 1948 technical education of farmers was separated from the experiment and research institutions, and entrusted to regular extension workers. Research, agricultural education, and extension are not coordinated or combined under the same roof or Ministry in Japan as in the United States. Ogura, *op. cit.*, p. 329.

7. During the 1880's outlays for agricultural research, extension, and related developmental activities in rural areas accounted for only 2–5 percent of the outlays for "non-conventional inputs" inclusive of expenditure on education. By the 1930's they accounted for nearly 10 percent. But even in 1936–40 expenditure on agricultural research by the central and prefectural governments together averaged 13 million yen annually. This represented .05 percent of the net national product and a little over 0.3 percent of the net income produced in agriculture during those years. It amounted to less than 0.4 percent of the total expenditure of the central government. Of the budget for agricultural experiment stations however, 75 percent was allocated to prefectural stations. *Agricultural Development and Economic Transformation: A Comparative Study of the Japanese Experience*, pp. 233–34.

8. For a more detailed analysis see, Hayami and Yamada in *Technological Progress in Agriculture,* especially pp. 7–8.

9. Ohkawa and Rosovsky believe that better seeds and commercial fertilizers were largely responsible for the rise in output in the 1878–1917 period, though the cost ratio to net output in agriculture was still very small—about 14 percent in 1890, and 16 percent in 1908. "The Role of Agriculture in Modern Japanese Economic Development," reprint from *Economic Development and Cultural Change,* p. 51.

10. Authors of a village report of 1782 from the Kinai set forth the view that good farming was simply a question of fertilization. *The Agrarian Origins of Modern Japan,* pp. 93–94.

11. By the early nineteenth century, fertilizer was being shipped from Osaka and other centers to all parts of the countryside. In 1714 fertilizer was the third largest (by value) item of 119 imports. *The Agrarian Origins of Modern Japan,* p. 83.

12. The government began to interfere in the marketing and pricing of fertilizer for the first time in 1930. See Ogura, *op. cit.,* p. 222 ff;

For reference to farmers in the U.S. in the following paragraph see earlier Chapter III, "Like Pigs in Clover."

13. Husked rice yield per 10 ares and per labor (day) also were greater on the smaller holdings due to more liberal inputs of fertilizer and labor. According to estimates published annually by the Ministry of Agriculture and Forestry in *The Economic Survey of Farm Households,* outlays for fertilizers increased from 36 percent of production costs of the average farm household during 1921–25 to 47 percent for the period of 1936–40. In fact, initially farmers often used chemical fertilizers indiscriminately, so that soil depletion began to occur. This was known as "denitrification," a condition brought to light by Dr. M. Shioiri in 1937–38. See Ogura, *op. cit.,* pp. 357, 358, 376, Table 19–7, 377. *Agricultural Development and Economic Transformation: A Comparative Study of the Japanese Experience,* p. 232.

14. There was a 15-fold increase in purchased fertilizers between 1878–82 and 1903–7. *Agricultural Development and Economic Transformation: A Comparative Study of the Japanese Experience,* p. 231.

15. Until then, tillage was done manually. Nevertheless, Toshio Shishido estimates that draft power in Japanese agricul-

ture increased only modestly from a million horse-power in 1878–82 to 1.2 million during 1913–17. See *Rural Economic Problems*, Vol. 1, No. 2 (November 1964), p. 89. *Agricultural Development and Economic Transformation: A Comparative Study of the Japanese Experience*, p. 231.

16. Aside from new strains of seed and the improved animal-drawn plow, farmers—*not* the government—were responsible for most of the other technological advances in agriculture of this period as well. Thus, successful land amelioration projects had been accomplished by peasants in several regions (Ishikawa and Shizuoka prefectures, for instance) in the early years of the Meiji era before government officials started a similar program. Regular planting of rice seedlings had taken place in several districts by the 1880's before government made it compulsory. *Ensuisen* method of selecting seed by using brine was an innovation of farmers in a district in Kyushu, before it was taken up by T. Yokoi, then chief of the local experiment station. The rotary weeder and treadle threshing machines also were not the inventions of qualified engineers. According to Shujiro Sawada, government experiment stations did not do much research on farm machinery during the Meiji period. See *Rural Economic Problems*, Vol. 1, No. 2 (November 1964), p. 90.

17. The diary of a farmer from Tohoku shows that the family was continually testing and discarding different varieties of rice between 1808 and 1866. Finally, he succeeded in lengthening the growing season by 17 days in this northern region by pushing forward the date of harvest from the sixth to the twenty-third day of the ninth month. It was a notable achievement and must have helped substantially to improve yields. *The Agrarian Origins of Modern Japan*, p. 95.

CHAPTER XXIV

1. Another innovation was the foot-pedal rotary thresher. It replaced the 200-years-old comb-toothed thresher after World War I. But this too had to be worked manually till the power thresher was introduced during the 1930's. The latter became widespread, however, only after the outbreak of World War II. Thresher was about the first farm implement in Japan to be mechanized. See *Rural Economic Problems*, Vol. 1, May 1964, p. 12. Ogura, *op. cit.*, pp. 411, 415–16.

Notes

2. *The Economic Development of Japan: Growth and Structural Change 1868-1938*, p. 194.

3. See Shujiro Sawada, in *The State of Economic Enterprise in Japan*, p. 331.

4. A series of government farms for experimenting and exhibiting Western methods of farming were established, such as the Naito Shinjuku Experiment Station (1872), the Botanical Experiment Yard in Mita (1874), the Shimofusa Sheep Farm in Chiba Prefecture (1875), a Tree Experiment Yard (1877), the Kobe Olive Farm (1879), and the Harima Grape Farm (1880). In addition to these, some of the prefectures set up several of their own demonstration farms and experiment stations to promote Western technology. By 1890, however, these institutions had all disappeared. Ogura, *op. cit.*, p. 321; see also, Chapter XIV, Section 3, and Chapter XVI, Section 3, of this book.

5. The extracts are from *A Woman Rice Planter*, by Patience Pennington (Cambridge, Massachusetts: Belknap Press, Harvard University Press, 1961), pp. 5, 8, 12–13, 35–36, 42, 44–45, 73–74, 78, 87.

Elizabeth used to plant 20 to 30 acres directly by hired hands on wages and rent from 100 to 150 acres on crop-sharing. Her father (1801–64) had owned seven plantations totaling 4000 acres, besides pasture and timberlands of about 9500 acres, and yet another 1900-acre plantation in North Carolina. He had 60 pairs of oxen. Rice cultivation was his major occupation. Since rice required so much labor, it was considered necessary to have it on a large scale—a conclusion exactly the opposite of that arrived at by the Japanese. In the old South, this meant plantation—using slave labor—as the producing unit. See *Ibid.*, Introduction, and pp. 3, 16.

CHAPTER XXV

1. By Elizabeth's time the slaves had long been emancipated. But her hired workers and share-croppers were almost all either former slaves of her father or their descendants. Their willingness and "capacity to work and to bear responsibilities," however, underwent a radical change, while she lacked the control that slavery gave to the master. On January 18, 1906, she writes: ". . . the hands positively refuse to come out to work when called. . . ." By the time Elizabeth gave up rice planting,

the crop had begun to shift to the coastal prairie areas of Louisiana, Texas and Arkansas, where the soil was better suited to the use of less truculent machines. Pennington, *op. cit.,* pp. xxvii–xxxi, 293, 446.

2. See Chapter XVI, Section 3.

3. See Chapter V, Section 4.

4. John M. Brewster, "Technological Advance and the Future of the Family Farm," *Journal of Farm Economics,* 40 (Dec. 1958), pp. 1957–59; see also, Hathaway, *op. cit.,* pp. 9–18.

5. *Farm Bureau Policies for 1960* (Chicago: American Farm Bureau Federation, Dec. 17, 1959), pp. 5–6.

6. *A Strategy for New Agriculture,* p. 17.

7. Absentee ownership was not permitted any more and the legal maximum limit on a family's total holding of agricultural land and of tenanted land imposed by the reform was 3 hectares and 1 hectare respectively (12 hectares and 4 hectares for Hokkaido). All land transfers were to be controlled and tenancy strictly regulated. In 1960, only 7 percent of all cultivated land was under tenancy. Ownership status among farm households in 1960 was as follows:

	Percent
Total farm households	100.0
Owner-cultivators	75.2
{Part-owner-cultivators part-tenants	18.0
{Part-tenants part-owner-cultivators	3.6
Tenants	2.9
Others	0.3

Note:

Owner-cultivators are those owning 90 percent or more of the land they cultivate.

Part-owner-cultivators part-tenants are those who own 50–90 percent of the land they cultivate.

Part-tenants part-owner-cultivators are those who own 10–50 percent of the land they cultivate.

Tenants are those who own less than 10 percent of the land they cultivate.

Others includes agriculturalists who do not cultivate land, such as sericulturists, livestock breeders, greenhouse keepers, etc.

Rural Economic Problems, Vol. 1 No. 1, May 1964, p. 80, Table–4; see also Ashikaga, *op. cit.,* p. 102; Dore, *Land Reform in Japan,* pp. 198, 371.

8. In 1940, of all states, South Dakota had the highest proportion of leased land—69.6 percent. North Dakota ranked next with 61.4 percent. Kansas, Illinois, Oklahoma, and Iowa were all in the group with 57 percent or more of the farm land under lease. *Family Farm Policy,* pp. 67, 93, Table 2.

9. *Fact Book of U.S. Agriculture, January 1965,* p. 103.

10. Similarly, nearly all the sugar beet in the country was grown under contract with processors. The contract specified acreage, delivery dates, payment schedules, seed, growing methods, and marketing procedures. Sugar companies employed specialists to advise farmers on production practices. The government, authorized by the Sugar Act, prevented excessive planting and regulated the price. Most commercial fruit and vegetables also were produced under contract farming or vertical integration—principally by grower-shippers and canning firms. *Ibid.,* pp. 103–6.

11. See Chapter XIII, Section 3.

12. The quote is from Dore, *Land Reform in Japan,* p. xvi.

13. In interview with the author.

14. In conversation with the author in Japan.

15. In all, Toynbee visited "three characteristic present-day Japanese farms in Hokkaido: an onion farm on the outskirts of Sapporo; a rice-farm in the irrigated country to the east of the city; and a dairy-farm in rougher country farther south-eastward." He gives no description of the onion farm. He also fails to mention that the "radical" dairy farmer was a Christian. Arnold J. Toynbee, *East to West* (Oxford University Press, 1958), pp. 72, 76–77.

CHAPTER XXVI

1. *Farm Bureau Policies for 1960,* p. 5.

2. See Chapters VII, Section 1, IX, X.

3. See Bogue, "Farming in the Prairie Peninsula, 1830–

Notes

1890," *The Journal of Economic History,* Vol. XXIII, No. 1 (March 1963), p. 14.

4. *New Approaches for Agricultural Extension in Problem Areas,* Extension Bulletin 1 (Madison: University of Wisconsin, College of Agriculture, September 1952), p. 14.

5. *Ibid.,* p. 4 n.1.

6. See Cochrane, *The City Man's Guide to the Farm Problem,* pp. 51, 111, 114.

7. Natural color of wood is preferred in Japan. It is not customary therefore to paint it.

8. Sources: Hayami and Yamada, *op. cit.,* pp. 1–3; *Japanese Import Requirement,* pp. 54–56; Ogura, *op. cit.,* p. 75; Ashikaga, *op. cit.,* pp. 55–56; *Rural Economic Problems,* Vol. 1, No. 1, May, 1964, pp. 15–16.

9. Nakamura, in *The State and Economic Enterprise in Japan,* p. 261.

10. Cited by Smith in *The Agrarian Origins of Modern Japan,* p. 76.

11. *Ibid.,* pp. 111–12; see also, Nakamura, *Agricultural Production and the Economic Development of Japan, 1873–1922,* p. 138.

12. Smith, *The Agrarian Origins of Modern Japan,* pp. 212–13.

13. Hayami and Yamada, *op. cit.,* p. 23.

14. After hitting a peak in 1962 the national average of rice yields per unit of planted area was as follows:

Metric tons per ha.
1962—4.07
1963—4.00
1964—3.96
1965—3.90

It was partly due to unfavorable weather, but also because of the steep reduction and deterioration in the quality of the labor force. Hayami and Yamada, *op. cit.,* pp. 21–23.

15. The postwar land reform made fundamental changes in ownership and thereby income patterns. But it was not responsible for a more or less equal division of land—and hence

of production as well, among *cultivating* households. Despite landlordism and absence of any legal restraint on accumulation of land in the prewar years, most of the actual production, whether by tenants or owners, was on holdings that averaged less than 1 hectare, comprising 66 percent of the cultivated area. Over 68 percent of the farm households worked less than 1 hectare of land. In 1940, only 9 percent of all farmers cultivated more than 2 hectares each, or less than 10 percent of the land. See Ogura, *op. cit.*, pp. 72, 684, Table 5; Dore, *Land Reform in Japan*, p. 181, Table 10.

16. See *Rural Economic Problems*, April 1963, p. 54, Table 1; Ashikaga, *op. cit.*, pp. 84–87; *Annual Report on the State of Agriculture 1962*, pp. 120–23.

17. Distribution of income was even more equable than production. As against an average per capita income (from *all* sources) of farm household members of 81,033 yen in 1961, those having less than 0.3 hectare had an income of 87,025 yen. The highest was of farms in the size group of 2 hectares or more. But it was only 101,579 yen. Ashikaga, *op. cit.*, pp. 80–112, Table 41, 113.

18. See *Rural Economic Problems*, April 1963, p. 9, Table 6.

19 (a). Regional variations in 1960 were as follows.

Region	1960 (koku per tan)
Japan	2.96
Tohoku	3.25
Hokuriku	3.13
Kanto	3.03
Tokai	2.75
Kinki	2.85
Chugoku	2.62
Shikoku	2.72
Kyushu	2.81

Rural Economic Problems, Vol. 1, No. 1 (May 1964), p. 45, Table 1.

Also see, Hayami and Yamada, *op. cit.*, pp. 33–34, Appendix C.

19 (b). *The Variation of Rice Crop Yields by Field, 1960*
(Otashinden Hamlet,* Sakata City, Yamagata Pref.)

| Farm No. | Average Yield Per 10 a | | Frequency Distribution | |
	No. of Fields*** owned by each farm	Average** Koku	Yield** per 10 a Koku	Frequency*** (No. of Fields)
1	39	3.67	2.8	1
2	38	3.73	2.9	1
3	36	3.86	3.0	4
4	34	3.84	3.1	1
5	32	3.70	3.2	4
6	29	3.75	3.3	1
7	30	3.88	3.4	13
8	34	3.74	3.5	33
9	33	3.75	3.6	74
10	28	3.63	3.7	81
11	22	3.73	3.8	125
12	23	3.61	3.9	57
13	23	3.85	4.0	43
14	19	3.87	4.1	9
15	17	3.70	4.2	7
16	7	3.83		
17	8	3.42		
18	2	3.90		

Standard deviation: 0.18601

Average yield per 10 a: 3.75 koku

* This hamlet consists of 18 farms.

** Unit: 1 (one) koku = 150 kg.

*** Average acreage per field is about 10 a.

20. See Chapter I.

21. See Akira Tanaka, *Potentialities in and Approaches to the Improvement of Rice Production in Tropical Asia*, (mimeo), Read at Symposium on the Research Problems of Rice Farming in Japan, on November 12, 1965, at the Institute

Notes

of Agricultural Research, Tohoku University, p. 15, Table 1. The same experiment was done in 6 countries in the Far East in 11 different locations involving 31 trials. For details see the whole paper. But in Indonesia, the Philippines, and Thailand, the experiments showed that yields of rice could be doubled over the national average simply by better "practising ordinary management."

22. Of several farm products in the United States, whereas exports are subsidized, imports are severely restricted by means of tariffs and import quotas. For a brief but concise discussion of import policies, see D. Gale Johnson, *United States Food Problems and Policies: Pricing Developments* (The University of Chicago, Office of Agr. Economics Research, Paper No. 67:4, Feb. 8, 1967), pp. 7–12 (mimeo).

CHAPTER XXVII

1.   SUPPLY OF FOODGRAINS
         (in million metric tons)

1950–51	Domestic Production	Net Imports
1950–51	54.9	4.00
1951–52	55.5	3.93
1952–53	61.7	2.04
1953–54	72.2	0.83
1954 55	72.6	0.60
1955–56	69.2	1.40
1956–57	72.3	3.63
1957–58	66.5	3.22
1958–59	70.7	3.86
1959–60	76.7	5.13
1960–61	82.0	3.49
1961–62	82.7	3.64
1962–63	78.4	6.55
1963–64	80.2	6.26
1964–65	89.0	7.45
1965–66	72.3	10.40
1966–67	74.2	8.70

Notes

2. TARGETS AND PERFORMANCE—FOODGRAINS UNDER THE FIRST TWO PLANS

	First Plan	Second Plan
1. Base Level Production (million long tons)	54.0 (1950–51)	65.0 (1955–56)
2. Original targets for last year of Plan: (million long tons)	61.6 (1955–56)	75.0 (1960–61)
3. Ratio of (2) : (1)	114	115
4. Average annual compound growth rate in percent	2.66	2.9
5. Performance in last year million long tons	65.8	79.6
6. Ratio of (4) : (1)	122	122
7. Compound growth rate percent p.a.	4.06	4.06

3. To 100 million metric tons. Even the subsequent downward revision of the target to 92 million tons implied a growth rate of 3.55 percent compound per annum.

4. *Notes on Perspective of Development, India; 1960–61 to 1975–76,* issued by the Planning Commission, Perspective Planning Division, April 1964, paragraph 76, page 25.

5. THIRD PLAN TARGETS OF DEVELOPMENT: ANTICIPATED ACHIEVEMENT (IN 1965)

	Target	Anticipated	Percent Achievement
I. Irrigation			
(a) Major M. acres	12.8	7.7	60
(b) Minor M. acres	12.8	13.8	108
II. Soil conservation Million acres	11.00	11.8	107
III. Land reclamation Million acres	3.60	3.00	83
IV. Consumption of chemical fertilizers			
(a) Nitrogenous (N) Million metric tons of which:	1.00	0.65	65

5. (Continued)

	Target	Anticipated	Percent Achievement
Domestic Production Million metric tons	0.80	.350	44
Imports Million metric tons	0.20	.350	175
(b) Phosphatic (P_2O_5) Million metric tons	0.40	0.25	63
(c) Potassic (K_2O) Million metric tons	0.20	0.15	75
V. Area under improved seeds-foodgrains, Million acres	204	164	80
VI. Organic and green manure (a) Urban compost Million metric tons	5.0	4.42	88
(b) Green manures Million metric tons	41.00	27.90	68
VII. Plant protection Million metric tons	50.00	40.00	80

Note: Derived from data in the *Memorandum on the Fourth Plan.*

6. Theodore W. Schultz, *U.S. Malinvestments in Food For the World.* Paper read at Ames Conference on Balancing Future World Food Production and Needs (Iowa State University, November 8–10, 1966), pp. 4, 6 (mimeo).

7. *Ibid.*, p. 5. See also, Theodore W. Schultz, *Economic Crisis in World Agriculture* (Ann Arbor: The University of Michigan Press, 1965), pp. 1–40.

Note: The data, statistics, and tables pertaining to Indian agriculture have been derived from several publications of the Ministry of Food and Agriculture and the Planning Commission of the government of India, and some evaluation studies made by external agencies. They are too numerous to list and many of them have not yet been published or made public.

Notes

1. *Memorandum on the Fourth Plan,* Planning Commission, Government of India, paragraphs, 6, 7.

2. The all-India index of wholesale prices of cereals in September 1967, stood at 228 (base 1952–53 = 100).

See Government of India, *Economic Survey, 1964–65,* Table 5:1; M. L. Dantwala, "Incentives and Disincentives in Indian Agriculture," reprinted from the *Indian Journal of Agricultural Economics,* Vol. XXII, No. 2 (April-June, 1967).

Review of the Food Situation (Government of India, July 1968), p. 1.

3. The Third Plan also had stressed that "For achieving the high targets of agricultural production set for the Third Plan, it is important that growers should have full confidence that the additional effort and investment which are called for will yield adequate return." *Third Five-Year Plan* (Planning Commission, Government of India, 1961), p. 323.

4. Also, since 1950–51 there has been a net inflow of funds from the nonagricultural to the agricultural sector via the capital budget of the government. See Dantwala, *op. cit.,* pp. 19, 20; Ved P. Gandhi, *Tax Burden on Indian Agriculture* (Cambridge: Law School of Harvard University, 1966).

5. As of *Taichung* (Native) 1, and the IR 8–288–3. These were developed at the International Rice Research Institute in the Philippines. Using these varieties, the Institute produced 10 tons of unhulled rice per ha in a single crop, and more than 20 tons per ha in 3 crops grown on the same land in a 12-month period. Wheat varieties from Mexico were *Sonora 64,* and *Lerma Rojo,* with Indian adaptations and selections (PV–18 and S–227).

6. YIELDS IN POUNDS PER ACRE OF THE OLD VARIETIES

	Rice	Jowar	Bajra	Maize	Wheat
1949–50	731	400	307	756	617
1950–51	637	358	264	662	624
1951–52	674	376	226	758	597
1952–53	721	378	250	847	690
1953–54	846	410	314	834	676
1954–55	769	471	270	843	724
1955–56	810	346	272	753	639
1956–57	835	404	228	876	626
1957–58	733	446	289	826	608
1958–59	862	450	302	788	703
1959–60	836	433	291	836	688

Notes

6. (Cont.) YIELDS IN POUNDS PER ACRE OF THE OLD VARIETIES

	Rice	Jowar	Bajra	Maize	Wheat
1960–61	909	485	252	821	755
1961–62	907	389	287	841	793
1962–63	816	477	321	879	707
1963–64	918	454	308	881	650

Source: Directorate of Economics and Statistics, Ministry of Food and Agriculture, Government of India.

7. Initial estimate was that the new strains of paddy and wheat would require around 100 lbs. of nitrogen per acre.

CONSUMPTION OF FERTILIZERS PER UNIT AREA OF AGRICULTURAL LAND 1963–64[1]

State	Consumption[2] in lbs. per acre			
	N	P_2O_5	K_2O	Total
Andhra Pradesh	4.87	1.95	0.10	6.92
Assam	0.14	0.16	0.12	0.42
Bihar	1.31	0.55	0.25	2.11
Gujarat & Maharashtra	1.82	0.79	0.23	2.84
Jammu & Kashmir	1.14	0.02	—	1.16
Kerala	4.20	1.18	3.56	8.94
Madhya Pradesh	0.34	0.18	—	0.52
Madras	5.56	1.29	1.37	8.22
Mysore	1.78	0.71	0.51	3.00
Orissa	0.40	0.10	0.06	0.56
Punjab	4.01	0.25	0.01	4.27
Rajasthan	0.34	0.10	—	0.44
Uttar Pradesh	2.75	0.24	0.01	3.00
West Bengal	2.38	1.06	0.80	4.24
Delhi	1.17	0.33	—	1.50
Himachal Pradesh	0.71	0.48	—	1.19
Manipur	0.99	0.22	—	1.21
Tripura	0.05	—	—	0.05
India	2.24	0.64	0.27	3.15

[1] Agricultural land includes net area sown, area sown more than once, permanent pastures and other grazing lands and land under miscellaneous tree crops and groves.

[2] Calculated on the basis of distribution figures.

Source: *Fertilizer Statistics, 1963–64* (New Delhi: The Fertilizer Association of India, 1965).

8. HIGH-YIELDING VARIETIES PROGRAMME: FOODGRAINS

	Target 1970–71 m. acres	Approx. Percent of normal acreage	Additional Production Expected m. tonnes
Rice (Paddy)	12.5	15	12.5
Wheat	8.0	24	8.0
Maize	4.0	9	2.0
Jowar	4.0	15	2.0
Bajra	4.0	36	1.0
Total	32.5	11	25.5

Source: *Agricultural Production in the Fourth Five Year Plan—Strategy and Programme* (Dept. of Agriculture, Government of India, August, 1965).

Re-orientation of Programmes of Agricultural Production (Dept. of Agriculture, Government of India, November, 1965).

9. AGRICULTURAL (FOODGRAINS) OUTPUT IN THE FOURTH PLAN (1970–71 ONLY)

1. Additional from Intensive High-Yielding Varieties Programme in already assured areas	m. tonnes 25.5
2. Outside the H.Y.V. Programme	
(a) Additional irrigation area of 26 m. acres	4.0
(b) "Soil conservation" on 20 m. acres	1.0
(c) 500,000 tonnes N. additional under old technology on irrigated and non-irrigated.[1]	5.0
(d) For double cropping "improved practice"	no allowance
Total	= 35.5
3. Base for 1965–66	= 90.0
4. Total production	125.5

[1] This assumes application of 1.3 m. tonnes N to the H.Y.V. Programme and a total availability of 2.4 m. N in 1970–71.

Notes

10. *Some Background Facts About Indian Agriculture*

Contribution of agriculture to national
income   45 percent approx.

Share of total work force dependent
on agriculture   70 percent

Total Area Under Specified Crops
1965–66 (anticipated)

	m. acres
Net area	330
Area harvested more than once	65
Gross area	395
Area under Irrigation	
Net area	73
Area harvested more than once	14
Gross area	87
Unirrigated Crop Area	
Net area	259
Area harvested more than once	49
Gross area	308

Total population at the end of 1966 had exceeded 500 million.

11. In an exclusive interview with the author on December 28, 1966, in New Delhi.

12. See Chapter III, Section 4.

13. In address by secretary of Agriculture, Orville L. Freeman, at the Sixty-Fifth Convention of the National Farmers Union, Oklahoma City, on March 14, 1967 (Washington, D.C.: USDA, mimeo), p. 12.

14. Hathaway, *Government and Agriculture*, p. 87.

15. *The State of Food and Agriculture 1965*, FAO, p. 19.

16. *Farm Programs and Dynamic Forces in Agriculture*, p. 1.

17. See Chapter V, Section 3.

18. *Ibid.* Also see Chapter III, Section 2.

19. T. W. Schultz, *Economic Crisis in World Agriculture*, p. 66.

20. See Chapter III, Section 2. See also, Martin L. Mosher, *Early Iowa Corn Yield Tests and Related Later Programs* (Ames, Iowa: Iowa State University Press, 1962), pp. 94, 97.

21. See Bray and Watkins, *op. cit.*, pp. 761–62.

22. Mosher, *op. cit.*, p. 30.

23. *Farm Programs and Dynamic Forces in Agriculture,* pp. 5–6.

24. Even prior to the introduction of the H.Y.V. program, agricultural scientists held the view "that based purely on existing knowledge and research tried out in India, it is possible to step up yields of wheat, rice, jowar, bajra, and barley in India more than four times their present yield. All that is needed is the application of improved strains already introduced in the country, use of fertilizers in the right quantity and at the right time, proper use of water and the right seeding practices."

The above opinion was expressed to the Food and Agriculture minister by an advisory panel of agricultural scientists set up by him, and stated in a speech by the minister on September 24, 1964, in New Delhi.

25. See B. S. Minhas and A. Vaidyanathan, *Analysis of Crop Output Growth by Component Elements: India 1951–54 to 1958–61,* Planning Commission, p. 16 (mimeo).

26. *Ibid.,* p. 17.

27. From data obtained from Economics and Statistics Directorate, Ministry of Food and Agriculture. Following is the yield of wheat in pounds per acre in the IADP District of Ludhiana:

Year	1st Decile	2nd Decile	Average	9th Decile	10th Decile
1961–62	3007	2317	1606	1102	653
1962–63	2700	2279	1580	1111	700
1963–64	3122	2575	1847	1312	822

Source: IADP Crop Cutting Data.

28. In 1964–65 there were 1,493,358 acres under rice cultivation in the district of Tanjore, which was nearly one-fourth of the total area under rice in the 14 districts of the state of Madras. It had an assured water supply for 1.4 million acres and was one of the first 7 districts selected to be in the IADP program—in April, 1960.

29. *Panchayat* is an elected village council in India.

30. In interview with the author in November 1964. The interviews that follow also took place at the same time.

31. Average yield of rough rice in Tanjore in 1964–65,

Notes

was 2348 pounds per acre. In clean rice it was 1565 pounds per acre for the same year.

32. *Mirasdar* means a landlord in Tanjore.

33. *Kuruvai, samba,* and *thaladi* are the 3 crops of rice grown in Tanjore during the rainy, winter, and spring seasons.

CHAPTER XXIX

1. In the first year only 400 farmers were involved. ADT–27 was developed at the Regional Research Station at Aduthurai in Madras State. For statistics, see *Accelerating India's Food Grain Production, 1967–68 to 1970–71,* Foreign Agricultural Economic Report No. 40 (Washington, D.C.: USDA, Economic Research Service, March 1968), p. 7.

2. He was referring to the region of South Asia. See T. W. Schultz, *Production Opportunities in Asian Agriculture: An Economist's Agenda.* Paper presented at a Symposium on Development and Change in Traditional Agriculture: Focus on South Asia (Michigan State University, Asian Studies Center, June 20–22, 1968), mimeo.

3. *Ibid.,* p. 10.

4. *Ibid.,* pp. 11, 12.

5. See, Willard W. Cochrane, *Food and Agricultural Policy for India* (New Delhi: The Ford Foundation, April 24, 1968), pp. 39–42.

6. Reference is to the Biblical parable of the tares: ". . . and in the time of harvest I will say to the reapers, Gather ye together first the tares, and bind them in bundles to burn them: but gather the wheat into my barn." Matthew 13, verses 24–30 (King James version).

7. Estimated Number and Cumulative Percentage of Farm Households and Area Owned by Size Holdings (1953–54 Crop Season).

Holding Size (acres)	No. of Households (000)	Area Owned (000 acres)	Cumulative Households	Percentage Area
1. 0.001	14669	——	23.09	——
2. 0.01–0.99	15360	4166	47.26	1.37
3. 1.00–2.49	8879	14839	61.24	6.23

305

Holding Size (acres)	No. of Households (000)	Area Owned (000 acres)	Cumulative Households	Percentage Area
4. 2.50–4.99	8569	30821	74.73	16.32
5. 5.00–7.49	4966	30411	82.55	26.28
6. 7.50–9.99	2972	25766	87.23	34.72
7. 10.00–14.99	3207	39053	92.28	47.50
8. 15.00–19.99	1690	29253	94.94	57.08
9. 20.00–24.99	929	20623	96.40	63.83
10. 25.00–29.99	636	17480	97.40	69.55
11. 30.00–49.99	1051	39439	99.06	82.46
12. 50.00 and above	604	53580	100.00	100.00
13. Total	63532	305431	63532	——

Source: *National Sample Survey Report on Land Holdings* (3) Number 36 (New Delhi: Cabinet Secretariat, Government of India).

8. It would be more than the *total* U. S. population of 189.9 million in March 1965. The total civilian labor force in America was 75.6 million in the same year, according to the Bureau of Labor Statistics.

9.	WORK FORCE DISPOSITION (in Millions)		
Year	Total Work Force	Workers in Agriculture	Workers in Nonagr. Section
1960–61	188.4	135.3	53.1
1970–71	237.7	170.7	67.0
1975–76	266.9	191.7	75.2

Assumptions:
(1) Population increases at the compound rate of 2.35 percent per year.
(2) Work force increases at the same rate as that of population.
(3) Proportions of workers in agricultural and non-agricultural sector remain the same as in 1961 (71.8 and 28.2).

Notes

Increase in Number of Workers (in Millions)		
	Agriculture	Nonagr.
1951–61	34.67	14.21
1961–75	56.4	22.1

Assuming that the proportion of work force in agriculture is reduced to 66.6, increases would be as follows:

| 1961–75 | 42.7 | 35.8 |

See M. L. Dantwalla, *Problem of Subsistence Farm Economy: The Indian Case*. Presented at Seminar on Subsistence and Peasant Economics (Honolulu: East-West Center, February 28-March 6, 1965), pp. 2–3 and appendix table 2, mimeo.

10. In 1962 a third of the rural households earned less than or the equivalent of Rs 2 per day.

Rural Income Distribution by Zones, Occasional Paper 17, National Council of Applied Economic Research (New Delhi, June 1966), p. 7. See also *All India Rural Household Survey*, Vol. II, National Council of Applied Economic Research (New Delhi, July 1965), p. 29.

11. *Asian Agricultural Survey*, Regional Report, Volume One (Manila, March 1968), pp. 44, 116.

12. The quote is from a statement by Orville L. Freeman, U.S. secretary of Agriculture, in *Rural Poverty*, Hearings before the National Advisory Commission on Rural Poverty, p. 13.

13. The quote is from Dantwalla, *Problem of Subsistence Farm Economy*, p. 1.

14. The history of mechanization in U.S. agriculture provides a very good lesson in how large and small machines are unable to coexist within the same economy.

15. Chief earners of only about 15.5 percent of the rural households had attended even a primary school according to Census of India, 1961. About 3 percent were educated up to and above the high-school level. See *All India Rural Household Survey*, Vol. II, pp. 10, 14.

16. Average input of labor per acre of an Indian rice farmer is a quarter or at best half that of the Japanese. See John W. Mellor, *The Economics of Agricultural Development* (Ithaca, New York: Cornell University Press, 1966), p. 160.

Notes

17. See Chapter XV, Section 4, and fn. 15–17.
18. *The Rural Economic Problems*, April 1963, *op. cit.*, p. 54. See also Ashikaga, *op. cit.*, p. 85.
19. See Chapter XXVIII, Sections 1, 2.
19a. See Preface, Section 4.
20. Means market in India. Usually it is held once every week for a group of villages.
21. Although there is a widespread conviction among economists that "the rate of diffusion is proportional to the profitability of the new inputs . . . ," no one claims to know "the size of increase in production that the use of the new inputs must give over traditional methods to generate enough farmer enthusiasm to establish a self-sustaining diffusion response." *Asian Agricultural Survey*, Volume One, pp. 60–61.
22. See Chapter XXVI, Section 4.
23. See Yujiro Hayami and Saburo Yamada, *Agricultural Productivity at the Beginning of Industrialization.* Paper presented at Agriculture and Economic Development: A Symposium on Japan's Experience, July 3–7, 1967. (The Nippon Agricultural Research Institute, Tokyo, 1967), mimeo, p. 5, table 1.
24. See Chapter XXVIII, Section 4. Also, for examples of differential response in production behavior and efficiency among farmers in India, see author's *Blossoms in the Dust* (London: Gerald Duckworth & Co. Ltd., New York/Washington: Fredrick A. Praeger, 1961).

TABLE OF WEIGHTS AND MEASURES

(A) Land Measure

Unit	Tan	Cho	Hectare	Acre
Tan	1	0.1	0.099	0.245
Chō	10	1	0.992	2.451
Hectare	10.083	1.008	1	2.471
Acre	4.080	0.408	0.404	1

(B) Capacity Measure

Unit	Koku	Liter	Bushel
Koku	1	180.39	(U.S.) 5.12 (Br.) 4.96
Liter	0.005	1	(U.S.) 0.028 (Br.) 0.027
Bushel	(U.S.) 0.195 (Br.) 0.201	(U.S.) 35.2 (Br.) 36.3	1

(C) Weights

Unit	Kan	Kilogram	Metric Ton
Kan	1	3.75	0.0037
Kilogram	0.266	1	0.001
Metric Ton	266.6	1,000	1

Monetary Units

360 yen = $1

1 rupee = $.21 prior to June 6, 1966; and 13.33 cents since June 1966.

Index

Index

Index